NATURE'S WONDERS
in FULL COLOR

NATURE'S
WONDERS
in FULL COLOR

Edited and Compiled by

Charles L. Sherman

WITH A NOTE ON NATURE COLOR PHOTOGRAPHY

INTRODUCTION BY

ROBERT S. LEMMON

HANOVER HOUSE   GARDEN CITY, N. Y.

PREFACE

I N THE FALL OF 1953 the National Audubon Society and Nelson Doubleday, Inc., joined forces to launch the now established Audubon Nature
Program—a unique experiment in direct-by-mail nature education for the
whole family.

For those who are unfamiliar with it, the Audubon Nature Program consists of an authoritative, 48-page pamphlet on a different nature topic each
month accompanied by a large expensively printed sheet of full color nature
stamps. Young and old alike have found these handsome real-life photographic illustrations stimulating of a wider, deeper interest in nature, while
teachers in the grades and on up through college are using them to aug-
ment the standard nature texts and guides.

Obviously pamphlets and separate stamps do not constitute permanent
publishing, although they are most necessary for wide low-cost distribution. Because the writer had a great deal to do with the concept and edi-
torial shaping of the Audubon Nature Program, he has been given the task
of welding this material into permanent form. This may well result in a series
of books similar to the present volume.

Immediate acknowledgment and credit must be given to the National
Audubon Society for their invaluable cooperation in securing competent
nature writers and photographers, and especial credit given to the naturalists whose original research and texts form the basis of this book. Robert S.
Lemmon for *Seeds and Seed Pods, Best Loved Song Birds, Favorite Wild
Flowers, Flowering Trees and Shrubs,* for his introduction to this volume,
and for his gracious cooperation in reading the entire manuscript before
publication; Alan Devoe for *Animal Children;* Norman D. Harris for *Eyes
of Nature;* Charles E. Mohr for *Life in a Woodland Pond,* and *Nature's Archi-
tects;* Alexander B. Klots for *Butterflies and Moths;* Alexander Sprunt, Jr. for
Life in the Everglades; Harold M. Moldenke for *Camouflage in Nature* and
Inventions in Nature; B. Bartram Cadbury for *Life In Shallow Sea Water;*
Kenneth D. Morrison for *Birds of Prey;* and Dr. Arthur A. Allen and D. Van
Nostrand Company, Inc. for the copyrighted passage on *The Wonders of
Bird Coloration,* which forms a section of the Chapter on *Camouflage in
Nature.* In this connection I would particularly like to thank my two invalu-
able assistants, C. Earl Cooley and Charlotte Galli for their continuing good
work in keeping up the high standards of the Audubon Nature Program.

Few nature books can boast of as many full color plates as are used here —over 450—and for full credit to the contributing photographers you will find a complete list in the back pages, with the numbers of the photographs for which each is responsible. Few people other than the photographers and their friends and possibly a few editors will find this information useful, but if it will encourage nature photographers to continue submitting their best work to the Program through the National Audubon Society, its inclusion here will have served its purpose.

Similarly, the special note on Nature Photography will be of interest only to advanced amateurs or professionals, for the simple reason that good nature color photography requires professional equipment and more than snapshot knowledge of photographic technique.

Lastly, may I mention my own personal gratitude to A. Milton Runyon of Doubleday and Company for his unfailing guidance and encouragement in the completion of this project and to my wife for her patience and co-operation in checking many of the scientific names and details.

CHARLES L. SHERMAN

CONTENTS

PREFACE v

INTRODUCTION x

ANIMAL CHILDREN 1

SEEDS AND SEED PODS 19

EYES OF NATURE 35

BEST LOVED SONG BIRDS 51

LIFE IN A WOODLAND POND 67

FAVORITE WILD FLOWERS 83

BUTTERFLIES AND MOTHS 99

LIFE IN THE EVERGLADES 115

CAMOUFLAGE IN NATURE 131

NATURE'S ARCHITECTS 147

FLOWERING TREES AND SHRUBS 163

INVENTIONS IN NATURE 179

LIFE IN SHALLOW SEA WATER 195

BIRDS OF PREY 211

A NOTE ON NATURE COLOR PHOTOGRAPHY 231

THE CONTRIBUTING PHOTOGRAPHERS 243

INDEX 245

INTRODUCTION

T HE RECORD of the earthly realm in which we live is the world's greatest story. It is a tale whose theme is as limitless as the oceans, as inevitable as the mountains and valleys, as colorful and minutely perfect as the heart of a rose or the million microscopic scales which clothe a butterfly's wing. More astonishing than all else, perhaps, it is an organized story of causes and effects, of ingenuities and objectives, of coordinated truths so rigidly tested and proved that we pause before them in wonder and admiration.

This far-flung world of nature that lies about us began millions upon millions of years ago when our planet *earth* was a lifeless mass of swirling vapors and cataclysmic upheavals. No creature of today could have survived for a single moment in that poisonous maelstrom, and yet the dawn of all life was even then preparing to break through the mists and perpetual rains. Feebly at first, and with a crudeness almost too primitive to believe, the marvel of reproduction finally struggled into being.

Then, as the eons passed, the earth's surface cooled, the vapors lost their lethal peril, and those dim beginnings of self-perpetuating life expanded and grew constantly more diversified and perfect. So gradual was their progress that in point of time you might almost say that one of our modern minutes would have represented a thousand of those primeval years. But they were actual changes, and as they became more numerous and definite there developed countless and always multiplying sub-changes as the processes of creation swung into their stride—a stride that is as strong and inexorable today as ever in all of Earth's history.

What directions has this astonishing evolutionary progress taken? There is no simple answer to such a question, for the ramifications of the developments defy calculation. They have brought us, among countless striking distinctions, the multitude of different bird songs; the incredible variety of plant sizes, types and individual forms; the thirty pound lobster in his armored coat and the pint-size hermit crab that lives in a snail shell; the swallowtail caterpillar whose false "eyes" look like a snake's real ones; the African lion with his thunderous roar and the giraffe which inhabits the same region but has no vocal cords at all.

Sometimes these individual racial characteristics have no purpose which we can clearly detect. Usually, however, they are tied in closely with the environment in which a creature or plant is found, the food it consumes, the perils it faces, and its particular niche in the throng of other lives around it. There is as sound a reason for the kangaroo's power to cover thirty feet in a single bound as there is for a hummingbird's ability to fly backwards or the beaver's skill in felling trees and building dams.

In very many instances, too, the peculiarities of a given species, or even a whole group of related species, are geared to a particular type of life pattern. Thus, a buck deer grows a complete new set of antlers every year, and they reach full development and fighting effectiveness in time for use in those battles of the autumn mating season whose underlying purpose is to determine the strongest, most vigorous fathers for the new generation that will be born the following spring. This principle that only the fittest shall survive to carry on the race is found throughout the world of nature, and it tolerates no exceptions.

In a somewhat different vein, although pointed in the same race-survival direction, are the heightened colors that many creatures and plants assume for their spring and summer breeding season. A male wood duck in normal condition displays his gorgeous courting clothes to the best possible advantage while wooing a potential mate, and so do the strange little spotted salamanders and numerous other animals large and small, winged, wingless or scaled. Not to be outdone by their mobile neighbors, thousands of diverse plants flaunt colorful, fragrant or nectar-bearing flowers to attract insects which, seeking sustenance, inadvertently transfer pollen from blossom to blossom and thereby help to insure the formation of seeds and hence the birth of new plant generations.

Behind all these peculiarities and behaviors lies the constant and vital need for food. It is here that we find some of the greatest surprises, for there is almost no natural substance, living or dead, which fails to contribute directly or indirectly to the sustenance of others that are still alive. To illustrate:

Without the presence of certain chemical elements in the soil, water or air, plants could not grow and produce the foliage on which a mighty array of insect forms and some mammals depend for food. If most of the insect forms were immune to interference they could well become masters of the world, for their potential rate of increase would reach fantastic figures even in a single year. But nature would sanction no such tragedy, and so we find many millions of birds, certain mammals, reptiles and other animals that feed primarily on insects and help materially to hold them in check while filling their own stomachs. The term "animal," incidentally, covers all living things except plants.

Comparable checks and balances exist throughout the natural world; in fact, they are the cornerstones without which the entire structure would eventually collapse. The situation reminds one of Jonathan Swift's lines, written over two centuries ago:

> "So, naturalists believe, a flea
> Hath smaller fleas that on him prey,
> And these have smaller still to bite 'em;
> And so proceed *ad infinitum.*"

Just to round out this interdependence principle, it should be noted that whenever a living thing dies a natural death at least some of the chemical elements in its tissues return to their original sources whence they can aid in starting some fresh cycle!

Another cardinal principle in nature's economy is that each type of environment shall have a quota of life forms especially adapted to meet its particular conditions. Among the obvious examples of this rule are the flightless but cold-proof penguins of the Antarctic; the hosts of aquatic animals and plants that can live only in fresh or salty water, as the case may be; the cacti and other succulent plants of arid regions with their astonishing ability to store up enough water during the rainy season to carry them through the many dry months which inevitably follow.

Considering whether an environment's peculiarities developed before or after those of its inhabitants is rather like speculating over whether the hen or the egg came first. Actually there is a good chance that the surroundings and their populations evolved more or less simultaneously over a period of countless centuries.

Does this matter of environments and adaptations to them seem rather remote or perhaps even unreal? Then consider for a moment the situations which are found on and around any suburban or country home—perhaps your own.

First, there are the plants, some of them doing best in full sun or damp soil, others thriving only in shady or dry places. Living on or in the earth itself is a varied population of moles, earthworms, toads, beetles and grubs that seldom if ever leave terra firma. Some of these eat plant roots or stems; others eat each other. And as a roving control force for them, so to speak, there are the sparrows, robins and other birds which, especially during the warm seasons of the year, do a large percentage of their feeding with their feet literally on the ground. Even a quick glance will disclose the remarkable agility of these birds while afoot, in sharp contrast to the waddling awkwardness of a web-footed duck whose proper feeding environment is a pond or other body of water.

Look upward into the trees, and you may catch a glimpse of a woodpecker, a bird so strikingly equipped for arboreal life that he seldom even touches the ground. And out across the fields your eyes will discover a wholly different example of specialized equipment in the graceful, long-winged swallows whose feeding region is so primarily aerial that their feet are mere perching devices on which they are barely able to hobble a few steps.

So much for a sketchy but I hope informative background for an understanding of what has been aptly termed the "web of life" that encircles this old planet of ours. It is time, now, to speak of the pages which comprise the major portion of this book and are the real reason for these introductory lines.

You have here, to my way of thinking, a volume that is unique in the field of nature publications. Its range of topics is exceptionally broad and stimulating, and the hundreds of color photographs, all of them taken direct from life, illustrate each page superbly. Of at least equal importance, from start to finish it is a book of facts, not fancies, for each of its contributors is a recognized authority in his field.

Within this general framework lies a wealth of specific information that more than justifies the title "Nature's Wonders." Much of it will astonish you and open completely new and rewarding horizons. And you will never find your interest flagging, whether you dip into the pages at random or follow the King of Hearts' instruction to the White Rabbit and "begin at the beginning and go on till you come to the end: then stop." For although the information imparted is scientifically accurate, its presentation moves along with refreshing zest and enthusiasm and is free of obscurities for readers of all ages.

And as you go from page to page two realizations of major importance will take form in your mind.

The first of them is that nature's world is peopled by no random assemblage of isolated, unrelated life forms jumbled together without rhyme or reason. Rather, it is an inconceivably vast and integrated organization, a network composed of myriads of tenuous yet vital connecting strands. Let one of these threads break, and dangerous added strains will fall upon its neighbors. Should they fail, too, a broadening rent could appear and seriously endanger the entire fabric. So nature, broadly speaking, never permits such threats to develop. Only man, with his heedless disregard of such fundamental stabilizers as the forests and natural watersheds, seems able to wreck her system, and in the end, conceivably imperil his own existence.

Your second great realization, I think, will be that all the members of nature's far-flung community live their lives exactly as they are intended to be lived. Among them you will find no disruptions by senseless wars, no self-seeking politicians, no conflicting ideologies, no artificial regulations such as we impose upon ourselves. Although some of nature's acts may seem cruel by our standards, they are rarely wanton. On the contrary, every one of them has its justified purpose and, in the long run, works out for the general good.

One final thought:

Not long ago a great naturalist explained the present growth of interest in nature's world in this way: "It is a means of escape—escape *into* reality."

How right he was! And now you, the reader, are ready to make that welcome escape yourself as you turn the pages of this book.

ROBERT S. LEMMON

NATURE'S WONDERS
in FULL COLOR

A baby *koala*, nature's teddy bear, is weaned on *eucalyptus* leaves. A koala's childhood is spent in the tree tops often as much as 150 feet above ground.

ANIMAL CHILDREN

M OST NATURALISTS believe that immeasurable ages ago life on our earth existed only in the primary form of a sort of seed or germ. This beginning of life on our planet was what biologists call protoplasm: basic life-substance, containing potentialities of growth and development, but at first so little organized as to contain only a hint of what we mean now when we speak of living creatures in their present variety.

Over long ages, under countless influences and agencies which we can only partly understand, the life-stuff developed and grew in complexity, becoming organized in variously shaped structures of pattern. Multiplying, increasing, unfolding, it "opened up," as a plant-seed sprouts, thrusts up its stem, puts forth branches and leaves, until it achieves a form that in the seed was only hidden promise.

Naturalists sometimes speak of the "tree of life." This is one way of saying that the earth-life around us began in seed, that it is all one united growth. Way out at one twig-tip of the tree, so to speak, we find life taking the form we call a fox. At another twig-tip we find a turtle. At another, a zebra. But under all the differences of these particular life forms there is unity, a vital relation among them, for they go back together to a common

1

Although lambs are symbols of meek-
ness, they train for life in rough games,
contests of strength, and mimic fights.

Because of his enormous size, the young
walrus, who will grow to over a ton, fears
only *killer whales* and *polar bears.*

source and an hour when the seed of life began growing, long long ago.

All animal life in our world is a single great organization: animaldom. This whole living entity—now vast, multiformed, comprising thousands of interrelated species functioning with an intricacy of parts united into a whole, but once only protoplasm—in a sense had a birth. It grew through seasons of increase, adaptation, trial-experience, the drawing out of capacities and potential. When human eyes and mind first looked upon animaldom, man found it richly differentiated, complex, a teeming integration of inter-work-ing parts. Once it was only foreshadowing protoplasm, only a seed of all this.

What seems to have been the story of animal life as a whole is the story of each individual animal life.

You and I start our existences as mere bits of life-stuff, mere seeds and eggs, as unlike a "person" as any particle of protoplasm was when the world began. We reach our fulfillment able to perform the complex process called thinking, able to perform acts requiring elaborate coordinations of muscle, nerve, and mind. The ape called a gibbon starts its existence, like you and me, as only a fertile egg. It reaches maturity crowned by such ape-lore as knowing how to swing expertly from limb to limb among jungle trees, how to make great leaps to catch passing birds, how to protect and raise its young-sters, how to quench thirst by dipping up a drink of water in its cupped hand.

When you and I are born, after the fertilized egg that was our begin-ning has developed into an embryo, and this embryo has developed to the point of readiness for life outside a parental body, we are infants with no observing or reflecting powers. Our "personality" amounts to hardly more than two traits: a fear of being let fall, and an urge to grasp any such offered object as a finger and hold on tight. A newborn gibbon's personality amounts to just about the same.

From that beginning, you and I have to make the almost incredible change to becoming *people:* thinkers, doers, dealers with the adventure of human living. From a similar beginning, baby gibbon has to make a change almost as tremendous. Looking at a helpless baby gibbon, who could guess he would grow to be such an accomplished ape?

2

We share many things with the animals of our earth: fundamental biological patterns, drives of impulse and emotion, sensory perceptions, experience of many kinds as we all go through the cycle of life together. Wherever we look in the world of nature, we see things to arouse our sense of kinship. There is perhaps no other thing that can so make us realize the bond among all creatures, as seeing how animals grow up during childhood.

Let's explore what life's beginning and unfolding is like, for some of nature's animal children. First, perhaps, we should talk about some differences as well as likenesses. Childhood, in anything like our human sense of the world and experience is a way in which nature gives protection and development to growing lives. We need to understand that among many lives in nature this kind of fostering does not occur.

Many creatures are not destined for an adulthood that requires any childhood period. They are born equipped with what powers they will need, "built in," in the form of instincts, automatic reflex behaviors, guiding kinds of unconscious impulses operative from their birth and very little modified by experience as life goes along.

Insects, or worms, or spiders, while having a period of youth and undergoing a process of growth, never develop even at the summit of their lives such "personality" as needs any protected and formative season of childhood in which to get under way. They have a time in their lives when they are young, but no real childhood.

A moth or butterfly is never a baby. From the egg of moth or butterfly there hatches a caterpillar, a completely different creature from its parent. The caterpillar, after a period of growing and moultings, transforms into a pupa: a life-form something like the insect-to-come, but different from both. There is at last another transformation and the mature butterfly or moth comes into being, ready to start a new cycle of lives that are a round of change and development without any period we can quite call a childhood anywhere along the line.

4

The youngsters of this *gibbon* and other apes are cared for and brought up almost as carefully as human children are.

Collie pups grow up to be "almost human," but they learn about the world in much the same way as *wolves* or *foxes*.

5

3

Among the very small animals that naturalists call animalcules—tiny creatures like the amoeba and paramecium, little organisms less than 1/100 of an inch long which teem in ponds, brooks, and the sea—there is not only no childhood, there is not even the experience of birth. One of these animals just feeds and grows until, at a certain size, it begins to narrow at its middle. This "waist" gets slimmer, and in a little while the animalcule divides into two. Each half of what was a single animal is now a small new animal. It starts a life of feeding, growing, and getting ready after a while to split in its turn and become two more individuals.

Lives without childhoods characterize that part of animaldom which has not grown too far from the psychic darkness, the original unconsciousness, of life's beginnings. All life grows; but it is only after a certain stage in the ascendance that growth begins to mean more than physical growth and starts involving the growth of consciousness. As animals are then more and more set free, by the development of increasingly plastic minds and ingenious bodies and ability to explore and enlarge their world of experience, they are more in need of a period of *introduction* to life: a time in which to accomplish the shift from the unconsciousness of infancy to the grown-up world they must master. This is how there comes to be need for childhood.

If we should come upon a litter of baby *snakes* just hatching from their eggs, in a sheltered place in the lee of a big stone or an old stump, we might expect to see mother snake somewhere nearby, watching out for her youngsters. We are not likely to find her. Snakes don't "mother" their babies. A mother snake of the egg-laying group (curious eggs they are, like birds' eggs but leathery-rubbery instead of brittle; they have so much "give"

Life for a baby *penguin* is an adventure in communal living. A penguin parent must cuddle the chick carefully on top of its feet to keep the downy baby's feet from touching the ice and freezing fast to it.

6

Though a young *giraffe* looks awkward and ungainly, it can toddle after its mother within a few minutes after birth.

Young *badgers* delight in such tricks as turning somersaults and prancing about in high-spirited dances and games.

7

8

that they grow in size after being laid, and bounce if dropped) often does not even stay protectively with her eggs until they hatch. She lays the eggs and then glides away forever, leaving them to be hatched by time and the sun. Baby snake is "on its own" from the start. Within seconds after it is born, a little snake is ready to use the instinctive technique of coiling and striking. Incidentally, if we go exploring the outdoors in regions where there are poisonous snakes, we should remember that babies of the poisonous species are born with fangs and venom, and with instinctive ability to use them. A baby snake comes into the world little in size, but in a sense "born old."

So are baby *turtles* "born old," baby *lizards*, most babies in the fish world, and many others. Lives like these—destined to be lived almost entirely according to instinct, in a limited kind of environment, with relatively few and simple adjustments to be made—can do without mothering because "Nature is mother enough for them." When a baby turtle hatches from its egg, shallowly buried in the sand or mud of the shore, it has the unconscious nature-given knowledge that the first thing to do is to go uphill. This brings it safely out of its birthplace. Then a second automatic response sets in. The turtle is attracted by the shine of water, or the brightness of sky over the water, and goes down-hill toward that. Such simple, uncomplicated responses as these are enough to guide the turtle all through its childhood and on through its long, dim life of turtlehood, without ever a need to learn much more. Like snakes, it can afford to be "born old."

In the lives of birds, though, we see there has come to be true childhood. It is a big transition from a helpless, blind nestling to a matured adult bird with powers of flight and song, feeding skills, wariness against enemies, and all the perfected endowments of bird-being. In bird life, we find mothers who are really devoted to mothering. Here a baby is born to be really a *baby*, developing its individuality more slowly and more fully than

5

9

10

A baby *horse,* or foal, can stand beside his mother on wobbly spindle-legs and nurse a few minutes after he is born!

Due to skillful raising and big families, *opossums* now appear in parts of this country where they were unknown.

youngsters lower in life's scale, for the child has the protection and care of a parent instead of just the earlier "parenthood of nature."

Where nature serves as the only "parent," broods of youngsters often have to be enormous, for so many of them die under that impersonal scheme. A mother fish has to lay hundreds of thousands of eggs. In many species, such as *cod,* the number may run to five or ten million. Insects often produce huge broods. A common garter snake, very often seen on a country walk, may give birth to thirty or forty or more babies in a litter. The batch of little *polliwogs* may consist of anywhere from several hundred youngsters to over ten thousand. Among the birds, where there has come to be a true season of childhood, with personal mothering, many species have only four or five youngsters in a brood, and many have fewer. Mother *dove* has only two children. So does tiny mother *hummingbird.* Mother *condor,* one of the biggest flying land birds, has just a single chick. She gives it probably the longest of all bird childhoods. Baby condor takes two years to grow!

Though birds' care of their youngsters is still largely a thing of instinct, only somewhat lit by awareness or intelligence, it is a foreshadowing of the kind of love that makes childhood a blessed season for the highest animals, the mammals, and at last for you and me.

A bird mother's attachment to her eggs is so strong and deep that if the eggs are taken away from a brooding *gull,* for instance, she will "mother" a ping-pong ball, a matchbox, or almost any small object offered to her. Toward nestlings, affection is even fiercer. Parent birds have such a deeply felt impulse to look after youngsters that they may undertake to feed and raise any stray fledgling in their vicinity. Among birds that live in flocks or communities, this devotion is often touchingly shown. Oriental bird-dealers sometimes impose the care of as many as fifty baby *finches* on a single pair of finch adults. The grown birds weary themselves to exhaustion, eager to look after them all. Solicitude for abandoned eggs or orphaned youngsters perhaps reaches its height in *penguins.* Penguins by the dozen cluster and sometimes fight among themselves for the privilege of brooding a stray egg. An orphaned penguin baby is overwhelmed by efforts of the whole colony to be its foster parents.

When we go from birds to mammals, we find nature's creatures protecting their children, helping to elicit their developing instincts and training them for grownup life, in ways like our own. In watching their behavior and seeking to understand them, however, we must guard against the mistake naturalists call anthropomorphism. It means reading too much of our human kind of personality into any non-human life. If we could experience things the way an animal experiences them, we would find that life seemed quite different to us from the way it seems when we experience it as humans.

An animal's world is not exactly ours. But it has become so like it—the relation between ourselves and other living beings has here come so close and clear—that we can look at the childhoods of animals, and think of our own childhood with a feelingof recognition and kinship, without any danger of "anthropomorphism."

A baby needs, most of all, protection, a sheltered place where mother can look after it. The animals called marsupials manage this by means of a portable nursery, a sort of internal one. "Marsupial" means "pouched." There are three famous animals of this kind: *kangaroos, koalas,* and *opossums.* They are the logical animals for us to talk about first, because they represent in the animal world a stage in the slow transition from an egg-laying way of life to the way of the highest mammals. With kangaroo, koala, and opos-

Red fox cubs must learn the cunning ways of the wild for survival. The curious youngsters start exploring the world at about the age of five weeks.

11

7

Baby *bobcats* usually first see the light of day in a well-concealed den in a hollow tree or high up among ledgy rocks.

sum, we find the old egg-laying pattern giving place to the egg-retention pattern that prevails among all the higher animals; but baby is born little prepared for external existence.

Mother kangaroo, a native of Australia and neighboring islands, has on the lower part of her body a big deep "pocket," a pouch that has a circular ribbon of muscle around its mouth so that she can either draw it almost completely closed or open it wide. If it were not for this furry receptacle in which her baby can be stored after birth, mother kangaroo could not possibly succeed in child-rearing. Though she is a good-sized animal (her mate stands taller than a man and may weigh around 200 pounds), her baby is born after it has had only five weeks in which to grow inside her body, and the incompletely formed little mite is less than an inch long.

Pink, blind, helpless, it is such a "premature" baby that its body is actually semi-transparent, like an earthworm's. The only part of the baby that is well developed and strong is its little "hands." Just as soon as tiny "Joey" (his Australian nickname) is born, he grips his mother's fur with all his might and, guided by instinct, makes his way toward the protective pouch on her abdomen. If the uncommon occasion should arise when he needs help, his mother takes him carefully in her lips and tucks him away in the pocket. The furry pouch belongs entirely to Joey, for there is only one baby kangaroo in a birth.

As soon as baby Joey is installed in the pouch, he takes hold of mother's milk gland and hangs on with an inseparable grip. Joey is not strong enough to feed himself by sucking. Nature provides mother kangaroo with special muscles by which she pumps milk into him.

With milk continually being pumped into his gullet, little Joey can still manage to breathe and avoid choking because while a nursling, he has a specially adapted breathing apparatus. An elongated upper part of his larynx projects into direct connection with the back part of his nasal passages, so that air can pass directly into his lungs without involving mouth and gullet at all. He can keep up his milk-drinking all the while and never choke.

At four months, a kangaroo youngster has grown a coat of fur, detached himself from his constant application to mother's milk supply, and has taken to peeking up out of the pouch. When young Joey's mother halts to graze, he clambers out, hops to the ground, and starts some nibbling on his own. At any sign of danger, he rushes for the pouch, dives in head-first, and then scrabbles around until he is right-side-up again and can poke his head out to see what happened.

As Joey grows up, he takes to hopping along beside mother for longer and longer periods, strengthening his legs in the leaping skill that enables a grown kangaroo to make a thirty foot broad jump or a sailing arc over a

10 foot fence. Only when serious danger threatens now does he still take refuge in his baby carriage and let himself be borne away on a bouncing flight to safety. If his mother should be run down and captured, little Joey is unlikely to be captured too. Mother kangaroo's strategy when she finds herself hard pressed is to lift her baby out of her pocket and tumble him into a hiding place somewhere in the bushes as she races and leaps along. When she has finally exhausted her pursuers by mile after mile of springing bounds, she quietly comes back and retrieves her waiting baby.

Childhood for the other celebrated Australian marsupial, the koala, is more sedate and not half as exciting. A grown-up koala is slow, gentle, woolly-coated animal that loves to clamber around in *eucalyptus* trees. It looks almost exactly like a real-life Teddy bear. Mother koala has a baby, as a rule, at intervals of two years—just a single baby, like mother kangaroo. Little koala stays in his fur-lined cradle only a short time, and then his mother transfers him to her furry back. He spends his whole childhood riding there, or taking climbing lessons by cautiously hitching his way around to her under side and then back up again. Koalas are as mild and gentle as they look, and baby's growing up has a placid slowness in keeping with the mild quality of koala life. The young Teddy-bear continues to cling to his mother until he is almost half as big as she is. When it comes time for him to be weaned from his milk diet to eucalyptus leaves—the exclusive food on which grown up koalas live—his mother helps him through the transition by one of the strangest features in animal childhood. Her body develops a temporary power to make eucalyptus "pap." This vegetable "soup" is produced only for a month or so, only every two or three days, and only at a special time in the afternoon.

American opossums are as slow and placid as their koala cousins. When baby opossum is born he is smaller than an acorn. Unlike kangaroo and koala, he is not a solitary baby but one of a brood that may number as many as a dozen. At birth, he hitches his way to mother's pouch and snuggles in as one of a host of brothers and sisters. Baby opossum stays six or seven weeks in the warm security of the pouch, suckling, dozing, growing a silky down of soft fur, presently opening bright black little

13

Baby *snakes,* "on their own" at birth, get out of their eggs by means of a sharp temporary egg tooth which is soon lost.

Mother *hens* are devoted parents, constantly caring for their helpless *chicks* and teaching them pecking skills.

14

9

15

16

Secure in his armor of quills, a baby *por-cupine* may spend two or three months exploring just one tree.

One of the most delightful sights in the moonlit woods is the gliding flight of these graceful little *flying squirrels*.

eyes. As the opossum children grow, it begins to get seriously crowded in their portable nursery, elastic as the pouch is. Cautiously at first, the young-sters take to peeping out of the pouch opening. Then, like baby koala, they climb out onto mother's back. On either side of her backbone they cling in rows, their sharp little chins hooked over the ridge to steady them, their strong-thumbed little hands holding fast to her pelt.

When mother opossum arches her tail, almost a foot long, up over her back the opossum children wrap the tips of their own little tails around her big strong one and hang from it upside down. The prehensile skill of their tails, learned this way, will be useful to them in adult life, as will the flex-ible strength of their small thumbs, perfected in clinging to mother's back and shaggy coat. Joggling and swaying, the young opossums ride their ma-ternal caravan.

They do not stay with mother as long as baby kola does. Opossums have large and frequent families. While the youthful passengers are still riding on mother's back, a new generation of tiny babies is already growing in the warm pouch. Mother begins to be impatient with her "teen-age" passen-gers. She takes to nipping at them, shaking herself to break their grip on her fur and tail. Before long the opossum striplings heed the increasingly vigorous messages. One by one, they climb down for the last time from their traveling swing and slip away into the dark woods and the adventure of adulthood.

For animal children that do not have the protected babyhood, constantly with mother, that marsupials have, there are three chief means by which protection may be secured. The baby may be born in such a good hiding-place—a tree-top nest, an underground burrow, a concealed hillside den— that it can safely be left unwatched while mother is away on errands. The baby animal may be dressed in a protectively colored coat, different from its parents', that tends to make it invisible. Or a baby may form so com-pletely during the period in its mother's body before birth—what is called the period of gestation—that it may be born able to overcome the complete helplessness of earliest babyhood with astonishing ability.

Marsupial babies, with a very short gestation period, are hardly even full-

10

formed little animals at all, and must have a slow further development in mother's pouch. A baby *white rat,* whose gestation is only 21 days, is a tiny, naked, blind baby, helpless and dependent, but the baby *guinea pig,* whose gestation is a long 67 or 68 days, is born with its eyes open and wearing a coat of fine fur. There are quite a number of wild animal children that are born in a sufficiently advanced state to enable them to overcome their first helplessness without delay.

A little foal, a *horse* baby, is able to get to his feet within minutes after coming into the world. Almost all the horse's wild relatives (odd-toed ungulates, as they are formally called) are similarly quick to "get their bearings" in babyhood. New-born baby *zebra* can struggle to his feet about five minutes after being born, and can totter after mother, begging for milk, within an hour or so. *Tapir* babies are extremely prompt toddlers. So are *rhinoceros* youngsters, even though their childhood is a long, slow one, lasting five or six years. Among other advanced animal babies are *antelopes* and *chamois.* A new-born chamois can walk around, slowly but sure-footedly, even before it has dried off in the strange air and sunshine of its new world. Many other animals of different kinds belong among the comparatively precocious babies. One of the most comical is baby *porcupine.* His bristly

mother, armed with upward of 25,000 quills, weighs only twelve or thirteen pounds; but little porky comes into the world weighing a full pound, shadowed with a stubble of quills that start growing promptly. Before he is two days old he is climbing trees and nibbling at leaves and twigs!

Less advanced animal babies are given the protection of many kinds of nurseries. The babies of *woodchucks, badgers, chipmunks* and *gophers* all start their childhoods in a dark, cozy nursery-room of an underground burrow. Mother *weasel* outfits a nursery in a stone-heap or a hollow log. Mother *white-footed mouse*—the little tawny-backed, soft-eyed wild mouse—likes to find an old abandoned bird's nest and then enlarge the structure and put a roof of

17

18

Australian *kangaroos* are the most famous of the pouched mammals called marsupials. A baby is called "Joey."

The sun-loving young *harbor seal's* coat of soft, white baby fur gradually mottles and darkens as the pup grows up.

11

When danger threatens, mother *woodchuck* whistles a shrill warning, and the youngsters dash for their bolt-hole.

Both mother and father *coyote* train their roly-poly children to become swift, wary, and resourceful hunters.

These calves live on the North American prairie. In 1900 only 800 *bison* were left; fortunately almost 25,000 exist today.

19

20

21

dried leaves and grasses over it, making it into a warm, snug house, in the heart of which is the nursery lined with soft mosses and shreds of cedar bark. Nurseries for baby *beaver* and baby *muskrat* are in the "lodges" the adults make, domed houses of twigs and sticks, or else in deep bank-side burrows that in the case of some beavers may extend into the bank as far as thirty feet and lead to a roomy chamber a yard wide with a foot-high ceiling. Fox cubs are born in an "earth," a tunnelled den in the ground, often an enlarged and made-over house that was originally the burrow of some other animal. Mother *cottontail rabbit* prepares a soft, warm ground-nest of grasses and leaves, hidden among the tall meadow grass, and lines it with fur from her body. Among the animals whose babies are born very helpless, and must be hidden securely for a long while, there are ingenious nurseries to fit every need.

Midway between these animal children that have sheltering nests and the precocious ones whose parents need not make such a provision, are the babies whose protection comes largely from their special coloring. Grown-up *lions* have solidly tawny coats; but baby lion is all mottled with an array of spots, and his tail shows a clear trace of dark circling rings. *Mountain lions,* or *pumas,* are almost uniformly reddish-tawny; but a puma cub in babyhood is strikingly splashed and dappled with markings: a broad band on each side of his face, spots on his legs and underneath his chest and stomach. We can see a striking instance of protective childhood coloration in *bobcat* kittens. The soft, thick fur of an adult bobcat is a light gray, grizzled with rufous brown, and there is only a very faint trace of some dusky spottings around its mouth, head, and tail. But baby bobcat in kittenhood is powdered with a dotting of speckles almost all over. The stripings and spottings

12

which show so plainly in some animals' baby days are probably the remnant of an old pattern that once may have characterized the adults too. Zebras, giraffes, and many other animals keep their protective coloring all their lives. Others lose it. Perhaps the best known of all the animals' babies that change their coats as they grow up is the *white-tail deer.*

Adult deers may measure six feet in length, stand three feet or so high at the shoulder, and may weigh nearly three hundred pounds; but baby fawn is tiny. When he stands he is a scant sixteen inches tall. He weighs only about five pounds. From soon after the time of his birth, his mother, the doe, quite often leaves him by himself for rather long periods. The woods-world has its dangers for a helpless little fawn, so his way is to lie exceedingly still, with his slim legs tucked under him. Hugging the ground, motionless, baby fawn gives off very little betraying scent. For protection against sharp eyes, he relies on his coat. While he lies unmoving, his dappled hide blends with the sun-flecked pattern of the leaves and in an almost magical way the quiet little youngster "disappears."

The little white-tail fawn must even have lessons in that art of stillness which is his chief source of safety. Often when he hears his mother coming, he struggles to his feet and wobbles eagerly to meet her; and often when she is leaving him, and he still feels hungry and lonesome, he tries to follow her on his insecure legs. She bunts and pushes him with her head, forcing him down. She keeps up these lessons until he has learned obedience. Later, when he is stronger and ready to make trips from home, she bleats softly to him and teaches him to understand the signal-flagging of her tail. A deer's tail is nearly a foot long and rather bushy. When held downward, pressed against her body, it shows only an inconspicuous brown,

22

23

A little *white-tail deer* with its concealing coat learns to watch—and follow the flashing signal of its mother's tail.

The shy, gentle *tapir* is related to both *horse* and *rhinoceros.* The streaks on his coat will disappear when it grows up.

Young *zebra's* hereditary stripes form a "ruptive" pattern. They break up the animal's contour and aid him in hiding.

24

the color of the rest of the deer's coat. But when it is raised it shows the flashing white of the underside. The youngster learns to watch for that quick white glimmer among the tree trunks and obey its message. It means "Get up! Come! Follow me!" The young fawn learns to bound forward, trot from cover, and follow where his mother leads. After that, traveling, exploring, he learns more and more. What the coughing deer-cry or bark—the blowing noise that sounds like *Kaaah!*—means (it means urgent danger); what different kinds of twig-snapping signify; what is the safe way by which a band of deer can cross a highway. The way for road-crossing, little whitetail learns, is for one member of the herd, usually a doe, to advance to within a few yards of the roadside while all the others hold back. If all seems well, she flirts her tail vigorously, showing the white signal-flag. Then she walks slowly and alertly forward to the road's edge, and the rest of the herd advances to where she was previously standing. At the roadside she again pauses, looks carefully both ways, raises her signal-flag, then vaults across the road. Reaching the far side, she makes one final reconnoiter. Then she gives her white flag a last triumphant flip. "All's well! Come ahead!", and the herd goes trooping across the road.

It may not surprise us that a little deer should have a lot to learn, in the course of growing up; but it does come as a surprise to find how many animals' "simplest" and most "natural" activities—activities that we might have supposed to be wholly instinctive—are actually things that have to be learned in childhood. We may think a baby *chick* automatically knows how to feed itself. But it must learn. A chick at first pecks at everything it finds. Only by childish trial-and-error experiment does it learn what is good to eat. We are almost sure to think that a predilection for water must be inborn in the graceful, gliding *swans*. But it isn't. Baby swan (called a cygnet) has to be coaxed and wheedled to take to the water, and in the beginning the little fellow hates it, making frantic efforts to climb out onto the bank, or sometimes climbing up on mother's safe, dry back.

The *harbour seals* live on rocky and craggy promontories around bays, loving to bask on the rocks in the sunlight when they are not cavorting happily in the water. When the time comes for mother seal to have a baby, she

In warm days, young *mud turtles* seek shallow water and shore-flats to bask in the sun. Their childhood lasts a year.

A *sow* must meet heavy family demands. She often has two litters a year with ten to twelve hungry *piglets* each time.

25

26

14

27

28

These appealing *lion cubs* with their "puppy markings" may be resting up from a mock fight, a favorite pastime.

Fond of clowning, frisky *bear cubs* constantly get into mischief and must be disciplined by their watchful mother.

usually swims up a river so that the baby is born some distance from the open sea. He is a sleek, chubby, and uncommonly winsome baby, his first fur a soft white, later a sort of dappled yellow-gray with variegated spottings. He loves the companionship of mother—a colony of nursling seals is a continual uproar of plaintive *wa-aa's* as the youngsters complain of their mother's absences—and he loves milk, on which he requires to be fed for about a month before he can be enticed to take an interest in fish. What he does not like is the water. Mother takes the pup to the edge of the rocks. She nudges him, nuzzles him, urges him tenderly. No result. She tries again, coaxing, pleading, slipping sleekly into the water herself and gliding around as if in a display of what fun it is. No. She flippers her way back up onto the rocks and again approaches her child. This time there is no pleading. With a quick, adroit shove she tumbles him—*whomp!*—into the water. Thrashing and spluttering, baby seal is all outrage and misery. He hurries back up onto the rocks. But then, come to think of it, that plunge *was* fun. He peeks over the rock-edge at the water, hitches a bit nearer, and suddenly—splash!—has made a dive on his own. He has made the grand initiation into being a grownup seal. It is an initiation that has to be made, with almost as much timidity and reluctance, even by the seal's huge relative, the *Arctic walrus*. Grunting and straining, mother walrus has to heave her enormous baby over the edge of the ice-floe into the dark, forbidding current.

A similar adventure, in a different element, marks the childhood of young *flying squirrels*. They must overcome fear of the air. A flying squirrel cannot really "fly," but it has a web of furry skin stretching between forelegs and hindlegs, and when it spreads out all four limbs the skin is extended to become something like a pair of wings. On these the squirrel can glide through the air, on a downward slant, sailing from a treetop to a slightly lower point on another tree a hundred feet or more away. Flying squirrels are gentle, playful, shy little animals, active almost exclusively at night. The babies are often born in a snug hollow high in an old tree. Gradually they must learn to make explorations from the nest, climbing around on the tree trunk and in the branches; but there is no gradual way to learn a long swooping glide through the empty air. This thrilling, breathtaking moment comes

29

30

31

Curious baby *raccoons* explore the world with the help of agile "hands" almost as skillful as a monkey's paw.

Domestic *cattle* may seem staid and placid, but a *calf* starts life as wild and rambunctious as any young animal.

Baboons can be fierce, but their home life is marked by tender affection and devotion for their children.

to baby flying squirrel when at a nudge from his mother, in the dusk of a summer evening in the woods, he suddenly finds himself dislodged from the edge of the tree-hollow and tumbling through space. Instinctively he spreads out his little legs. His soft-furred, broad tail is thrust out straight as a kind of combination rudder and parachute. Wobble . . . side-slip . . . head-over-heels . . . and then all of a sudden he finds himself riding lightly on the air, flying downhill upon it as serenely as a young boy coasting down a slope on a sled. The minute a flying squirrel youngster has completed his first flight, he is permanently enchanted by the adventure. He can hardly wait to scramble back up to the top of the tree and take off again. It is a practicing for life; but it is also a great game.

Mother *lioness* offers her children the tip of her tail as a plaything, twitching and vibrating it to attract their notice, then moving it slowly or thrashing it quickly as the youngsters make rushing pounces in an attempt to catch it. Many other mothers among the big cats teach hunting-skills by the same game. *Wildcat* kittens, like our domestic ones, spend hours in frisky games that perfect their capacities for climbing, jumping, and pinning their prey with an adroit forepaw. Little *lynxes,* no less than little house-kittens, are great ones for making sudden stiff-legged prances and leaps almost straight in the air; and they will chase a pebble or twig, batting it with their paws, rolling over, kicking with their hind feet, in a wild game that exactly duplicates the way of a pet kitten. In young *lambs* and *calves* we can see play-antics that show the youngsters getting ready for such lives as their wild ancestors led. They take part in exuberant mimic fights. They butt, buck, and jump. A baby lamb by nature hates to be left by its mother even for a little while. As it grows, the lamb's urge to follow develops into training

16

games of follow-the-leader. They are a preparation for the kind of gregarious life that sheep lead in the wild state. Calves' favorite games are playful stampedes. Young *puppies* rush after each other in circles, each trying to "head off" the other fellow. It is the same game—a life-training game—played by the wild dogs, the *wolves, foxes* and *coyotes.*

Almost all young animals love to tussle and wrestle together, in mock fights that train them for possible serious emergencies in their grown-up days. Baby *bear* is one of the animal babies that are born tiny and unready for life. His mother gives birth to him while she is still drowsing in her winter den, and he is a tiny, toothless infant often weighing under a pound. But he grows prodigiously, and he gets to be one of the most high-spirited youngsters in all outdoors. When a couple of bear cubs get to cuffing and nipping each other too uproariously, mother bear growls a warning. That failing, she may deliver a whole-hearted swat that tumbles the little fellows head over heels. Animal mothers are patient, but not given to tolerating nonsense.

Much of animal children's playing and learning comes from following mother and imitating her. *Raccoons* pick up the life-lores they need in the course of evening and night-time excursions, following mother 'coon from their hollow tree den. A 'coon family outing is a charming sight to see: mother trundling solemnly along, at a rolling flat-footed gait like a little bear's, her coonlets following earnestly behind her. Every animal child has its special knowledges and habits to acquire; and little raccoons acquire a particularly odd one. Fishing with mother along the moonlit brook, dipping their paws in the dark flowing water for frogs and crawfish, they learn

Mother *skunk* leads her family in a woodland procession. Young skunks display a calm confidence. Their scent weapon makes them feared by almost all enemies but the great *horned owl.*

the curious 'coon trick of washing every morsel of food before they eat it. Another family outing-procession that is delightful to watch—and rather easier to see, for it often takes place in early evening instead of the deeper darkness that 'coons prefer—is a parade of *skunks*. The children, who look like miniatures of mother, imitate her every turn and detour, her every pause to flip over a flat stone or scratch at a tussock in search of grubs and beetles.

In our talking about animals' childhoods, and how the little ones are prepared for life under their mothers' protection and tutelage, we don't seem to have given any consideration to animal *fathers*. The reason is that among a great many of our world's animals, father plays no part in bringing up the family. Having sired the children, he goes his way and either lives a solitary life or joins a group of his fellow males. Among quite a few gregarious animals, however, the children are attended by mother only while they are very small and helpless, and then are brought together with the adult herd and turned over to the mixed guardianship of its adult members. *Bison* babies enjoy the protection of the whole herd while they are growing up. At any hint of danger, the male elders form a protective ring, lowering their formidable heads. Baby *giraffe* is under a disadvantage very strange for an animal child. He cannot cry, as giraffes have no vocal chords. The young giraffe is introduced at the age of a few weeks to a group of youngsters looked after watchfully by older giraffe "nurses." They keep the little fellows rounded up and in order.

It is in those animal families where father is an intimate part of the household, sharing the children's feeding and training, that we see the animal world and our human world become most recognizably akin.

It is a long way from the animalcules to the apes: a range of childhoods as broad as the range spanned in the individual childhoods of you and me. Once, our world itself was only a sort of baby, the life on it as simple (if as miraculous) as the primary life-stuff that starts the life of every child. Once, there was only protoplasm. Then came the shaping and growing, the slow maturing of animaldom from this start in seed. We can see the whole wide range of the growth-story, in its evolving order, in the hierarchy of animal lives around us. A tiny *paramecium*, mindless, unconscious, just reproduces itself by splitting in two. A family of *gibbons* is a family so close akin to us that our relation has become unmistakable. Mother gibbon cradles her baby in her arms as a human mother does. She holds him gently by the hand and guides his steps. She watches constantly over his diet. She scolds him, pets him, encourages his initiative and assuages his fears; she cherishes him with all her heart.

The story of animals' childhoods is one of the most revealing stories we can learn outdoors. It may make us think about a lot of things. Perhaps it may make us feel most vividly the oneness of all creation, the bond among all the many forms of life from humblest to highest. For we see that under the creative scheme of nature all of us, each in our fashion, each in our appropriate ways of birth and growth and learning, as the great life of the world has been evolved are really members together of a single family of children.

33

The combination of both husks and berries produces the striking two-tone effect of the *American bittersweet* autumn fruits.

SEEDS AND SEED PODS

T HE SEED OF A PLANT is one of nature's most ingenious devices. It begins life as a speck so small that you can see it only with the help of a good microscope. Yet when it has ripened and reached the ground it has the power to absorb moisture, produce a root and stem of its own, and feed on itself until that root is large enough to gather the necessary liquid nourishment from the soil. From that point on the growth becomes faster and stronger until the one-time seed stands as a complete new plant which, unless human hands have interfered with nature's ways, is almost always an exact copy of the one from which it came. Some seeds no larger than pinheads can even wait for years until the right combination of light, temperature and dampness come along, and then sprout and grow as strongly as if they had just fallen from the plant that created them.

In the following pages, wherever you come across the word "fruit," remember that it does not necessarily mean something good to eat. Rather, as used here, it means the entire package in which seeds come—pod or other covering, pulp or inner coating, and of course the actual seeds. Sometimes parts of the package are good to eat, like the pulp or "flesh" of Apples, Cherries and Strawberries. In other cases, such as Walnuts and Pecans, only the true seed—the part that does the sprouting—is worth eating. And in many other instances the entire "fruit" is completely inedible.

19

34

35

36

Corn, or *maize,* is believed to have originated in Mexico, no one knows how long ago. Today it is known the world over.

Okra, a favorite Southern vegetable, produces pods such as few other plants can match. Sometimes they are a foot long.

When they ripen in autumn the splendid red of the *Japanese barberry's* fruits is echoed by the color of its leaves.

An American *bittersweet* in fall and winter can be as pretty a vine as you could wish to see. After its leaves have fallen its twigs are often tipped with such showy clusters of two-toned yellow and red fruits that hundreds of pounds of them are cut for sale in city shops where people buy them to decorate their rooms at home. These gay ornaments are the genuine fruits of the vine, and outdoors they will stay bright and fresh-looking all winter unless the wild birds eat them. The yellow part is the husk or overcoat of the actual berry. When the latter is ripe this covering splits into three cup-like pieces which spread out and backward and expose the bright red berry itself, a soft, tough-skinned little ball that is divided into sections or segments somewhat like those in an Orange. There are not many of them, though —only six, as a matter of fact. Hidden inside each one is a single hard, smooth, light brown seed only about 1/8 of an inch long.

Mankind has been eating *corn* for so many hundreds of years that today we think of it as just another fine vegetable. We seldom stop to remember that actually it is a member of the grass family and was grown for food by the North American Indians long before the first white men came to this country from Europe. It has long been a tremendously important crop for feeding cattle and poultry as well as human beings all over the world.

Most of the sweet corn that we eat nowadays has seeds, or kernels, that are either white or yellow, as you know. Long ago, parti-colored varieties were much more common than they are now and were eaten freely, but the improved solid colored varieties of today taste much better.

If you live in the South you are probably very familiar with a certain long, rubbery pod known as *okra,* and you have often eaten it in "Gumbos." Okra's native home is in tropical Asia, and since it cannot stand frosty weather it is not grown much in the United States outside of the South. The okra pod began as a handsome yellow, red-centered blossom growing on a stiff, three- or four-foot branching plant with huge leaves. Cooks who know their business pick okra pods while they are still young and green, for later on they would lose their fine flavor and be too tough.

There are more than 200 different kinds of *barberry*. The Japanese barberry is the sort that you are most likely to see in the United States. Most of the barberries are dense, thorny shrubs whose spines have a mean way of pricking your fingers painfully unless you handle them with care. They all have colored berries, too, but none are prettier than those which hang from the twigs of the Japanese species from early autumn until the end of the winter. Heavy snows have little effect on them, and when the ground is white their glistening scarlet seems brighter than ever. Only when other kinds of food become scarce do a few species of wild birds eat them eagerly, thus giving the two dark brown seeds inside a chance to fall to the ground some distance away and perhaps eventually grow into new bushes.

Many remarkable fruits grow in the tropics of the Western Hemisphere, and the *avocado* is one of the strangest of them all. It is almost round and has a slightly rough skin. It is big, too—sometimes nearly six inches in di-

The fruit of the *avocado* tree gives you no hint of the fact that it contains only a single huge seed.

The space inside the thin walls of the *eucalyptus* pods is divided into equal-sized compartments to hold the seeds.

Both *wild* and *brown rice* grow perfectly in parts of the United States, but not many people have seen them growing.

These *grapes* and *raisins* don't look much alike. Yet they came from the same flowers and grew side by side.

37

39

38

40

ameter—and inside it is a single seed a couple of inches thick and shaped somewhat like a hen's egg. Between this seed and the outside skin is the layer of yellow, butterlike flesh which, when properly seasoned, is so popular for use in salads. Avocado trees are grown in cultivated orchards in Florida or California, where the climate is suitable.

The story of *wild rice* and *brown rice* is a record from opposite sides of the world, for the first of these two famous grains originally hailed from North America and the second from the warm regions of the Far East. Ordinary white rice, like that in your kitchen cupboard, is simply brown rice grains that have been cleaned and polished to make them look nicer. Both wild and brown rice belong to the grass family, and both grow in muddy, watery places. They are slender, graceful plants with rather feathery seed heads somewhat like those of Wheat and Oats. Neither one lives for more than a single season, so fresh seeds must be planted every year.

There is a good reason why the native American one of these two important food plants is often called Indian Rice, for several Indian tribes have eaten its long, slender seeds for centuries. It has a good deal more flavor than the usual rice to which we are all accustomed, but so few people know about it that groceries rarely carry it.

41

There are more than 300 species of evergreen *eucalyptus* trees, all of them natives of Australia and the Malayan region. This means that they are not grown much in the United States outside of California and some parts of the deep South. Californians plant various kinds along their streets to break the wind in exposed places, or to provide valuable oil as well as timber and firewood. The biggest of the eucalyptus tribe may stand 300 feet with seed pods a half-inch across.

42

Some *yuccas* have no seeds. The white moth is the only insect that carries pollen to yucca flowers to form seeds.

A cluster of *firehorn* fruits will stay on bushes and hold their color all winter, a cheery sight on a bleak day.

A *sycamore's* multiple seed head, or "buttonball," is made of soft fibers and seeds, the seeds being on the outside.

43

A *raisin* is simply a carefully dried *grape* of a special kind, and the seeds of both are exactly alike. The reason why many raisins have no seeds is that they were made from grape varieties that were seedless, too.

Most grapes intended for raisin-making are picked when they are fully ripe. Next, they are carefully dried in the sun for from ten days to a month. The best variety for this purpose is called Muscat or Alexandria, a deliciously sweet, juicy one that is a very pale green color which darkens when it dries. Many thousands of pounds of raisins are made from this variety every year in California, where the climate is just right for growing as well as drying it.

There is something about the appearance of *yucca* plants which tells you that they come from warm dry regions or even deserts. Nearly all of the thirty-odd different species have stiff, sharply pointed and swordlike leaves growing in a tuft at ground level. Out of the center of this bunch, when the proper time comes, a single

44

45

The strange pods of a *wood rose* have hard nutlike skins. Just as lovely are the yellow flowers of this plant.

Most people like the flavor of these odd-looking *caraway* seeds, but have no idea that they can be grown in a garden.

leafless stalk rises straight into the air for from three to as many as twelve feet, depending on what species it is. This stiff stem is rather ugly at first, but after a while buds appear along the upper two-thirds of it and soon there is a splendid spire of strong-scented whitish flowers that can be seen for a long distance.

There is no doubt about where the *firethorn* got its name, with its clusters of ripe little fruits as bright as any fire and the spiky thorns along its twigs. Several kinds of firethorns are grown in gardens in this country, and all of them came from eastern Europe and Asia. They are dense, stiff-branched shrubs with small white flowers in flat bunches during the late spring. One attraction of firethorns, of course, is their showy little fruits whose pulp is a popular bird food even though each berry contains five, small stony seeds.

One look at the seed heads of an American *sycamore* or *plane-tree* will tell you why the parent plant is so often called buttonball or buttonwood. They are made up entirely of little brown seeds, each one equipped with long, very fine hairs. It is the seeds that give the surface of the ball its curious pinhead roughness. Sycamores are giants among trees, sometimes becoming 150 or more feet high. When they have grown to some size their brownish old bark has a peculiar way of falling off in places and exposing patches

46

47

48

Black beans and *black-eyed peas* are closely related but quite different seeds. The peas have rings around their eyes.

In spite of its hard-luck name, *poverty grass* produces quantities of tiny seeds that have marvelous silky parachutes.

Melaleuca pods get quite hard and woody and stay on the twigs for some time after their seeds ripen and fall off.

of creamy white younger bark scattered all over the larger limbs and the upper part of the trunk. This peeling is an entirely natural habit, too, and does not result from any injury or disease.

Would you ever guess that a *"wood rose"* is a cousin of the *sweet potato?* Well, it is; and it is also related to those gorgeous blue *morning-glories* that you often see climbing on trellises or along fences and walls.

Inside the peculiar rounded pods or capsules of the wood rose, which split open when fully ripe, are quantities of black seeds that feel almost as though they were covered with metal. In fact, their "skin" is so hard that moisture has a tough time softening it enough to get inside and start the life germ swelling enough to burst the walls around it.

Caraway seeds often are used to give a special flavor to rye bread, cakes, apple pie and even soup. There is an aromatic oil in them, too, and when this has been distilled from them it is put into liqueurs, perfumes and sachets to improve their taste or scent. Sometimes the plant's roots are cooked as a vegetable, while its leaves go into salads.

Taken together, *beans* and *peas* make up one of the world's most-used food crops, not only for human beings but also for cattle and poultry. There are scores of different varieties of each, but all peas and beans are genuine seeds which grow inside fairly long, narrow pods.

Down South, where great quantities of *black beans* and *black-eyed peas* are grown in big fields as well as gardens, both of them are often called Cowpeas. There are more than sixty kinds of them, and when fully ripe they may be either light or dark, solid colored or mottled. The eye marks the spot where the seed was attached to the pod.

24

Poverty grass won its name by growing cheerfully in poor, dry, worn-out soil where many other kinds of plants could not make a decent living. Yet this does not prevent its being one of the prettiest of the whole grass family. To the farmer it is only a weed, so worthless for cattle food or bedding that he won't even bother to mow it. But perhaps we should be glad he leaves it alone and gives it a chance to spread its beauty freely across otherwise dreary fields. There, autumn after autumn, it puts on a delightful show with its graceful, lavender-brown leafy stalks and feathery seed heads.

Most plants carry their flowers at the ends of special stems of one sort or another, but you'd never catch a *melaleuca* following a rule like that. Instead, its flower-bearing stems form the blossoms and then keep on growing through and beyond them. So what you finally have is a strong twig surrounded by a cylinder of rich red, yellow or white fuzzy-looking blooms with a leafy shoot sticking out of its top! Altogether there are about a hundred species of these odd Australian shrubs and trees.

There are several species of *dock,* and all live for several years. They are the toughest of the weeds, partly because they have astonishingly long roots that go straight down into the ground and develop side branches for extra feeding and anchorage. An old one gets such a grip underground that often you cannot pull it out until you have loosened the soil with a spade or a big fork. The upper part of the root finally becomes almost as hard as wood, but that doesn't keep it from sending a fresh green stalk three feet into the air every spring. This stem has several side branches near the top on which the flowers are borne. Each produces three seeds.

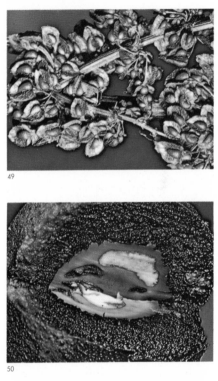

49

50

When the fruits of a *black walnut* tree first fall from their lofty twigs you would never suspect that the kernels inside their thick, rough shells

51

Dock are troublesome weeds. Yet the handsome brown seeds themselves are as neat as the surrounding flat flanges.

The white "meat" found in the heart of a *black walnut* seed gives flavor and richness to many desserts and tidbits.

The *Chinese lantern's* seed container is more like a bag than a pod. It is as thin as paper and hides its seeds.

25

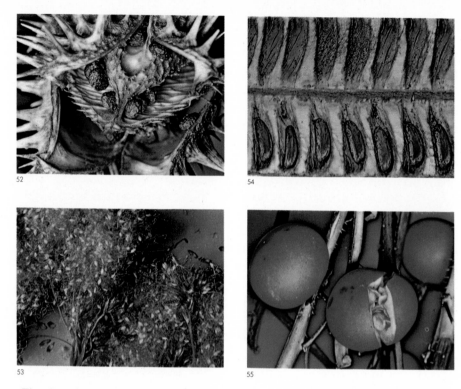

52

54

53

55

The *Canada thistle* seed heads are well protected by prickles in order that their numerous seeds may ripen safely.

Sedge seeds are very small, but the part the plants play in covering chilly parts of the world with beauty is great.

When the long, flat pod of *royal poinciana* is split open, one can see the amazing way the seeds are lined up.

No one seems to know why these showy pods are called *love apples,* a name they have carried for a long, long time.

could be so rich and finely flavored. Indeed, the nuts themselves are completely hidden by strong-smelling green husks which must rot away or dry up before the "meat" is fully ripe and ready to be eaten.

The tree which bears these singular seeds is famous for its size as well as the remarkable beauty of its dark brown wood. This is the same hard, heavy lumber that is so greatly valued for making gun stocks, cabinets and other wooden articles where a handsome "figure" or pattern in the grain is especially important. A really old black walnut tree may be 150 feet high and eight feet thick at the base of its trunk.

The *Chinese lantern plant* is quite common in gardens all around the country. Each husk is a couple of inches long, and sometimes several of them are strung along a stem like real Chinese lanterns.

When you cut open a husk, you find the round berry, a rather sticky one, that contains many seeds. Once a Chinese lantern plants gets well started in your garden it's hard to get rid of, for its yellow roots grow fast and far, making whole new plants.

Probably the *Canada thistle* serves some useful purpose in nature's world, but many of the people on whose land it grows look upon it as just about the worst of troublesome weeds. Its creeping roots start new plants and its numerous seeds sprout many years after they have fallen. Its origin is Europe and Asia. Like all thistles, this unwelcome foreigner has so many prickles on its leaves and around the flowers that you'd better not touch them unless you are wearing gloves. The plant seldom grows more than two or three feet tall—less than half the height of the *Scotch thistle.* Both species have similar flowers, but the Canada's are much smaller and less handsome.

Cool climates are the ones where *sedges* grow best—all 900 species of them. They are grasslike plants, and in some places, such as the upper Mississippi River valley, they thrive in such enormous numbers that there is quite a business in weaving their leaves into attractive grass carpets.

One of the important reasons for the great size of these colonies of sedges is that each plant lives for years and every season produces a large number of the little seeds. Sedge flowers and seed heads take the form of either spikes or bunchy clumps which are often pretty as well as odd.

The big scarlet blossoms of the *royal poinciana* produce narrow, bony seeds nearly an inch long, and their dark brown coats are decorated from end to end with four whitish stripes. The inside part, where growth begins, is canary yellow. There may be three dozen of these handsome seeds in a single flattened, beanlike pod two feet long which, when ripe and dry, looks like a strip of old purple-brown leather and is as hard as wood. The big island of Madagascar, in the Indian Ocean, is the ancestral home of this flaming tree.

You might well search for a long time without finding a more colorful fruit than that of the *love apple.* Its two-inch scarlet fruit, loaded with pale, flat seeds, is so decorative that some gardeners grow it just to brighten up their rooms in the fall. The plant stands a couple of feet high, lives for only a year, and has to be in a warm, sunny spot. But its seeds sprout easily, so the job of planting a few of them every spring doesn't amount to anything.

The two-foot leaves and arching branches of the *tree of heaven* make it look as though it came from the tropics, although China is the real home of the species we usually see in this country.

The most interesting thing about the seeds of this peculiar tree is the way each of them is flattened between the paper-thin sides of a narrow,

Although the seeds of the *tree of heaven* are small, their samaras are twisted to cause a spinning motion in the air.

After the autumn leaves have fallen, the rich colors of fat bunches of *Indian currants* seem to brighten the entire bush.

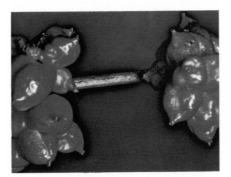

58

59

Although *grapefruits* are related to *oranges* and have similar seeds, they grow in an entirely different way.

The large *sunflower* and the small *millet* seeds serve the same purpose, although their appearance is so very different.

oblong samara, or wing, about 1½ inches long. The seeds are so small and light, and their samaras so perfectly shâped, that they can ride for a long distance in a strong wind before settling to the ground.

White men long ago gave one American shrub the name of *Indian currant* because its fruits reminded them of cultivated *red currants.* It may be, too, that the Indians liked to eat them, as do our wild birds. Actually, however, the bush is the first cousin of the *Snowberry* and not even distantly related to currants. Each of the clustered little berries contains two hard, very small seeds. When the low, rather slender-stemmed plants on which they grow are well developed the berries cling to their places all winter long and so are seldom covered by snow. Even the leaves drop only when real winter has arrived.

You would not expect anything as big and heavy as a *grapefruit* to grow in bunches. Yet it is actually true that they hang from tree branches in clusters of four to a dozen or more, like gigantic yellow grapes.

There are several varieties of grapefruit, all with the same general appearance but some containing many more seeds than others and one, at least, having pink instead of pale yellow "flesh."

Grapefruit trees, which reach a height of thirty feet or more, were apparently introduced into Florida from the West Indies about 150 years ago.

The plants that the *sunflower* and *millet* grow on are completely different, for sunflowers are coarse, big-leaved, straight and sometimes fifteen feet high, while millet is grasslike and only one-quarter as tall.

Sunflower blossoms look somewhat like gigantic yellow *daisies,* and their name comes from their peculiar habit of turning so as to keep their faces to the sun as it moves from east to west. When the seeds develop from the masses of little blossoms, they form one of the most amazing geometrical patterns in the whole plant world.

The seeds of true millet, on the other hand, are small, shiny and grow in drooping, quite slender sprays. Men have raised them for food since prehistoric times.

Dogbane is a real native American. Its stems are filled with sticky white sap, like that in a *milkweed,* and the Indians used to make string out of its tough bark. That's why it is sometimes called *Indian hemp.* And because those same Indians, as well as the early white settlers, also utilized its roots to cure sicknesses, it still bears other names like Choctaw root, Indian physic, Bowman's root and Rheumatism-weed.

Have you ever looked closely at the ripe, round seed head of a common lawn *dandelion?* You see, what seems at a distance to be an almost solid ball is actually so airy and fragile that if you hold it in the palm of your hand it apparently has no weight at all. Beneath its surface it is merely a network of hair-thin stems, each with a scrap of a seed at its inner end and a parasol of delicate fuzz at the other. In the center of the ball you can see the little dull white mound to which the seeds are attached and the withered remains of the blossom that was so jolly and golden only a few days ago.

Perhaps the strangest seed arrangement of them all is the "boll" of the *cotton plant.* This fluffy white mass of fibers is the material which, after it has been separated from the seeds attached to it and cleaned of bits of leaves and other odds-and-ends, is made into our familiar cotton cloths and threads. Cotton plants grow like small bushes, and their large flowers are white, yellow or purplish, and quite showy.

60

Honesty is probably the only garden plant with five different names resulting from the appearance of its peculiar seed pods. The names *St. Peter's penny* and *moneyplant* come from the shape and thinness of the pods. It is also called *satin-flower* and *moonwort* because each pod has a satiny sheen and a color and form that suggest a clear, bright moon. The satiny parts last indoors for several years and are popular decorations, particularly when combined with other dried plant materials.

61

Most *waterlilies,* as you probably know, have round leaves or "pads"

The feathery parts of *dogbane* seeds are ready to set sail, and in a strong wind they often travel very long distances.

Dandelion seed heads form and ripen very quickly. They will scatter a week after the yellow blossoms open.

Many thousands of acres of *cotton* are planted for just one purpose: to produce bales of fluffy cotton "bolls."

62

29

63

65

64

66

Many people grow *honesty* in their gardens. The pale, silvery pods are tissue-thin, so thin that the flat seeds are visible.

This section of a *lotus* pod's flat top shows a good way to drop seeds. It just bends over and they fall to the ground.

The berries of *honeysuckle* plants may be black, blue, yellow, red or white fruits, depending on the species of the plant.

Sumac seed heads are softly beautiful from early autumn until well into the winter. Each seed wears a downy coat.

that float right on top of the water and big flowers on rubbery stems only a few inches higher. But the East Indian *lotus,* although it belongs to the waterlily tribes, does things differently. For instance, its two-foot leaves often stand five feet out of the water and, even at that, they are below the fragrant, usually pink blossoms. A lotus seed pod is bowl-shaped and has a flat top with many round holes in it. When ripe this seed head is quite heavy, so that when the wind blows the stem bends enough to allow the seeds to fall out of the holes.

The fruits of the *honeysuckle,* whose tubular white to yellowish blossoms are so deliciously fragrant in warm June evenings, are hardly more than a quarter-inch in diameter. Each shining coat contains from six to ten jet-black seeds buried in soft, juicy green pulp not unlike that in a grape.

This pretty vine came originally from Japan. Long ago we Americans began planting it around our homes, and after a while the birds scattered its seeds widely around the country.

About fifteen kinds of *sumac* grow in the United States, and most of them look pretty much alike except to an experienced botanist. You may find them in the form of either straggly bushes or crooked small trees, and often they form big thickets in sunny fields or along the edges of woods. It may surprise you to know that three members of the tribe have a bad reputation for getting people into trouble, while the rest are perfectly harmless. These bad actors are the vine-like *poison ivy,* the *poison oak* and the dangerous *poison sumac,* which is seldom found except in swamps. Sumac flowers are so small and greenish that you'd hardly notice them except for the way they grow in pointed, closely packed clusters perhaps 9 to 10 inches tall.

The seed head of *sweet gum* looks like a green and later a brown ball such as no other tree can match. The actual seeds are at the bottoms of separate cases, all of which meet in the center of the head. The other ends of the cases form the outside of the ball. They are curved and sharp-pointed, and when fully ripe their hard tips split open enough for the winged seeds inside to escape and go their way.

Sweet gum is a good-sized tree with large, shining, star-shaped leaves that turn to a rich crimson mixed with yellow in the fall. There's a very good reason for its peculiar name: in the South, where the tree is common, they make a sort of chewing gum out of its resinous, pleasant-smelling sap.

Apple seeds have more value than you'd think! Every once in a while a single apple seed out of hundreds or thousands grows into a tree which, when it is old enough, bears fruits which are different from and better than those on the tree it came from. In this way McIntosh, Wealthy, and many other famous varieties first came into existence. Mankind had nothing to do with producing them in the beginning. You might say that they were out-and-out presents from nature. And here is another strange fact! If you were to plant the seeds of apples picked from such a special tree they would sprout and grow all right, and in time would produce fruits of their own. There is little chance, however, that these new apples would be exactly like those on the original tree.—The genetic reasons for this are not well known.

The seed head of the *sweet gum* tree is round, covered with hard points, and looks almost like a thistle.

Apples are one of the fruits whose "flesh" is thick in relation to the few small seeds buried in the center.

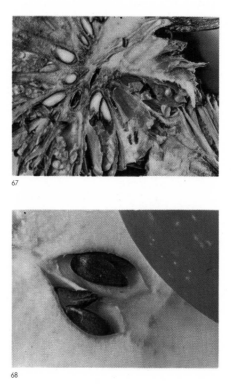

67

68

Peanuts are produced by sprawling vines that belong to the same family as peas, beans and clovers, and live for only one season. They have two kinds of flowers: big yellow fellows that supply nothing but pollen, and much smaller, hardly noticeable ones close to the ground. When these little blossoms have been fertilized by the pollen from their big companions their stems

69

About the strangest seed pod of all is the *peanut* shell. It always grows where not even the sharpest eyes can see it.

70

A *fern* has "seeds" on its leaves. Although they form no roots of their own, new ferns come from them just the same!

turn downward, grow longer, and bury themselves in the ground. There, completely out of sight, the pods develop and finally ripen the seeds, at which time they are dug up like potatoes! Most of the pods will have two seeds or "nuts" inside the shell, as you know, but an extra-big one may contain three and a little runt has only one.

One of Earth's very oldest plants is the *giant holly fern.* The two lines of brownish spots found on the underside of the big plant's leaf are groups of spores—dustlike particles which serve the fern as seeds. When they ripen and reach the ground, however, they do not behave at all like regular seeds. Instead of rooting they slowly develop into thin, flat green bodies called thalli which simply lie on the surface of the soil like scraps of damp paper. Several months later tiny fernlike shoots appear on the upper sides of some of the thalli and, growing taller, finally send down roots and become real ferns just like the parent.

Nutmegs, although you might not believe it if you saw a whole one among the other spices in the kitchen cupboard, are genuine seeds. They grow on trees, mostly in the tropical East Indies, and even in that part of the world they wear what you might call two coats and a shirt. The outside coat is a thick, pulpy husk, somewhat like that of a hickory nut. Inside this is the scarlet "shirt," a stringy layer out of which mace, another kind of spice, is made. And under the mace is the thin shell that surrounds the real seed.

The common names of plants sometimes seem to have no particular meaning, but certainly this is not the case with *foxtail grass.* This bushy, hairy-looking object would make anyone think of a fox's tail, and that's that! The seeds are at the base of the "hairs" and close to what would be the bone if it were a real animal's tail.

In some species the whole head is a foot long and a couple of inches thick, but most of them are smaller than that. Taken as a group, foxtail grasses are of no real use to men except as fodder for their cattle.

The *white oak* is a sturdy American tree which may reach a height of more than a hundred feet and a spread of eighty. It will take many years to do that, for white oaks grow slowly. But they can afford to take their time, since it is entirely possible for one of them to live for 700 or 800 years!

Its acorns are any oak's seeds, and those of the white oak are particularly pretty and neat-looking. A ripe one is nearly an inch long, and when it falls from the tree in early autumn, an interesting thing happens. Within a few weeks a single thick, white root pokes out through the pointed end of the shell and goes into the ground.

White oak acorns are sweet and rather good to eat. Squirrels are crazy about them, and so are pigs and several kinds of birds. The Indians used to make a sort of meal out of them. And, as you probably know, the hard wood of this splendid tree is highly valued by white men for house timbers.

There are only two members of the *pomegranate* tribe. One is an ornamental shrub. The other is a small tree from tropical and subtropical Asia which bears juicy fruits the size of an orange and containing edible seeds. Some of us Americans think it is rather tasteless, but in foreign countries it is rated very highly indeed. The fleshy part of the fruit is eaten. Yet the seeds have considerable value, for, in addition to being used as a garnish, they are also used to make grenadine, a pink liquid for flavoring and coloring certain kinds of mixed drinks.

You have seen that there is almost no limit to the sizes, shapes and colors of seeds. They may be as light as scraps of feathers or as heavy as a base-

Nutmegs grow on 60-foot trees. They look like solid wood, but they are real seeds and valuable for food flavoring.

All *white oak* acorns wear caps. The dark little point at the opposite end of the cap marks the spot where the roots appear.

Although there are many kinds of these handsome *foxtail grasses*, every one has seed heads that suggest foxes' tails.

Grenadine is made from *pomegranate* seeds. The fruit around the seeds has been a famous delicacy for centuries.

71

73

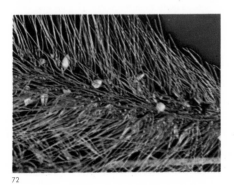
72

74

ball bat. Some are long and slim, others circular, three-cornered, flat, curved, pear-shaped, sharp-pointed or round as tiny balls. Many are black, and many more are brown, yellow, gray or orange. Certain kinds have parachutes to carry them to distant places; others thump to the ground like falling stones; and a few leave their sheltering pods as if they were being shot from little guns. There are seeds completely hidden in tasty pulp, like apples and cherries; and seeds that stick to the outsides of pulp, such as strawberries. You can find seeds that are as soft as butter, and nutlike ones that can be broken only with a heavy hammer.

And every last one of them, no matter what its size or shape, has the same important reason for existence: to grow into a new plant like its parent, and so keep the species from dying out.

Nearly all kinds of seeds originate in the heart of a flower and many stay in the same place until they are nearly ripe. In the case of most garden flowers this means that they remain there from a few weeks to a couple of months, although some seeds take a year or more to ripen. On the other hand, the blossoms lose all their beauty and wither away before their seeds are fully grown. You might almost say that a flower gives its life so that its seeds may live.

Not every flower on a particular plant produces seeds. In fact, large numbers of them shrivel and disappear without starting a single one. Each of those that is successful, though, may leave behind it from one to many thousands of seeds. If you were to figure out an average of all the different flowering plants in the world, some of which bear almost countless blossoms apiece, you would probably find that each individual one forms at least a few hundred seeds.

Certain kinds of seeds do far better than that. For instance, it has been estimated that a single seed pod of our American *moccasin-flower,* or *pink ladyslipper,* contains no less than 200,000 seeds, although it is only about an inch long and half as thick.

Only the very lucky seed ever lives to grow up. All the rest—billions and trillions of them—are wasted as far as their job of keeping up the future supply of plants is concerned. Birds, insects, mice and sometimes people eat them. Great numbers fall where there is no soil to grow in. Many more "drown" in too much water, are buried by fallen leaves, or die of thirst or starvation because there is not enough rain or the soil is unsuitable. Enormous quantities start to grow but are killed by insects, rodents, disease, unfavorable weather, or overcrowding.

These are a few of the many dangers that lie in wait for a seed. And so nature, almost as though she knew what each of her seeds is going to be up against, turns out huge quantities of them in order that enough can survive to keep the show on the road.

75

The alert eyes of the *tiger* are indicative of its nature, and these sharp eyes
seem to imply a thorough understanding of all the animal sees. The brain
of the tiger, however, limits its understanding to what its eyes perceive.

EYES OF NATURE

OVER THE LAST 500 million years of evolutionary history, a wondrous
succession of visual "inventions" has been developing in nature. This
process, though slow, is a continuing one. All these visual "inventions" trace
their origin to an elementary light sensitivity that is a vital characteristic of
every living thing, even the simplest one-celled plant or animal. Of the two
great kingdoms, animal and vegetable, only one has evolved specialized organs of sight. Although plants must find light to live, not a single plant
species has developed an eye of any kind. By contrast, in the animal kingdom, functional eyes are to be found in the majority of species, both vertebrate (those animals whose organs are supported by a backbone) and
invertebrate (those creatures that possess no backbones).

In instances where animal species have completely given up locomotion
there is usually complete absence of visual organs. *Shrimps, crabs,* and *lobsters* have well developed eyes but their very close relatives, the sessile *barnacles,* have no eyes at all! In a slow moving animal such as the *horseshoe
crab,* we find a relatively simple eye that can bring only the crudest of pictures to its armor-plated owner. If we turn to a bird like the *ostrich,* whose
safety is dependent upon its speed, we discover an extremely large and spe-

76

Shortsightedness is adequate for the *wood turtle.* Its eyes are tipped downward to help it see what it is eating.

77

The *crayfish* has several pairs of antennae and two bulbous eyes. Stalked eyes have swivel attachment and move freely.

cialized eye that can form an image of the outer world in the most exquisite detail. Highly specialized sense organs are always found in those animals whose very way of life seems dependent upon them. The nocturnal Mouse Opossum is able to elude his enemies in the forests of South America only because he is endowed with extra large eyes and ears, a keen sense of smell, and a set of long and sensitive whiskers. The senses of hearing, of smell, and of touch are all vital to his safety, but it is his sight that is far and away his most important sense.

The animal kingdom as a whole presents many different plans and styles for organs of special sight. None, however, can compare with the wonderful "camera eye" that reaches its finest perfection in the present-day birds and mammals. All vertebrate eyes are built much along the lines of a modern camera, but the all around precision and adaptability of the eye far surpasses our most modern and expensive cameras. Though the eyes of the vertebrate animals show considerable variation, the basic plan of construction is ever the same. For that reason a discussion of one vertebrate eye can serve as a basis for an understanding of any vertebrate eye. The eye of a *pygmy shrew* is little larger than the head of a pin, but it has the same camera-like arrangement as the grapefruit-sized eye of a *great blue whale*.

Even in the lowly one celled creatures we find structures popularly referred to as "eyes." The *euglena,* for example, has a tiny spot of red pigment that is specialized for the detection of changes in light intensity. This plant-animal (biologists are still debating the issue) contains green units of chlorophyll and must seek the right light intensities for carrying out photosynthesis. Of course, such a pigment spot in a one celled organism can do absolutely nothing by way of giving its owner an actual picture or image of the surroundings. Such a primitive eye spot represents only the first step toward a structure specialized for the detection of light.

Cottontail rabbit's eyes are opposite one another on sides of his head. This provides an extremely wide circle of vision.

78

As we move up in the animal kingdom to the larger and more complicated invertebrates we find a great variety of pigmented eye spots specifically designed as light detectors. The prominent eye spots of the *planaria*, a primitive flatworm, seem to suggest that this little animal might observe its surrounding in some detail. Microscopic study of the planaria's eyes, however, shows that these structures have absolutely nothing by way of a lens with which to focus an image of the surroundings. The planaria merely senses the major variations in light intensities, much as we can sense the direction of a strong light through our closed eyelids.

Again, the radially symmetrical *starfish* has several eye spots, one at the tip of each arm. As the arms swing about, while the starfish climbs among the rocks, his "eyes" will serve to tell him where the open clam flats are, in contrast to the dark hollows amongst the rocks.

There are many different methods of forming an image of the outer world, and an example of nearly every method can be found among the vast variety of living animals. The utilitarian eye of the *chambered nautilus* lacks a lens but functions satisfactorily on the principle of the pinhole camera, where a very tiny opening gives a universal focus. The *cuttlefish*, *squid* and *octopus*, close relatives of the nautilus, have eyes equipped with true lenses, the most specialized eyes of any of the invertebrates. The eye design of these three marine mollusks is remarkably similar to that of the higher vertebrates, a striking example of two different evolutionary lines that have developed very similar structures to meet a similar need.

If we next turn to the *arthropods*, by far the largest and most successful group of invertebrate animals, we find a fascinating variety of both simple and complex eyes. This great phylum of joint-footed animals includes all the *insects, spiders, crabs, centipedes,* and *millipedes.* The spider's eyes are known as simple eyes because each has but one transparent lens to focus light rays on the sensi-

The *African ostrich,* largest living bird, has eyes proportionately large—and the biggest eyes of any land animal alive.

The *toad's* eyes are set in a raised position to enable it to look around when buried in soft earth.

79

80

37

tive nerve cells beneath it. From its simple structure such an eye is presumed to give only a very limited picture of the outer world. To some extent the spider makes up for this inadequacy by having eight of these simple eyes placed strategically at the front of the head. Even such simple eyes have proven so useful to their owners that sight has become the most important sense to some spiders.

It is in the insect world that we find the most remarkable development of the compound style of eye. A *grasshopper* has five separate and distinct eyes, three small simple ones hardly to be noticed and two large compound eyes prominently placed at the sides of the head. Such a compound eye proves to be a very remarkable and elaborate structure. In essence it is a combination of hundreds, or even thousands, of simple eyes all combined into one compact structure. Each individual unit has its own lens and sensory nerves to record the light that it receives. Though the stalked eye of the *crayfish* is not especially large, it is, nevertheless, of a compound nature. Under a powerful hand lens the surface of such an eye resembles a honeycomb, made up of many tiny individual lenses. The structure of a compound eye is so completely different from our camera-type eye that it is difficult to make even a good guess as to the sort of visual image it records. We must assume that the scene is reproduced as a lot of small patches of lights and darks.

In the extreme development of the compound eye we find insects with enormous eyes that nearly encompass their heads. The *dragonfly* represents such an extreme since it needs the very best of sight if it is successfully to capture flying insects on the wing. A single eye of the dragonfly is an elab-

The *Indian elephant* is such a large and powerful beast that it does not depend on eyesight for safety. Though it has a very keen sense of smell, its relatively small eyes are all that it needs for satisfactory vision.

81

38

orate composite of nearly 20,000 individual units!

If you observe a *praying mantis* in the act of stalking a spider you will likely conclude, as the entomologists have, that the mantis has little ability to distinguish motionless forms. If a praying mantis suddenly spies a spider moving within its reach, it will promptly turn its head in the direction of the prey, obviously having detected the motion. If the spider now elects to remain motionless however, as spiders frequently do, the mantis will stand poised and immobile, staring in the spider's direction but apparently unable to distinguish the prey as long as it remains still. When tired of waiting, the mantis will advance, its grasping forelegs raised and ready to strike the instant it detects any motion.

It is believed that birds have very highly developed long distance vision. The remarkable vision of the *vultures* found in southern United States has been clearly demonstrated. If a dead sheep is placed in the open when not one vulture can be seen in the sky, it may be only a matter of minutes before several vultures will have gathered for the feast. The prompt appearance of the birds results from a broad and effective spotting system. Each long-winged scavenger soars in large

82

83

The powerful *mandrill* is thought to have good color vision; hence its bright hues are to attract its mate.

One eye of the *gray squirrel* records a different scene from the other. Such "dual vision" is of life-saving value.

circles high in the sky, keen eyes scanning the details of the earth below. Where possible a weather eye is also kept on other vultures soaring over neighboring sections of the adjoining countryside. If one spies a likely meal and drops down to investigate, several others, taking the cue from the first, will take the long glide in with the hope that there will be enough carrion to go around.

The eyes of most animals are designed to focus either on near objects or on distant objects, but usually not equally well on both. The spider, with eight simple eyes, is so near-sighted that it probably cannot distinguish objects at all clearly if they are more than five or six inches away. Most birds of prey have a special ability to view distant objects in sharp detail one in-

84

85

The *mouse opossum* has extra large eyes and ears, a keen sense of smell, and a set of long and sensitive whiskers.

Even the homely *toad* has an attractive eye when observed at close range. The pigmented iris sparkles like metal.

stant and then change to a sharp short range focus the next.

The *osprey* serves as an excellent example of this specialization. When looking for a meal this large fish hawk often hovers on beating wings as much as three hundred feet above the water. From this distance it can spot even a small fish if one rises near the surface of the water.

In proportion to body size the eyes of birds are usually much larger than those of mammals. A large *owl*, only 1/30 the weight of a man, may have eyes slightly larger than those of a man. That part of a bird's eye which we see in the eye opening is really deceptively small. It is surprising to see how much of the total space within the head is taken up by the eyes. The large eyes of the owl give him a wise expression, but we should not overlook the fact that the space devoted to his brain is only half of that devoted to his two eyes! What land animal has the largest eye? An *elephant* or perhaps a *hippopotamus*? No, the largest terrestrial eye is found in a bird—the *ostrich*. The eyes of day-living birds can produce a sharper picture over a broader area than can our eyes.

The vision of most animals on this earth is concentrated primarily on the detection of movement. Many creatures, like the snakes and the toads, appear almost entirely blind to objects that remain motionless. A *frog* being chased by a *garter snake* will sometimes take a few big jumps and then freeze instinctively. By remaining perfectly still the frog makes it much more difficult for the snake to relocate him. Our *dogs* and *cats* seem to see and interpret motion much more readily than they do stationary objects.

The most difficult visual problem is that of adapting to the extremes in light conditions that prevail during an animal's active hours. Unlike the camera, the eye is not in a position to make a simple replacement and change to a film of a different speed. To adjust to sudden shifts in light intensity the eye must make very special internal alterations. For better light adaptation there is an actual migration of pigment in the eyes of some insects. In the dark the praying mantis's eyes are deeply pigmented, but when brought into the bright light they soon turn to a beautiful green.

In the camera-eye of the vertebrates the amount of light admitted is first controlled by the iris diaphragm. In our eyes the round pupil opening automatically expands and contracts to let more or less light into the retina. In our domestic *cat* the enormous pupil opening will close to a vertical slit in the presence of bright light. In direct sunlight the pupil opening in the eye of a *horse* will be found to take the shape of a horizontal bar. *Lizards* and other lower vertebrates reduce their pupil openings to a great variety of odd shapes and patterns. In the *alligator* we have a reptile that is by nature regularly active in bright sunlight as well as in the dark of the night. Its retina must be extremely sensitive to record a satisfactory image when there is very little light available, and yet it must somehow avoid being completely dazzled by the brilliance of the sun. To help with this extreme adjustment the pupil can change from a large round opening to a paper-thin vertical slit which will admit only a tiny portion of light. A vertical eye pupil indicates an animal that is active day and night.

Nocturnal creatures (such as the *owl* and the *flying squirrel*) always have proportionately enormous eyes, designed to admit just as much of the dim illumination as possible. Those animals with particularly large and sensitive eyes usually remain hidden during the daylight hours for comfort.

The great variety of eyes found in nature seem to cover all the extremes of adaptation to special light conditions. Where we would be dazzled by the brilliance of the sun on an expanse of glistening snow, the *polar bear* views the world without the slightest discomfort. Where we would be helpless in a deep forest on a dark night, the owls and flying squirrels glide through the trees with the greatest of ease.

There is also the matter of a color sense. It is hard for us to realize that an animal with good eyesight may still fail completely to see the brilliant

The *African lion* in repose seems only a big, friendly cat. Set in such an enormous head the eyes of this animal seem extremely small and insignificant. This is deceptive for the African lion has very excellent vision.

86

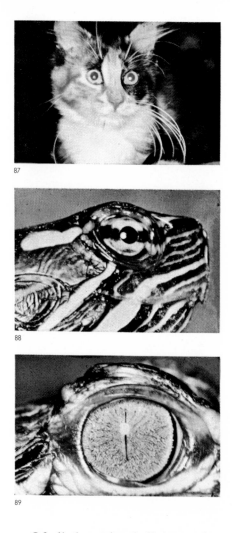

87

88

89

Excellent vision, acute hearing, and sensitive whiskers make the domestic *cat* a successful night-time hunter.

The young *painted turtle* has camouflaged eyes. Pigmentation of the iris carries head striping right through the eye.

Exposed to brilliant light, *alligator's* pupil contracts to vertical slit admitting only a fraction of the light.

colors in a sunset. The human eye itself does not actually see all the colors in sunlight. The ultraviolet portion of the sun's spectrum, lying just outside the visible, remains invisible to us because these very short wave lengths are absorbed in the lens and never reach the sensitive retina. Fantastic as it sounds, a person who has had a diseased lens removed from one eye can (with a substitute glass lens) see quite satisfactorily in pure ultraviolet light!

Zoologists tell us that most animals live in a dull, gray, colorless world. None of the nocturnal animals have much of a color sense because eyes that are adapted for night sight lack the "cones" in the retina that are responsible for color vision.

Of all the animals living today only the birds and the primates (*lemurs, monkeys,* and *man*) show full awareness of colors. The color-blind mammals for the most part have extremely drab markings whereas the *mandrill,* a primate with good color vision, is permanently outfitted in rather startling hues. In an animal possessing color vision bold coloration usually serves as an attraction between the sexes. The brilliant plumages of male birds are, similarly, sexual adornment designed to impress the female.

There are some eyes in nature that normally see as well in ultraviolet light as they do in the rainbow colors that are visible to our eyes. Our own well developed color consciousness makes us try to explain the actions of all other animals, at least in part, on the basis of color. The oft-repeated statement that *bulls* are infuriated by the color red serves as a good example of such conclusion-jumping. Tests seem to indicate that bulls are in reality quite color blind. An entire herd of European stud bulls was once outfitted with bright red veils and not even a minor case of infuriation was reported.

Birds have a more highly developed color sense than man but the color emphasis in birds is somewhat different. A *robin* is believed to see the world somewhat as we might through a pair of orange-tinted spectacles. Some birds apparently have a favorite color. Bright orange-red paper petals will quickly draw the *hummingbird* to the small vials of sugar syrup often put out to attract him.

The feeding habits of many of the backboned animals can be judged not only from an examination of their teeth but also from a study of their eyes! The position of the eyes in many of the higher vertebrates can serve to identify them as either a herbivore or a carnivore. In a plant-eating mammal such as a *rabbit,* the eyes are of first importance as sense organs to warn of approaching danger. To give the rabbit as wide a circle of vision as possible its eyes are positioned on opposite sides of its head. By contrast, a predatory mammal like the cheetah has both eyes squarely set in front of its head and directed straight forward. To capture the elusive animals that make up its diet requires the hunting advantage that is gained by having both eyes concentrate on the same scene. Being a powerful and dangerous fighter, the cheetah has little need for a "360° lookout." An animal with eyes on opposite sides of its head must, of course, see two completely different scenes at one and the same time which to us would be quite confusing.

The position of the eyes in the head of an animal can show great specialization. The *alligator* (a reptile) and the *hippopotamus* (a mammal) both have their eyes set in a raised position on the tops of their heads. With "periscopic eyes" they can float in the water, almost entirely submerged, and still keep an eye on their surroundings. The *bittern,* a marsh heron, has its eyes placed unusually low on the sides of its head. As a result, with its bill pointing skyward to make it blend with the cattails, the bittern can still look forward with its underslung eyes to observe any danger. The *woodcock,* or *timberdoodle,* has its eyes placed so far back on its head that it can ac-

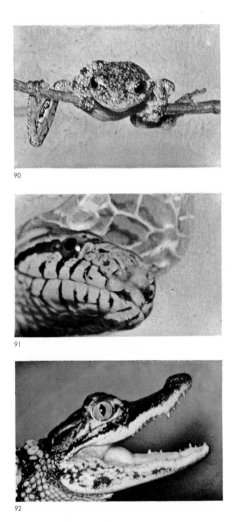

90

91

92

The little *tree frog* has sticky toes to aid in climbing, and prominent eyes to help it catch fast-flying insects.

The *milk snake* cannot close its eyes (snakes have no eyelids!) but depends on an "eyeshield" for protection.

In shade, the *alligator's* eye pupil is a vertical ellipse. On a dark night, it expands to almost fill the eye.

43

tually see better to the rear than it can to the front. This odd, rear-view arrangement enables it to maintain a lookout while its long bill probes deep into the mud in search of earthworms.

In many of the invertebrate animals, like the crabs and the snails, we find the eyes positioned at the ends of elongated stalks that can be moved about and, in some cases, actually retracted. To crawling creatures such a periscopic arrangement would seem to be of distinct advantage. There is one backboned animal with its eyes positioned at the ends of two bizarre extensions of the sides of the head—the *hammerhead shark*.

Animals with both eyes directed forward have sacrificed the extremely wide field of view enjoyed by the side-eyed animals like the rabbit. This loss, however, is compensated for by an entirely different visual advantage called depth perception or, in modern photographic terms, three dimensions or 3-D. This ability to judge the distance of an object at close range, and with extreme accuracy, results from the fact that two eyes do not really see identical pictures. Since our eyes are separated by about two and a half inches they each see nearby objects positioned just a little differently against the more distant background.

The advantage of three-dimensional sight can be of prime importance to a wildcat about to spring on a scurrying squirrel, also to an animal like a *chimpanzee* that has developed the skillful use of its hands. Birds that do not have binocular (stereoscopic) vision often try to compensate for the lack of it by bobbing their heads from side to side as a means of obtaining two slightly different views of the same scene.

Along with the impressive advantages that the eyes of nature bring to their owners, one very real disadvantage must be conceded. Most animals of the world are outfitted in colors and textures that help them to blend inconspicuously with their natural surroundings. Little has been done, however, to disguise the bright, round reflective surface of the eye. An *iguana's* green scales will serve as excellent camouflage in association with leafy vegetation, but one glimpse of its gleaming eye is all that is needed to fix his position for an enemy. Few animals have achieved much in the way of eye disguise. One of the rare examples of eye camouflage is found in young specimens of the common *painted turtle*. Here prominent colored stripes on

Spice bush swallowtail caterpillar has two grotesque false eyes. Real eyes are well forward, and inconspicuous.

The binocular vision of the *chimpanzee* greatly increases the skill with which it can use its well-developed hands.

93

94

The *iguana's* green coloring helps to blend it with vegetation. Its bright eyes, however, spoil the camouflage.

Extremely large eyes enable the *flying squirrel* to glide safely from tree to tree —even on the darkest of nights.

As added protection, the *owl*, like most birds, has a third transparent eyelid that covers without impairing vision.

95

96

97

the head are carried right across the eyes, with the pigment of the iris involved in the pattern.

It is common knowledge that the eyes of some animals actually glow in the dark, so that their luminous orbs can easily be seen on the darkest of nights. This "common knowledge," however, is actually a bit of folklore and is quite unfounded. Every eye in nature is designed to receive light energy, and though some animals, such as the *firefly*, have the ability to create light within their bodies, this "cold light" is never emitted from the eye itself. True, if the headlights of an automobile at night strike a nocturnal mammal sitting in the road, its eyes will sometimes glow like incandescent lamps, with a weird light that seems to come right from inside the eyes. This ghostly glow *does* actually come from inside the eyeball! It is simply light from the headlights that has been concentrated and reflected back again by a special mirror membrane that lines the back of the eye. This reflective layer has a bright metallic luster of silver and gold and is found in varying degrees in the eyes of most nocturnal animals. Its purpose, a rather surprising one, is to give the retina a second opportunity to absorb the energy of any particular light ray. The retina itself is so thin that it is able to absorb only a portion of the light that first strikes it. For this reason having a mirror layer directly behind the retina can be advantageous to animals that must see in very dim light. With such an arrangement light that passes through the retina when it enters the eye may still be absorbed when it reverses itself after striking the mirror membrane. Your cat's eyes will be seen to glow in the dark because of this efficient reflective arrangement but, remember, they glow only by reflected light and will remain entirely invisible to you on a dark night unless you shine a light in their direction.

Because of the great importance of eyes to their animal owners, many

45

special structures have been evolved for their care and protection. Insects have special brushes on the inside of their forelegs an aid in keeping the eyes clean and free of dust. You may have observed that the *housefly,* in cleaning its eyes, rolls its head about in its forelegs as if it were a marble it is trying to polish. The smooth and transparent surface of the vertebrate eye is easily kept moist and clean if it belongs to a *fish* that spends its life in the water. For this reason fish have no movable eyelids, but only a fixed transparent shield over the front of the eye.

A fish that comes out on land, like the little *mud skipper* that spends its time flipping about on the mud banks in pursuit of insects, is in great danger of having its eye surfaces dry up. To prevent this, the mud skipper, whose protruding eyes are placed high on its head, moistens its eyes at regular intervals by rolling them downward into a socket in the head. This odd action is necessary if the eyes of this semi-terrestrial fish are to be kept clear and moist while exposed to the drying air.

To prevent the eyes from drying, most land vertebrates have well developed eyelids which they blink many times each minute to keep the eyeball clear and moist. Since a slow blink would tend to interrupt the vision, we find that the "wink of an eye" can be an amazingly rapid motion—sometimes too quick to be seen. Only the snakes have no eyelids at all, their eyes being fixed in a permanent glassy stare. The "hypnotic effect" of the serpent's stare is a bit of superstition, however, with no basis of fact. To protect the delicate and lidless eyes of the snake, there is a transparent shield permanently in place over the entire eye opening. This "spectacle" is an integral part of the snake's scaly covering and hence is shed each time the snake molts.

One of the small lizards, a *gecko,* has an astounding method of keeping its eyes moist and clear. Rather than blinking its eyelids, as we might expect it to do, it runs out a very long tongue that reaches easily to its eyes. Then, in the most casual manner, it uses the expanded tip of its tongue to wash the surface of its eyes as if this were really no trick at all. To the *horned toad* that spends its days running over the dusty earth, or burrowing in the sand, a pair of responsive eyelids is highly essential.

We think of most animals as having two eyelids, an upper lid and a lower

The *black-footed ferret's* eyes glow here as if luminous, but only reflect the photographer's flash bulb.

The male *purple finch* has a thick bill for cracking seeds and a wide field of view for spotting danger.

98

99

The *horned toad* lives in dusty areas, blinks to keep eyes clean and moist. (Shown here eating a *grain beetle*.)

100

Alligator's raised eyes serve as natural periscopes when this reptile floats motionless in a quiet swamp.

lid, but some animals have three! The birds, and a few other vertebrates, have a distinct and very specialized third eyelid—the nictitating membrane. In the owl, for example, this extra eyelid can be seen as a complete transparent membrane that sweeps down across the surface of the eye, starting from the inner corner. In part it is used to moisten the surface of the eyeball, making it unnecessary for the large feathered eyelids to blink shut for this purpose. The great advantage of this special

101

eyelid, however, lies in its ability to protect the eye when its owner is forced to fly through such hazards as windblown dust and the closely laced branches of trees. The transparent nictitating membrane is drawn across the eyes of many birds whenever they are in flight, since this offers the eye important added protection while impairing vision to only a slight degree. It may surprise many equestrians to learn that even the horse, with the largest eye of any land mammal, has a well developed third eyelid designed to protect the eye while he grazes on sharp edged grasses. The special safeguards and protected position given to the eyes of all vertebrates is simple proof of the prime importance attached to vision.

So far as is known every one of the 38,000 species of vertebrate animals known to zoologists (4,000 mammals, 14,000 birds, 4,000 reptiles, 2,000 amphibians and 14,000 fish) is born with functional camera-style eyes. There are a few of these vertebrates, however, adapted to situations of total darkness, that completely give up their functional eyes as they mature. In the pools and streams that exist deep in subterranean caves—where there is no night and day, but only eternal blackness—several blind fish and a few blind *salamanders* live out their sightless days. Many thousands of years ago the ancestors of these blind cave species must have been carried in from the outer world by a surface stream that at some point found its way underground. Over a long, long period of time new species gradually evolved with greatly reduced, non-functional eyes.

That a fish could learn to adapt to total darkness is not surprising since most fish of the northern United States continue their activities in total darkness for several months each year. Remember, absolutely no light gets through to the water in a pond or a lake while its surface is frozen solid and covered with a deep reflective blanket of snow. Under these circum-

102

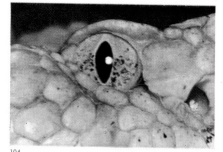

104

103

105

The *sunfish* cannot turn its head—because it has no neck—so it has need of eyes that swivel freely.

The *crab spider* has eight individual eyes on its head. Here it feeds on an unwary fly, caught in *goldenrod.*

The vertical pupil of the *timber rattlesnake* indicates that it is active both by day and by night.

Unlike man's, the large eyes of the *honeybee* use the ultra-violet portion of sun's spectrum to see with.

stances the fish learn to live by their other senses, particularly those of taste, touch, and hearing. In the oceans of the polar regions, where the ice and snow cover are a permanent fixture, a great variety of marine animals exists in a perpetually lightless world.

Only in the most eye-minded class of vertebrates—the birds—do we find not a single blind species. In the mammals we find several *moles* and a few subterranean *rodents* that have completely lost their sight. There is even a kind of fresh-water *dolphin* (a porpoise-like mammal) living in the mud-laden rivers of India that grows to be nine feet in length but has no functional eyes. It feeds on fish and small crustaceans captured by probing in the mud with its sensitive beak.

Those creatures that habitually live in semi-darkness frequently develop structures to make better use of one of the senses other than sight. A scurrying *cockroach,* for example, can literally find its way by feel, using its extremely long and sensitive antennae. The *catfish* that live in muddy waters have all developed long and mobile whiskers to compensate for their poor vision. The *star-nosed mole* has a set of little fleshy fingers arranged in a neat ring around the end of its nose.

There is one vast territory of inky darkness on our earth that we might easily overlook—the ocean deeps. In some places the oceans of our world are as much as five or six miles deep, but the bright light of the world above is entirely filtered out when we go below the two mile mark. This means, of course, that the vast number of deep water fish must live in the same eternal blackness that our fresh-water cave fish have adapted to. It comes as a surprise, therefore, to find that, instead of being blind, most of our deep water marine fish have eyes that are extremely prominent and more sensitive to light than any other eyes found in nature! The answer lies in the fact that most deep sea creatures (unlike the cave fish) possess characteristic luminous organs which they flash as a visible identification badge in their otherwise lightless world. Their luminous organs are not bright enough to illuminate other objects by reflected light but they can be directly seen by the eyes of other fish.

There is one odd group of shallow water fish that has solved an eye problem in surprising fashion. The *flounders* are fish that by nature lie on their sides on the ocean bottom. It would seem that one of their eyes, therefore, would be doomed to uselessness, lying as it would against the ocean bottom. Through ages of evolution the flounder has found a way to avoid this particular calamity. One eye of each newborn flounder promptly starts an actual migration that shortly brings it to the other side of the head, right alongside the non-migratory eye! This gives the flounder a grotesque appearance, but he has both eyes where he can use them.

The invertebrate animals show a great variation in the number of eyes that an individual may possess. The vertebrate animals, on the other hand, have settled for two eyes and adapted them to meet the demands of the various environments. The oddity known as the *four-eyed fish* is really a South American *minnow* that habitually swims with its eyes half in and

The two piercing eyes of the *African cheetah*, the world's fastest land mammal, face directly forward and can be focused simultaneously on the same scene. To a predator such binocular vision can be of major importance.

106

49

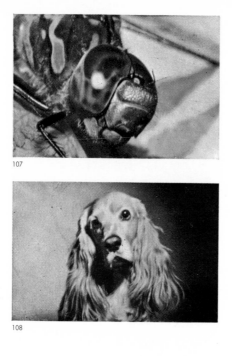

107

108

The compound eyes of the *dragonfly* nearly encompass its head. Each is composed of 20,000 individual units!

The plaintive eyes of a *cocker spaniel* are so expressive that we are misled to believe he thinks and sees as we do.

half out of the water. Though it has only two eyes, each of them is equipped with two distinct pupils—one to allow for vision above the water, and one for below the water. In New Zealand we find one rare exception to the two-eyed rule. The *tuatera*, a primitive lizard reaching a length of two feet, has in the middle of its forehead a small but functional third eye with a tiny lens and a sensitive retina. Though the eye is too simple to form a good image it still stands as a tie with the past.

Eyes are, of course, to see with, but the amphibians have added an ingenious secondary use for their eyes! This can be observed if you watch a toad in the act of swallowing a large insect. To help push the body of the insect down its throat the toad retracts its bulging eyes deep into their sockets so that they press on the roof of the mouth and help force the insect along. To be sure, the toad must "swallow blind" since it cannot use its eyes for vision at the same time it is using them as a food press.

In thinking of the vision of any animal, whether an octopus or an elephant, we must always remember that the real "seeing" is done in the mind. The eye is an organ specialized for recording light stimuli and setting off a pattern of nervous impulses that can be sent to the brain. Only in the brain can an image be recorded on the consciousness itself.

If humans could see with their eyes alone they would be greatly confused for the image that is formed on the retina is invariably upside-down! This poses no problem to our brains, since images are *always* upside-down in the eye and it is merely a matter of properly interpreting them.

When you consider the vision of any other animal, always remember that its "seeing ability" is dependent not only on the perfection of its eyes but also on the capacity of its brain to record and interpret the visual impulses received. Many creatures have larger and more elaborate eye structures than does man, but these more efficient eyes are always connected to much simpler brains. *No other living animal* can begin to appreciate—as man does—the information received through the eyes.

109

A *bluebird* in a fruit tree makes a colorful springtime picture. A nesting box may successfully attract him.

BEST LOVED SONG BIRDS

S PRING DAYS without the songs of birds would seem as incomplete as a layer cake minus its icing. The basic flavor and nourishment would be there, but you would sadly miss the final touch. Imagine a mild April morning in which no *bluebirds* warbled, or a fragrant May dusk deprived of the *wood thrushes'* rich cadences among the darkening trees! Could anything be more lacking in its crowning savor than this?

There is a popular belief that birds sing in the spring and early summer because they are happy over the return of warmer weather. This is unlikely, since birds act by instinct, without reasoning why. Well then, if they don't sing to express their joyous zest, why *do* birds sing?

The primary cause has to do with mating and nesting. Lady birds seem to be susceptible to first class vocalizing by good-looking males of their own kind, particularly when the songs are accompanied by much display of handsome plumage, fancy strutting and occasional bursts of manly flying powers. So the ardent suitors put on the loudest and showiest campaigns they can, and most of them succeed in winning brides. The uninhibited bursts of song from the male of the species reach their climax during the actual mating and breeding season, and recede steadily after the new families have been raised. In this fact lies one explanation of the almost complete absence of bird songs after midsummer. Since the breeding activity caused the songs, they ended when it did.

The second cause of bird songs is the parents' need to protect the family food supply. The burden of this task is assumed by the prospective father, which largely explains why, with very few exceptions, male birds do all the singing. Here is the background of it:

A male *redwing blackbird* with his red and buff epaulettes is one of the best-dressed birds in North America.

The softly blended subtle colors of the parent *field sparrows* provide protective coloration for a nestful of babies.

110

111

All members of any given species eat the same kinds of food and find them in the same sorts of places and by the same methods. Some species do most of their foraging in trees, some on the ground, and so on. So what happens? Each male must get complete ownership of a "nest neighborhood" that contains enough of its own special kinds of food. He therefore cruises around until he finds a spot well stocked with junior as well as adult foods. Then he instinctively bursts into song, thereby laying claim to his chosen territory. Once established, he issues constantly repeated warnings to all other males of his own kind to keep out or face him in battle. He does, however, proclaim his territorial rights far more courteously than we would if we were in his place, for instead of shouting gruff orders to "keep out," he just sings and sings as if he were too happy to contain himself. Birds of *other* species are, however, welcome to come in and settle if they wish, for they eat other foods or hunt in different ways or locations.

Nearly all of our smaller land birds sing, but many of them can scarcely qualify as fine vocalizers. Since this is a story about real singers, we have consequently made our final selections firmly on that basis. The twenty-six kinds of birds presented here are far from being a complete collection of this country's outstanding vocalists, but they do comprise a fair sampling of the most popular.

The picturesque *bluebird*, "with the sky on his back and good red soil on his breast," is one of the pleasantest singers of the thrush clan. No early spring in the Midwest and the East would be complete without his warm-hearted warbling. There is nothing strident about it, nor is it so frequent as to become monotonous. The male, of course, with his sky blue hue, is more brightly colored than his spouse, although even she out-shines most of the other females.

Although bluebirds are definitely migratory, a few of them commonly remain in New England all winter long. Many an abandoned field well grown up with red-cedars holds its half-dozen or so contented tenants even on the coldest days, for the dense leafage offers both excellent protection and a generous store of berries.

112

From babyhood onward, *wood thrushes* are exceptionally appealing birds. They seem to give the impression of being well-bred ladies and gentlemen.

Traces of winter are still in the air when the throaty *konk-a-ree-ee-ee* song of *red-winged blackbirds* rings out from countless marshes across the country. Another snowy day or two may lie ahead but more certainly than the first robin's chant, the far-carrying song of this shining black fellow with the buff-edged scarlet epaulettes brings the message that spring is really at hand.

Redwings habitually nest near water, and so it is not surprising that the first spring singing of the males is done in marshy places. They seek out such spots as soon as they arrive from the South, usually a couple of weeks in advance of the females. After a few days, this advance guard gathers in groups that range the countryside, often mass-singing from the treetops like college glee clubs on their Easter vacation tours. Apparently they enjoy their barbershop harmonies. But their free wanderings are short-lived, for courting begins with the appearance of the females, and with it comes the breakup of the songfests. By the time the trees are in young leaf most of the red-

53

wings have mated, and the pairs are settling down in marshy places for the nesting season.

While the soberly clad females attend to the chores of family-raising, their mates stand guard in bush tops or other commanding spots close by. Often they sing while on duty, but if a crow or other possible robber comes into sight every man jack of them joins in a mass attack that seldom fails to drive the enemy far out of sight.

The *field sparrow* is a modest, soft hued and completely engaging little fellow. Both sexes are similarly marked in a delightfully blended symphony of browns, red-browns, buffs and grays, and their light flesh-colored bills and pale eye rings give them a gentle, almost wondering expression.

This appealing mite ought really to be called "pasture" sparrow, since it does not live in open fields. Its neatly made cup nest of soft stems and grasses is built on or close to the ground in places where clumps of bayberry and other dense, twiggy bushes or wild blackberry tangles provide good coverage.

You might think that the long sunny hours of spring and early summer days would be ample for any field sparrow to sing his fill, but not so. Sometimes, on quiet moonlight nights, his brave little ditty comes lilting through the stillness with inexpressible sweetness.

113

The *wood thrush,* as they say, has "got everything." There is refined beauty as well as style in his chestnut back and dotted breast, and he is such a good mixer that he is equally at home in damp, thickety farm woods and among the lawns and

Though their name implies a fondness for forests, *wood thrushes* are just as happy near well planted human homes.

Meadowlark nests are built on the ground hidden among tall grasses. Access is by a tunnel-like path.

Down South they call the slim and showy *brown thrasher* a "sandy mockingbird," for he is one of the mimic-birds.

114

115

shade trees of private estates and small suburban homes. His rich, delightfully modulated phrases, rising and falling with all the feeling and perfection of a great musician, immediately appeal to every ear.

Wood thrushes are as devoted parents as one could find. Their substantial nests, well strengthened with mixed mud and fibrous stuff, are firmly planted in forks or branch clumps, neither dangerously close to the ground nor so high and exposed as to suffer from strong winds. Both parents noisily defend their young.

The *meadowlark* is a handsome, sturdy all-American. He delights in open grasslands where sun and wind have full play. Even his song is strong and far-reaching, and it sweeps out from tree or fence post with memorable clearness. Meadowlark nests are right on the ground of grasslands, and grass not only forms them but is also pulled together over-

116

While mother *red-winged blackbirds* tend their young in the home nests, their mates mount guard near by and drive off crows and other enemies.

head in a rough, concealing roof. Through the surrounding network of slender stems and blades a short hidden pathway completes a home almost too secret for belief. (You see it all in the photograph—all, that is, except the greatest secret of all, the nest itself and its complement of delicately spotted eggs.) The nesting birds are extremely wary in approaching and leaving their home, and while the female is brooding, her mate mounts guard on a distant post or tree from which he can see any approaching danger and call a loud warning. Neither bird leaves or alights on the ground close to the nest; there is always that stealthy walk through the sheltering grass as an ultimate precaution against discovery.

The strikingly marked *brown thrashers* with their gleaming yellow eyes are nearly a foot long from bill-tip to tail-tip. They may build their bulky, twiggy nests in shrubs at the edge of your lawn and freely display their beauty as they hop or trot across the open turf in search of grubs and beetles. They are also tireless hunters among fallen leaves, and if your garden contains raspberries or strawberries your admiration for brown thrashers may weaken

55

117

118

119

Chipping sparrow nests, like their owners, are trim and unassuming. Often they are built close to populated spots.

Slate-colored *juncos* keep their jauntiness in winter. Give them food and shelter and they face winter fearlessly.

The popular *song sparrows* are found, in various forms, all over the country. They are appealing garden birds.

considerably, for they relish fresh fruit and help themselves generously!

Song-wise, this thrasher is rather like the *mockingbird* in volume and general style. There are few startling imitations, however, and practically no harsh notes. The performance wears much better than the mocker's, being less strident and insistent. Besides, you never have to listen to it all night, for apparently thrashers like to get a little sleep themselves.

Chipping sparrows are the most sociable of dooryard birds, and the best behaved. They seem to have an abiding faith in the good will of human beings and may nest within arm's length of a front gate or kitchen porch.

In nest-building they are neater than most of the other sparrows and nearly always line their structure with long hairs such as those from horses' manes and the tails of cattle. They are excellent providers, too, and the youngsters are well prepared to leave the nest by the tenth day.

As for singing, "chippies" really put their hearts into long songs of "chips" crowded together like beads on a string. Their performance is one of the most soothing sounds of the long, contented summer days.

Whether you call it *slate-colored junco* or simply *snowbird,* this little bundle of grays and whites is never down-hearted, never dismayed by the deepest snows and lowest temperatures. During the nesting season you will find it only in our higher mountains and also at low altitudes up toward Canada, for it loves cool weather. Trimly dressed and flashing conspicuous white

56

outer tail feathers when it takes wing, the slate-colored junco is as much at home floundering in deep snow as on the bare, drab ground. Bread crumbs, small seeds and fine-cracked corn are all grist for its small mill, and for sleeping quarters this hardy fellow asks nothing better than frosty brush piles, shrubs, and—for special luxury—the shelter of small evergreens. Its song is sometimes a trill, sometimes a mixture of warble and twitter. And when its song ceases and the snowbird departs, you know that true spring is close at hand.

The *song sparrow,* time-honored favorite of garden, field and roadside, never seeks the spotlight and asks only to live its quiet life in its own way. It can face the discomforts of winter with perfect courage. No bird of its size is more determined in defense of its nest, yet few allow such close approach by quiet people to whom they are accustomed. There are many geographical forms or "races" of this well loved little chap, and one or more of them can be found in any region across the country.

Out west, the *western tanager* takes over the role of his scarlet cousin in the east. Their songs are almost identical, and both species prefer the same type of surroundings. But what a contrast there is between the formal red-and-black dress of the scarlet tanager and the riotous black, yellow, white and red pattern of the male western's spring suit! It seems strange to see such splendor in northern woodlands, and in a sense both these species are birds out of place. The tropics are the real home of the tanager tribe — some three hundred kinds of them — and only three members of it visit the northern states in spring and summer.

120

All tanagers are first of all insect eaters, but the western tanager sometimes forgets his family habit and raids the ripening cherry crops so hungrily that the orchard owners wish he'd go right back to the tropics, and stay there!

If a nationwide contest were to be held to choose America's most popular bird there is a fair chance that the good old *robin* would fly away with top honors. Robust, hearty, and

The *western tanager* is more fantastically colored than his eastern cousin, but the songs of both sound alike.

Baby *robins* show their kinship to the thrush tribe by sporting generously spotted vests before molting.

121

57

abundantly distributed from coast to coast, he also holds high rank as a singer. He is a friendly fellow, too, and likes open rural and suburban country where men live among lawns, gardens and even farm fields. There is no more characteristic morning and evening sound in such settings than his bubbly "cheer-up, cheer-up, cheerily, cheer-up."

Robins belong to the thrush family, which may help to explain the often continuous tendency of their singing performance. There is a thrush-like reminder, too, in the speckled markings of their children's breasts.

These rollicking characters are first class house builders. They not only construct substantial nests in stout tree forks or perhaps on exposed flat beams around house porches and barn eaves, but they plaster their walls with mud-and-grass, which they mold to fit their bodies before it dries and hardens. The nest lining is of fine grasses and rootlets, to provide a soft bed.

Winter wrens are ludicrously tubby little fellows, hardly bigger than golf balls, but possessed of terrific curiosity. They have perky tails that tilt skyward or even forward toward their owners' heads, and a consuming passion for mouse-like skipping in and out of dark crannies among rocks and tangled windfalls. But as singers they

Photographing the ever active *winter wren* in its haunts is a challenge to camera fans. Its nest is hidden in this tree-root tangle.

are in the top rank, full of trills, runs, and grace notes, the volume startling from a bird of such small size. Because of their highly secretive ways and remote nests, this is perhaps the least familiar of our wrens. The usual breeding ground is up around the Canadian border.

Since she is the one who does most of the household chores, the female *scarlet tanager* in her dull yellow and greenish dress is inconspicuous enough to avoid drawing attention to the nestful of eggs and young. But her husband has no such need, so he blazes like a torch until, with the approach of the southward flight in September, his colors change from scarlet, with jet-black wings and tail, to the restrained hues of his mate.

This tanager's loud, vigorous song reminds one of a robin's, but it is more hurried, broken, and, when heard at

122

58

close quarters, a bit on the rough side. Furthermore, this bird's song may baffle you, for one minute it sounds near by, then far away. Tanagers are excellent ventriloquists.

The tanager's nest is a shallow, rather loose mass of twigs and softer odds and ends. It is usually set out on a horizontal limb, perhaps as much as forty feet from the ground.

Scarlet tanagers spend their winters in western South America as far down as Peru, and return to the States about the time the new tree leaves begin to take definite form. At this season the almost dazzling males are not uncommon sights among lawn trees and even in landscaped city parks. But once hot weather is here the best place to find them is well up in the forest trees.

Goldfinches pack more delightful characteristics into their small frames than almost any other bird. Merry and replete with energy and the spirit of adventure, little parties of them rove the countryside with a bounding, joyous flight, often voicing their good spirits with a jolly "perchic-o-ree." All through the spring and early summer when most other birds are tied down by family tasks, they range hither and yon without an apparent care in the world, for

123

124

Baby *robins,* always hungry, proclaim this fact constantly. In one day they eat twice their own weight in food.

Baby *goldfinches,* still too young to fly, already show signs of inheriting their parents' independent nature.

their own nesting time rarely comes in the North before late July or even August. Meanwhile, the males keep bursting into their twittering, canary-like song, sometimes so prolonged that you wonder why they don't run out of breath.

Apparently goldfinches have two good reasons for putting off their family duties. One is that thistle-down seems to be a "must" for lining their nests, and even the earliest thistle flowers won't produce it until summer is well advanced. And the second is that these little gadabouts have a peculiar habit of feeding their young on predigested seeds, which cannot be had in sufficient quantity until late summer.

By mid-autumn all the gold in that glowing earlier plumage of the old males has become a dull olive yellow, so much like the female's that it is hard to tell one from the other.

Robin nests are strongly built and placed on firm supports like tree crotches and wooden beams. The beautiful eggs are of course robin's-egg blue. 125

Scarlet tanagers are illustrations of the fact that when the male is brightly colored the female is usually dowdy. 126

When a mother *goldfinch* grows hungry while brooding her eggs, her husband will serve her breakfast in bed. 127

The *house wren* has a capacity for bubbly song that literally shakes every feather on his small body. He also has the unhappy habit of occasionally pecking holes in other birds' unprotected eggs.

A typical male house wren is likely to be a bit of a Don Juan in spring and early summer. He marries readily enough, after building a nest—which his bride scornfully throws out to make room for another one constructed by herself. But once the eggs are laid, her mate apparently keeps an eye open for further female conquests, and if he can find a promising opportunity he may wind up with two households instead of one!

There is no telling what sort of home site he may select. House wrens have been known to nest in a clothes-pin bag hanging in a shed, an old coat pocket, a scare-crow's hat, a fishing creel. The only real requirement seems to be some sort of hole, crevice or dark nook in which a fantastic number of small twigs and soft stuff can be assembled in a hollowed pile.

A lot of work is involved in raising a house wren family, for meals must be served several hundred times a day when the project is at its peak. But Pop never forgets to sing, even though he is limited to moments snatched between dishing up one caterpillar and dashing off to catch another.

The *cardinal* has just about every quality that makes for bird greatness: beauty, vigor, friendliness, unusual devotion to mate and family, and a frank and enthusiastic singing voice. The male is one of the very few birds that continues to sing right through the winter, and his clear, vibrant whistling has all the free spirit of a country boy on his way to the swimming hole.

Cardinals used to be primarily birds of the South and lower Mid-west, but for years they have been extending their range northward and eastward and today are well established in southern New England and northern Illinois. They apparently have no fear of severe cold, and wherever you find them they habitually stay throughout the year.

The home life of a pair of cardinals is the next thing to ideal. Unless one or the other bird dies there is strong evidence that they will remain mated for life. They are completely devoted to each other, and although mother does all the nest building, father brings food to her while she is brooding the eggs, helps care for the youngsters when they hatch, and takes full charge of their welfare for several weeks after they leave home. This last service leaves the lady free to start a second nest and another family, an opportunity of which she may avail herself twice in a single season.

128

The *yellowthroat* is known far and wide for the black mask which the male wears across his eyes, and the clog-dance tempo of his clear, merry "wichity, wichity, wichity" song. These will-o'-the-wisp little fellows have a preference for nesting in lush, damp, or actually wet places. But if there is no such location around, they'll settle for a tangle of wild blackberries in a dry old field.

Like nearly all highly colored birds, female yellowthroats are less conspicuously marked than their mates. Thus, the lady wears no facial

If the *house wren* had a first name, it should be "curiosity." This small brown imp is a tireless busybody.

Male *cardinals* are popular showmen and gifted singers. Their cheery whistling continues all winter long.

129

61

mask and so is less likely to be seen as she broods the family eggs.

A male *rose-breasted grosbeak* is so stunning in his color scheme of black, white and clear rose, and so obviously overflowing with good fellowship as he tosses his rich rapid warble far and wide through the sunshine, that you know at once he is a bird of birds. When conditions are right you can hear him a quarter-mile away.

The urge to sing day in and day out is one of the rose-breasted's strongest traits. Even after his brown-streaked mate has built her twiggy nest and he takes his turn at brooding their several eggs while she is off duty, he often sings softly to himself during the job.

This heavy-billed, stout-hearted bird is highly useful as well as attractive to eye and ear. It eats an astonishing variety of insect pests, including potato beetles, tent caterpillars, and those of the destructive gypsy moth. Home gardeners sometimes claim that the rose-breasted grosbeak raids their pea crops as the pods approach picking time, and there is plenty of evidence that it nibbles certain tree leaf and flower buds before they have a chance to open. But on over-all balance, there is no doubt that the good it does far outweighs its sins.

All *vireos* have strong, emphatic songs, most of which are composed of two- to four-note phrases repeated over and over at curiously regular intervals while the singers move about in the treetops in a constant search for insects. The *red-eyed vireo,* in particular, prolongs his singing season far into the summer. Even on scorching July afternoons, when the heat has silenced almost every other bird, his off-and-on monologue drops through the concealing leaves with never a trace of drowsiness.

130

Red-eyes build beautifully woven basket nests ingeniously lashed by their rims to the two arms of small branch forks. Soft weed and bark fibers are bound in place with caterpillar silk, and bits of cocoon, moss and lichens superbly camouflage the outer walls. The finished home is exquisitely dainty and yet so enduring that it remains intact for months after its builders have flown away.

131

Low, dense bushes and grass tufts in old pastures are the best places to find the well hidden nests of *field sparrows.*

Yellowthroats are habitual dwellers in thickets where there are endless hidden nooks to explore for good food.

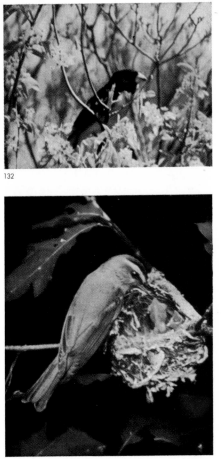

132

134

133

The showy, gay *rose-breasted grosbeak* is in a class by himself when it comes to fine singing and fine dress. 132

The beautifully woven and camouflaged basket nest of a *red-eyed vireo* always swings from a forked branch. 133

One never knows just what the mimicking *catbird* will do next, but it's sure to be something interesting, or entertaining. 134

The slim, sleek, gray-and-rusty *catbird* is a home-body with a consuming sense of curiosity and a passion for commenting on practically everything it sees. Many of its remarks are couched in the mew-like tones which justify its name, and this scolding note, supplemented by an utterly different subdued cluck, is its unfailing warning that there may be danger about. But when it wants to the catbird really can sing! Its usual refrain is a medley of notes that tumble after each other every which way. Some are sweet and subdued, many others seem to be imitations of other species, for catbirds are well known for their knack of mimicry. On occasion, however, a catbird seems to drop his clowning and sings on and on in a soft, murmuring tone which is completely delightful. You can hardly believe that the hidden singer is the same vociferous imp that scolded you only a few minutes ago.

By and large, our northern finches and other finch-like birds are an adventurous crew. Hardy, strong of wing and as self-reliant as the Declaration

135

136

A hardy bird and a superb singer, the *purple finch* has a roving spirit as intriguing as his own handsome plumage.

The female *cardinal* isn't as showy as her handsome mate, but she is an admirable mother, gentle and good tempered.

of Independence, they range hither and yon in loose, fast-flying bands, often for hundreds of miles and for no apparent reason other than to see what the country looks like out beyond the horizon. Only when the return of warm spring weather signals the approach of their late nesting season do their journeys have a definite purpose. It is then they head for the northern tier of States and lower Canada, or perhaps into our higher mountains whose altitude assures them of the Canadian life zone conditions in which to raise new families.

The *purple finch* is no exception to this tradition. Perhaps "purple" is the wrong name for it, for many birders feel that "rose" would be a better word for the color that glows on most of the male's plumage throughout the year and in February begins to brighten toward its maximum display in the months to follow.

On mild days in late winter, too, you are likely to hear brief snatches of his full courtship song, a swift, liquid warble that rushes forward as gaily as a brooklet on a hillside. Other birds may surpass it in sweetness, but you could listen for a long, long time without hearing one that could match it for jollity, tempo and delightfully fresh, unfettered spirit.

Purple finches are welcome visitors at thousands of winter feeding stations where they shell and devour sunflower seed with deftness and obvious relish. No bird visitors are better behaved, or more self-possessed. And none repays your bounty with a heartier song.

In the shade and dampness of woods whose trees are few enough to permit the growth of plentiful ferns and shrubs beneath them, you may hear in May and June the eerily descending song of the *veery,* one of our most retiring thrushes. It souds like neither voice nor instrument, a thin, vibrant whistle, faraway, wild, remote.

Veeries are partial to early morning and evening singing and often continue their distinctive solos until darkness has settled under the canopy of trees. They seem to be rather lonely, aloof birds, and their somewhat bulky nests of leaves and grass strengthened with fibers blend perfectly into the background of tussock, fern clump or ancient rotted stump on which they are often places. When the tawny-backed female is brooding her eggs, you might easily pass by within a couple of yards without suspecting that a bird home was only a few steps away.

To know the *hermit thrush* at its best you should visit its breeding grounds in the north country on a still June evening. There, from the depths of the spruce and hardwood forest, or perhaps along the edge of a long-abandoned clearing or wood-road, you will hear one of the most ethereal of all songs, a leisurely series of rising cadences so bell-like, so spiritual in tone and rendering, that they seem beyond the ability of even a bird. At regular intervals, and with no group ever quite the same as the one before, the singing goes on and on, often until full darkness has settled in the woods.

Hermits are both modest in appearance and reticent in manner, yet they are hardy and self-sufficient, and quite indifferent to frosty weather. Scattered individuals even spend the entire winter in sheltered spots only a few hundred miles south of their summer haunts and have been known to survive heavy snows and temperatures close to zero.

Among birds, bright colors do not always stand for brilliant singing. Take the *mockingbird,* for instance. Here is an undeniably modest color scheme of soft gray and whites, yet nowhere in this country will you find a bird having such a varied program, or one more vigorous and persistent in singing it. Apparently not satisfied with hundreds of daily performances, a springtime male mocker will often continue his vocalizing at intervals throughout the night. Even devout Southerners, who rightly champion the mockingbird, have been known to grumble their wish that he would either shut up or leave that tree just outside the window and let them get to sleep.

Mockers are not only superb mimics, as their name implies; they also appear to create many compositions of their own. Their recognizable imitations include such diverse

137

138

Veery nests, with their lovely greenish-blue eggs, are built on the ground or very close to it, in shady places.

On its north country nesting grounds the *hermit thrush* sings with a purity that seems to be a reflection of Heaven.

65

139

For vocal variety, vigor and durability, the slim gray and white *mockingbird* is the most famous singer of them all.

themes as the barking of dogs, the creaking of gate hinges, crowing of roosters and cackling of hens, and the songs and calls of many other birds. As for describing their original concoctions—well, let's just say that if you hear a snatch of song that doesn't fit any other bird you might take a chance and put it down as coming from a mockingbird. Mockers are born scrappers as well as singers, and will do their best to terrorize any creature from mouse to man that they think may have designs on the safety of their nests. Where most birds would hesitate to go beyond scolding, mockingbirds are likely to wade right in with highly effective claws, beaks and beating wings. They may not always win, but you may be sure they're perfectly willing to try!

Broadly speaking, nobody could grant much singing ability to our numerous tribe of American Warblers—more properly *wood* warblers, to distinguish them from the European group of similar name. In the majority of cases their songs are high-pitched, thin and far from musical, although they render them with an almost pathetic earnestness and effort. If their voices matched their colors, they'd have everything—including excellent manners.

The *chestnut-sided warbler* is one of the more gifted species in this family of about fifty American warbler members. Its song, which has been well described as saying "tawee, tawee, tawee, tawee, tawee, tawee-cha," rings out clearly and often from bush-grown pastures and long-abandoned fields for several weeks in mid-spring, and it will be a long-remembered day when you get your first good view of the yellow-capped singer with his black and white face markings and those rich chestnut brown sides for which he is named. Like most of his relatives, he is an incessant skipper, flutterer and climber among the twigs where he snatches scores of insect dainties with amazing skill.

140

The *Virginia rail* builds its nest among the cattails. Hidden from view, it is heard more often than seen.

LIFE IN A
WOODLAND POND

A POND IS like a miniature world in a goldfish bowl. Exposed to view more clearly than in any other type of environment or habitat are all the essential elements of life. It presents a lively package—for virtually everything visible through its transparent surface is engaged in an unending struggle for existence.

Here you can watch ferocious creatures attack and overcome animals many times their own weight. You can study each step in a graduated series of living things as each in turn becomes food for its next larger neighbor. Life in a pond presents a full range of nature from plants and animals of pin-point minuteness to flesh-eaters, large and dangerous.

The waters of ponds provide homes for an astounding variety of animal forms. Many of them spend a major part of their lives in its waters. Often they pass their infancy there in a form that in no way resembles their eventual appearance. As adults they may frequent the woods and fields, or even

67

linger about city street lights far from their birthplaces. Voracious as some are during their water life, once they leave the ponds, certain of them will never consume another particle of food.

To the timid, a pond may seem a fearsome place. Actually a pond is safe enough. The faint suggestions of danger and the certainty of exciting discovery appeals to the adventurous person of any age. Even more alluring is the prospect of the chase.

Let's go! Let's visit a pond! Let's pick one not too far from the woods. If it's been built by man, go first to the dam; if a natural pond, find the steepest side. Dipping in with a net, it's easier to catch things in fairly deep than in shallow water. *Turtles* and *newts* will be coming up for air, *fish* swim in close to the bank, and many other creatures will be travelling on or below the surface.

If you've come equipped with rubber boots, and with a net, collecting can or jar, then we're ready to explore the shallow part of the pond. Perhaps there are stones which you can turn over and examine for blobs of jelly that turn into *snails* or *leeches,* and for many creatures clinging to the stone or skittering away to hide in the mud.

Certainly there will be a marshy spot at the upper shallow end of the pond. Croaking in alarm, *frogs* jump in with a splash as we approach. A harmless *snake* slithers off a stump. As you step from the solid shoreline

141

142

143

144

The male *yellow-headed blackbird* is a Beau Brummell. Guarding his nest, he drives away crows, even hawks.

The conspicuous *spotted salamanders* appear but once a year when they come to the ponds to mate and lay their eggs.

After they are hatched the young *leeches* remain fastened to the mother until they are able to fend for themselves.

Out of the water for the first time, the transforming *dragonfly* hangs head down while its exoskeleton hardens.

68

145

146

Muscles now can operate the stiffened *dragonfly* body. It pushes away the old skin to extract the rest of its body.

After blood is pumped into the *dragonfly's* tiny folded-back wings, they expand, dry and swing into position.

your feet sink alarmingly in the soft mud. But soon you will get the feel of walking slowly among the lily pads. It's better that you can't move too quickly—that would frighten the frogs that watch you from between the lily pads, only their eyes above the water level, like twin periscopes. *Sunfish* swim about among the water plants looking for worms and insects. Young *dragonflies* and *mayflies* are climbing out of the water on taller plants, soon to be transformed into air-bound creatures.

A pond is fascinating all year long. Life goes on even beneath a covering of ice, but it will be most fun to study about the time the ice has melted, when the first warm rain stirs the hibernating creatures to life.

You'll never forget an evening in the rain at the edge of a woodland pond. Decked in hip boots, raincoat and hat, and carrying a hand flashlight or wearing an electric headlamp, you are ready for adventure.

A rattling, clacking sound, almost like quacking ducks, is steadily growing louder. Abruptly it stops and nothing is heard but the patter of raindrops. The open water of the pond is just ahead. Minutes pass, then suddenly a burst of high, grating clacks breaks the silence, and a rattling chorus rises again. Cautiously you switch on a single light—discovering that the surface of the pond is stippled with floating *wood frogs.*

The wood frogs are not alone. Slithering through the wet leaves and moss bordering the pond is a *spotted salamander* with yellow dots on its head, back and tail. In the water are many more, while still others are emerging from rotting stumps, under logs, joining the migration to the pond.

Scooping up one of the wriggling "spring lizards," as these amphibians are popularly but erroneously known, you examine it more closely. Nearly eight inches long, it has a moist rubbery skin and bulging eyes that give it a pop-eyed expression. Its toes are short and stubby compared to the long scaly claws of true lizards, members of the reptile family.

What are they doing? Dozens of the spotted salamanders are congregating in certain parts of the pond. Your beam of light reveals a mass of salamanders, twenty or thirty of them. Swimming in and out among each other, over and under, they are leading up to the climax of egg laying. Only a few females have arrived, more will come later on. They are recognized by their greater girth, indicating a large supply of unlaid eggs.

147

148

This 1½ inch long *diving beetle,* the adult of the vicious *"water tiger,"* can devour a *tadpole* or suck its blood.

By filling its throat sac with air the male *toad* produces a trilling sound guiding the female to the pond.

The slender males occasionally stop their gyrations, settle over a leaf or twig, and gently wave their long tails. Then they rejoin the weaving procession, each leaving behind a tiny white-capped gelatinous cone, scarcely a third of an inch tall. Its white cap contains sperm cells, the male's contribution to the reproductive process.

Excited by the churning dance, a female swims over one of these "spermatophores." When she swims away a few seconds later fertilization of the unlaid eggs has been assured. The reproductive cells unite internally, a highly efficient system not possessed by fish and frogs. Instead of laying tens of thousands of eggs as fish must do, or thousands as frogs and toads do, salamanders of the pond variety may lay less than 150 eggs, some land-dwelling species only three or four.

As they are laid, the individual eggs are only an eighth of an inch in diameter. Left completely to themselves, the embryonic salamanders steadily develop in their transparent incubator. Unguarded, they are safe from most enemies at least until they hatch.

If you visit a pond which holds water all year long you'll find tadpoles every month. The wood frog eggs will hatch into tadpoles in early spring, and transform into land-dwelling frogs during the summer. So will most other species. But the biggest frog of all, the *bullfrog,* and its smaller relative, the *green frog,* generally live for two years (in the North) in the tadpole stage. By the time they are about ready to leave the pond, they may be five inches long. But remarkable changes must be made before they are fitted to live on land.

As tadpoles, scraping food from leaves and stems of water plants, they needed a very long alimentary tract to break down and digest cellulose. As carnivorous, protein-eating land animals, a short simple digestive system will suffice. During the period of "re-tooling," nourishment is drawn from the tadpole's energy reserve, stored in its tail. No longer needed for locomotion, the tail is resorbed. Meanwhile further preparations for land life are made. First the hind legs, and then the forelegs appear. By the time the tail has disappeared the re-styled amphibian is only half its former length. Now it is ready to go ashore.

In contrast to the long larval life of the bullfrog is the brief tadpole stage of some toads. *Hop toads* of one species or another are found virtually everywhere except in the highest mountains. In spring the males come to the pond and sit erect in the shallow water, blow up their throat pouches and sing in a high-pitched musical trill.

The friendly, familiar hop toad comes to the pond only to mate. Each female lays from 5,000 to 15,000 eggs in ropes or strings, sometimes totalling 70 feet in length. They are deposited in shallow water warmed by the sun's rays. In contrast to the wood frog eggs which often take three weeks to hatch in the icy water, toad eggs may hatch in three or four days, transforming in 40 to 60 days.

Often the bottom of a shallow pond will be black with the hundreds of thousands of tadpoles which a few dozen pairs of toads can produce. Most of them will be eaten by fishes, turtles, and water snakes. *Green herons* stalk them offshore while land birds like *crows, blackbirds, starlings,* and many others scoop them out of the shallowest pools.

Many tadpoles escape the ever-hungry birds by fleeing to deeper water. Here they meet new dangers, predacious insects; some so fierce that they can kill a full grown frog! Especially noted for its ferocity is the big *electric light bug,* characterized by piercing, sucking mouth parts. While pinioning its victim with powerful forelegs, it drives its large strong beak deeply into the captive's body and sucks its blood.

Still larger is the *giant electric light bug,* reaching a length of two and a half inches. If you capture any of these big bugs, avoid handling them—a puncture caused by the ever-ready beak is deep and painful.

Most common of the predatory insects of the pond are the *dytiscus* or *diving beetles.* Their sleek dark bodies are propelled through the water by swift strokes of the oar-like hind legs. Longer than the other legs and

Boots, a bottom scraper for ensnaring specimens, and a minnow can, to bring them back alive, spell adventure when exploring a pond.

149

flattened, the last pair is equipped with long hairs which spread out to produce a broad surface on the back stroke. On the forward stroke the hairs fold down, offering little resistance to the water.

As an air breather a diving beetle must go to the surface at intervals. Possessing a breathing pore at the end of the abdomen it simply "backs up" to the surface, pushing the end of its body into the air. When preparing for trips to lower levels the beetle may take on an extra supply of air. The back of a diving beetle has a felt-like coat beneath the wings. When it surfaces for air the beetle raises its wings slightly. Air clings to the hairs. When submerging it carries a large flat bubble of air which is utilized slowly through small breathing pores beneath the wings.

Powerful as the beetle's large cutting jaws undoubtedly are, it further protects itself by giving off offensive secretions strong enough to deter almost any attacker.

Equally voracious are the long segmented larvae appropriately called *"water tigers."* Rapacious hunters, they have sharp, wide-spreading jaws. Like a pair of synchronized scythes they swing inward, cutting deeply into a victim until each blade is completely imbedded. Amazing as it may seem the deadly blades are hollow—the blood of the victim is sucked through them. Later the beetle larva may withdraw these jaws, perhaps to dismember and swallow its victim, more often to cast it aside.

Oddest looking insect to be found in the pond is the *water-scorpion.* Its name evidently refers to its breathing tube, extending from the end of its body. The water-scorpion's appendage is really a remarkable snorkel-like breathing device. The insect's fragile appearance is deceptive. Camouflaged among dried, water-logged grasses it seizes and feeds gluttonously upon the nymphs of dragonflies and mayflies. Firmly grasping its prey, it sucks

The *great blue heron* helps to control the overproduction of fish in the pond.

The *mayfly* emerges from the water just long enough to mate and lay eggs.

Like the larger, flat-tailed *beaver*, a *muskrat* builds a lodge snug among the cattails. When wet, its fur is dark.

Scavengers by nature and never at a loss for food, *snails* flourish wherever there is water and plant life to feed them.

Many ponds, canals, and even rivers in the far south are choked by this attractive plant that floats on the water.

Water lilies have exquisite blossoms; of pink or yellow. Their roots are anchored to the pond bottom.

blood through its hollow pointed beak.

About the time the wood frogs and spotted salamanders are awakening from hibernation, the first flocks of migrant birds are dropping in along the margins of the woodland ponds. En route from the Southern States to the vast expanse of territory north of the Canadian border are dozens of *rusty blackbirds*. Wading into shallow water, they search for food among the dead leaves and hummocks of moss. Any tadpole, frog or insect within reach will be devoured instantly.

Among the reeds in the deeper waters of the open ponds of central and western United States, the *yellow-headed blackbirds* will be looking for nesting sites. Like the familiar red-wing they will weave deep, firm baskets of dead cattails and marsh grasses, anchoring them to the tall reeds.

Best known blackbird in most of North America is the handsome *red-wing* whose "*konk-la-reeee*" is the most familiar song of open ponds and marshes. The thin advance guard of red-wings, arriving while there are still margins of ice around the ponds, represents scattered males that dallied farther north than the bulk of the blackbird population. About two weeks later the trees around the ponds and the nearby open fields are swarming with the first big wave of migrants. Then comes a second great wave of males. These birds are eager to set up housekeeping but they must wait at least two

Like masses of *frog* eggs, *snail* eggs are protected by a frothy gelatin film that holds the egg mass out of the water.

A host of pond dwellers live on the underside of a single *lily pad,* eating the leaf itself, or making it a home.

weeks before they can hope to attract a mate. Finally, about six weeks later, flocks of females arrive and settle down. Now the serious business of courtship can get under way.

When the modestly attired female has finished incubating her eggs and the hungry youngsters have hatched, both parents will be kept busy providing food for them. Though they themselves often eat weed seeds and grain during migration, now they depend largely on a diet of insects. Often they fly to nearby farmlands and pick up grubs, worms, and caterpillars.

Sometimes they strike a bonanza in their own backyard—the emergence of vast swarms of mayflies. These delicately beautiful insects swarm over ponds or lakes at twilight. Mayflies are important members of the water world, because they are so incredibly abundant. They are an exceedingly important food source for fishes, birds and many other creatures.

They are easily recognized, either as adults or young (nymphs) by the three or sometimes two long filaments on the end of the body. The nymphs are distinguished by having seven pairs of gills on the abdomen. When the mayfly approaches the climax of its life, when it climbs up the stem of some water plant into a new world of air, its feathery filaments are replaced by thread-like ones.

Other great changes occur. Like most insects they develop wings, but unlike any other insect they molt or shed their skin again, after they have developed wings. As nymphs they feed on microscopic plants, *diatoms* and *desmids,* abundantly present in the ooze that covers the pond bottom. Living in the mud, mayflies can dig with the speed of moles. Only this burrowing skill keeps them from the jaws of their enemies. As imagos (adults) they live only a few hours or at most a day or two. They eat nothing; their mouth parts are shrunken and useless.

At dusk hundreds or thousands take wing. The "spinners," as fishermen know them, hover over the water, alternately rising and falling as though tossed skyward by strong puffs of air. As soon as they have mated the females lay their eggs in the water, then drop exhausted upon the surface where they may be taken instantly by a hungry fish.

Many a woodland pond dries up as water accumulated from the spring rains gradually evaporates. The spotted salamander larvae are two inches long now and are shedding their gills. Wood frog tadpoles are becoming frogs while tiny toads by the thousands are impatient to go ashore.

At last it rains. Little pools and streams form everywhere as the dry woodlands become as wet as the pond. This is D-day for transformed amphibians. Squirming and hopping up on shore they spread out like ripples on the water. Wave after wave, they fan out through the woods. One can almost believe that it is actually "raining toads." Some are trampled, many are eaten, but enough survive to amply maintain the breeding stock of each species.

Every summer in more open country, particularly through the prairie states and the prairie provinces of Canada, thousands of ponds become *duck* factories. Millions of ducks build their nests among the *cat-tails, reed,* and *rushes,* or close by. Throughout the northeastern states the familiar *black duck* nests on shore at the edge of a pond.

Ducks which have wintered mostly in the southern states or in bays and other sheltered coastal waters, reach their nesting grounds via well-traveled migration routes. The routes serve as feeder highways which merge into great arterial boulevards. These are known as "flyways," and it is in this region that most of the sport shooting of ducks takes place.

Where the cat-tails are extensive, bird life will be abundant. Yet you might ride or even walk past a cat-tail marsh without knowing that anything but blackbirds lived there. But you will have a chance to see the marsh birds, especially if you set up a "blind," as the photographers do, and patiently wait inside. Often the marsh settles back to normal more quickly if two persons go up to the blind, and one leaves. Birds cannot count; evidently they are satisfied that they are alone. Ducks and *coots* swim out into full view; *rails, gallinules,* and *bitterns* work out to the edge of the open water. *Herons* and *egrets* feed in full view.

If woods are near, the handsome, multicolored *wood duck* will hunt a hollow tree, or perhaps use the abandoned hole of a *pileated woodpecker,* and the female will lay her eggs there. When the young are ready to leave the nest they leap out in rapid succession, though it may be twenty feet or more to the ground. Cushioned by a "pillow" of fat they escape injury and go chasing after their mother, who leads them unerringly to water.

Metamorphosis is what scientists call the change-over that enables the *tadpole* to take up life on land as a *frog.*

A hollow tree or an old nail keg may induce the small *wood ducks* to take up house-keeping around a pond.

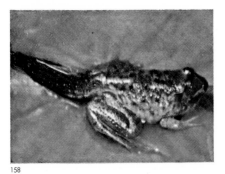

160

162

161

163

After the eggs are laid in a hollow in the sand, the male *sunfish* zealously guards the nest against all enemies.

These vicious larvae eventually transform into *diving beetles.* Here they fight over a defenseless *tadpole.*

A breathing-tube grows from the tail of this *water-scorpion* which feeds upon nymphs of *damselflies* and *mayflies.*

Swiftly a *backswimmer* captures a *water boatman* while remaining constantly alert to larger enemy creatures.

Once they reach the waters of the pond, mother wood duck conveys her fluffy family into well hidden channels. But the ducklings may have been spotted by the terror of the pond, the *snapping turtle.*

In many ponds the snapper population is kept in balance by *skunks!* While no living thing dares an encounter with the powerful jaws of a thirty-pound snapper, the mighty reptiles are not completely invulnerable. Each summer the female snapper lumbers up on shore, selects an open sandy spot and scoops a hole with her hind legs. In it she lays 25 to 30 spherical, white, hard-shelled eggs, nearly an inch in diameter. Then she scratches soil over the eggs and drags her way back to the pond. A skunk digging up insects may uncover the eggs and partake of the feast. Those that are not eaten by the skunk hatch before their embryonic food supply is exhausted. The yolk sac attached to their under shell will nourish them until they reach the pond and succeed in catching their own food.

A young turtle represents a tasty morsel for *raccoons, herons* or even for the parent snapper. The few that survive are likely to become the Methuselahs of the pond, safe from any attack. Troubles they have, in the form of leeches which attach themselves to the few exposed fleshy portions of the body and feed on the turtle's blood. Frogs and fishes also serve as unwilling blood donors for these remarkable parasites.

Painted turtles are quite different in appearance and disposition. Small and colorfully marked, they make good pets, never bite unless provoked. They are scavengers, but will eat small fishes, worms and other food washed into the pond. They eat only under water.

It's always fun to watch *sunfish*—"bream" or "pumpkin seeds" as they are also known, especially in summer when the males head for shallow water near shore. Swimming round and round, sometimes on its side, a male violently swishes its tail, sweeping sand and gravel out to the sides of the depression which forms the nest.

When a female comes along he "corrals" her, both swimming over the nest in a circle, the male on the outside. She lays about 5,000 eggs. As they settle into the nest the male releases a colorless cloud of "milt" or sperm which immediately fertilizes the eggs. These eggs and the transparent developing larvae are guarded zealously by the male.

Most of the eggs, or the young fish, will be eaten. This is not only inevitable but necessary for the welfare of the fish themselves. The female will lay a second 5,000 eggs later in the summer. In 12 months the young fish will be mature. If all lived, within two years the offspring from a single pair could total more than fifty million!

The introduction of the right proportion of predatory fish, like *large-mouthed black bass*, will result in the excess sunfish population being eaten and a "balance" being established. *Herons, kingfishers,* and *water snakes* also take some of the fish crop and help maintain a fish population that stays within the "carrying capacity" of the pond.

As we have seen already, a pond is full of life. But there are far greater numbers and kinds of living things than anyone would suspect. This is demonstrated by dragging a fine-mesh net through the water. Held up to

The microscope reveals the tiny plants and animals that live in every drop of water, forming the lower links in a chain of life.

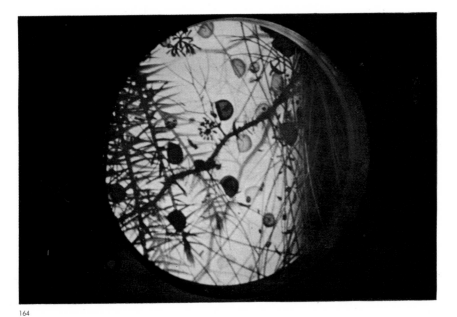

164

the light in a test tube or a vial, dozens of tiny creatures can be seen with the unaided eye. For a real thrill examine a single drop of this water under a microscope, magnifying the contents from 30 to 100 times.

Many of the fisherman's greatest tribulations are biting insects whose larval life is spent in the water. They include *midges, horseflies* and *deerflies* that bite deeply and painfully. One that looks like a bee but actually is a harmless fly has a larva known widely as "the rat-tailed maggot." This larva lives in shallow water breathing through a long collapsible tube. If the water becomes deeper the tube may extend until it is more than ten times the length of the maggot itself.

The eggs of most pond creatures are left unguarded, but the male *water bug* provides constant protection, because the female has forcibly cemented a mat of eggs to his back. A few may be scraped off but enough survive to insure their perpetuation.

Sometimes, as we walk toward the pond's edge the water's surface is agitated by dozens of gyrating, bronzy-black insects—*whirligig beetles.* The big compound eyes of these "whirling dervishes" of the pond world are divided by the sharp margin of the head so that each has an upper half gazing skyward, and a submerged half facing downward. When a number of whirligig beetles are alarmed they give off an offensive odor.

Also commonly found are *water boatmen* which swim with their backs upward, and *backswimmers,* which generally hang head downward from the surface. Both propel themselves with powerful oarlike back legs. These bugs are air-breathers and when they descend to the bottom they carry a supply of air in two large grooves on the underside of the body. Predacious themselves, they are eaten by almost all the other carnivorous pond creatures.

Even a *leopard frog* is helpless in the powerful grasping forelegs of the ferocious *electric light bug* who pumps blood out of its victim through its sharp, hollow beak.

165

166

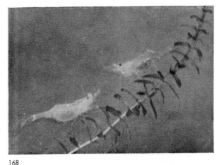
168

167

169

Powerful hind legs propel the *bullfrog* from land to water, and hence to safety, in a fraction of a second.

This colorful young *painted turtle* is swimming among the branches of *bladderwort* which traps tiny pond dwellers.

Freshwater shrimp are related to the edible deep saltwater shrimp of coastal waters, but not to *fairy shrimp.*

Only *snapping turtles* and *soft-shelled turtles* lay spherical eggs; other species lay elongated eggs.

Even stranger are the slender, long-limbed *water striders,* that skate about on the surface film by resting on their front and hind feet while pushing with the middle ones. Their weight is just enough to depress the surface into six concave lenses, which on a sunny day throw six dark round shadows on the bottom of a shallow pond. Often the six shadow spots are seen before the insect itself is discovered. Water striders also can leap into the air to catch insects that may be flying past and then land back on the water without sinking beneath the surface.

Stalks of cattails, reeds and rushes often serve as support for nymphs or larval insects which must climb out of the water before they can transform into their adult form. The immature dragonfly or naiad, like the more streamlined water tiger, is a ferocious killer, feeding on other insects, tadpoles and small salamanders. Many species live for two or three years in this stage. As the time nears for it to leave the water its developing wings become noticeable. At last it starts to crawl up along the stem of some plant that extends above the water.

The naiad climbs for several inches in its new environment then stops. Soon its skin splits along the head and thorax and the insect begins to emerge. For many minutes the dragonfly will be completely vulnerable to attack. As it climbs out of its old skin it gradually extracts its three pairs of long legs then falls backward, held only by the abdomen, not yet completely withdrawn.

Hanging head downward the insect is helpless for its external skeleton is still so soft that most of the muscles within have no firm attachment. When the "skin" has hardened, the dragonfly reaches up and grasps the stem, quickly freeing its long abdomen.

It must wait a little longer for the soft, limp wings to expand and harden. Hollow tubes functioning as wing struts will be pumped full of blood. Then the wings will be swung into the final horizontal position in which they will remain for the rest of the insect's life.

As adults the dragonflies continue to prey on insects. Large numbers of *mosquitoes* and other flying pests are devoured by them. They often can be seen dipping down into the water laying eggs, sometimes in the water, often in slits in the submerged stems of water plants, or on the underside of floating leaves.

Rather similar to dragonflies in appearance and development are the more delicate *damselflies* which rest with their silky black wings in erect position above their shiny green or blue bodies.

Plants like *cat-tails, sedges, bulrushes, arrowhead, burreed, pickerel weed* and *water plantain* grow in shallow water and lift their leaves and blossoms fairly high into the air. Where they grow and die year after year their remains help to fill the pond, eventually building up soil until it rises above the water level.

Small, shallow ponds eventually disappear as they are transformed first into marsh and then into dry land. Even plants growing in deeper water contribute to this slow but relentless system of destruction. Most of them are rooted in the mud of the pond bottom, sending up stalks which produce attractive flowers above or at the water level.

Large, armored and powerful, the hungry *snapping turtle* is the most dangerous enemy of all the pond dwellers.

170

Most familiar and beautiful of pond blossoms is the pure white *water lily* of eastern North America. The big, round, flat floating lily pads represent the pond's most important "community center." They operate as landing fields for dragonflies of many species, and are also the favorite basking spots for green frogs and young bullfrogs.

The leaf and stem of the water lily are slippery with *algae*. Often with a magnifying lens one can discover numerous little red hairs which wave constantly but never in unison. Called *bristleworms,* they live on decaying organic matter.

Sometimes the surface of a pond is blanketed by a myriad of tiny green plants. Generally they are one of the species of *duckweed*, a group notable for including the smallest of all flowering plants, *wolffia*. Duckweeds produce such a light-tight mat that submerged plants die for lack of sunlight, and herbivorous creatures must go elsewhere or perish.

There are two other plants, much larger, which likewise monopolize the surface space, *pickerel weed* and *water hyacinth*. In many localities they choke out all other vegetation. In this case, too, submerged vegetation is deprived of life-giving sunlight and the whole balance of the pond is upset. The largest planteaters living in the water are two mammals, the big, flat-tailed *beaver*

171

This inch-long male *water bug* might be called a hen-pecked baby-sitter, for his spouse glues her young to his back.

and the small, narrow-tailed muskrat. Beaver are partial to running water, but muskrats live in quiet waters of ponds and marshes where they feed on cattails, bulrushes, burreeds; also on arrowhead, water lily, and various grasses. Sometimes they add a bit of animal food to their diet, usually *freshwater clams* and *mussels, crayfish,* and *snails;* sometimes they catch fish and aquatic insects.

Two kinds of houses are built by muskrats. One is a tunnel into a clay bank, the entrance below water level, the living quarters above. This type of den often is extended into a system of tunnels which join other dens made by the offspring. Usually the muskrat builds a roof vent at a point near the surface, blocking it with sticks.

Much like a beaver lodge is the house a muskrat builds by piling rushes and cat-tails on an island in the pond. Then the muskrat tunnels up into it from below the water's surface, excavating a den about a foot across.

The muskrat is clumsy and slow on land but often speeds up his travels by digging canals through the muck and water weeds, which permit him to swim effortlessly in six to eight inches of water.

Muskrats are good swimmers. Webs between the bases of their long hind toes and rows of short hairs along the toes increase the propelling area. They steer partly with their hind feet, mostly with their vertically flattened tails. Climbing out of the water their wet fur looks black. Completely hidden is the very dense, short inner fur which keeps them warm.

Unlike beaver, these smaller rodents do not store up food for the winter. Instead they forage daily for stems and roots of cattails and other plants which they can easily get, even under the ice. The fact that they must come up for air is actually no hardship, since pockets of air occur quite commonly beneath the ice. Also there generally are spots where floating water plants keep the water from freezing.

Vegetation growing completely below the surface is extremely important to the creatures that live in the water and to many others that visit the pond. Like the floating duckweed, the submerged, rooted *freshwater eelgrass* or *vallisneria* is a favorite food of the *canvasback* and other ducks.

A considerable amount of oxygen enters the water from the surface of a pond. Also, stirring by the wind and changes in water density during spring and fall help distribute oxygen to lower levels in a pond. Nevertheless it is the amount of algae and higher forms of plant life and their production of oxygen which may determine the limit of animal life that the pond can support.

This vital interrelationship can be demonstrated in an aquarium, where a balance between plants and animals can be maintained. The animals contribute their share, giving off carbon dioxide which the plants need in photosynthesis, and discharging wastes which fertilize the water.

Winter comes slowly in a pond. There are no sudden temperature changes. Heat absorbed during the summer dissipates slowly until the depths of the pond reach a temperature of 39.2 degrees. The surface waters, of course, fall to freezing if the air temperature is sufficiently low. A layer of ice actually conserves heat stored in the water, preventing it from being radiated into the air.

Fall brings a brief return visit from the rusty blackbirds. Most of the herons depart if there is likelihood of the pond freezing over. Green frogs and bullfrogs take to the water as the daily temperature falls to 40 degrees and bury themselves in the muddy bottom. Young newts straggle through the fallen leaves and drying grasses to take up an aquatic existence.

Insects of the surface, whirligig beetles and water striders, "go below", descending the plant stems into the deeper water. Dragonfly and damselfly nymphs, pond snails, and even fishes, move to the deeper central part of the pond. Activity drops to its lowest point in the year. Food is scarcest now and must be conserved.

The hibernators are virtually in a state of "suspended animation". Enough food has been stored in their bodies to barely keep them alive. So low is their use of energy, so faint are their heartbeats and breathing that spring will be near before they need to eat again.

Then, some night after day-long rains have been drenching and thawing the frozen earth, the most restless of the land hibernating creatures will stir, worm their way upward to the surface, then crawl, hop, and slide toward the pond to renew the annual, age-old ritual of reproduction, and to re-enter the fierce battle for food and for survival.

Round leaf sundews catch bugs like the *venus flytrap* but are so small that you have to hunt long and hard for them.

The *hedgehog cactus* has showy flowers half as big as the whole plant, and huge fruit like large strawberries.

Dainty little *dutchman's breeches* are an old garden favorite, well named and related to *bleeding heart.*

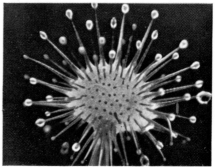

172

173

FAVORITE WILDFLOWERS

174

THE THOUSANDS OF different flowers that grow wild in North America are as varied as any other form of life you care to name. Some of them are only an inch or so tall. Others reach a height of fifteen or twenty feet with flowers of every possible color except black. Most are particular about where they live. You will find certain kinds in deep, dark woods, different ones in sunny meadows, dry fields, marshes, deserts, deep water, on ocean beaches, or among the mountain tops. Wherever there are differences in climate, there are wildflowers to fit them. Wildflowers have one characteristic in common. They have rather soft stems that do not turn into real wood, as do those of trees and shrubs. Beyond this fact they vary widely as to whether they are annuals, biennials, perennials or aquatics, as more fully explained later.

83

175

176

Several feet of water often lie between the roots of a *white waterlily* and its intensely fragrant summer blossoms.

Each leaf of the *venus flytrap* is hinged in the middle so that it can close tightly and grab venturesome insects.

The *round-leaf sundew* isn't a blossom at all, but a leaf. Those knobs at the ends of the slender spikes are drops of sticky liquid whose job it is to catch insects! A sundew does have real flowers, to be sure, but they are small, white and not nearly as interesting as these bug-trapping leaves.

Before it appears in May the *hedgehog cactus* looks rather drab. But as soon as the spring rains appear it takes on new life and quickly blossoms. These flowers bring dozens of hungry bees, and soon the glowing "strawberries" climax the season of activity with stunning color.

Dutchman's breeches is delicately formed, with ferny, faintly bluish green foliage massed below its leafless flower stalks. A well established clump may cover a ten inch circle, with its top-most blossoms six or eight inches above the ground. Often, when soil conditions are perfect and the plants have been undisturbed for years, they form an almost continuous carpet whose beauty during the short spring season is unmatched by any other wildflowers.

When early summer comes, however, there are no remaining traces of either leaves or stems. The crumbly buried clusters or root tubers, like grains of popcorn held loosely together, have done their work and earned a well deserved rest until spring rolls around.

Milkweed seeds are perfectly equipped with puffs of silky gossamer strands on which they can sail away in the wind.

Mound cactus, like many desert plants, stores water in its leaves to live through rainless months.

177

178

The name *dutchman's breeches* comes from the form of the individual blossoms. The moment you see them you notice their amusing resemblance to pairs of baggy Holland trousers dangling upside down from a clothesline.

White *waterlilies* have a curious habit of opening about six o'clock in the morning, closing around midnight, and waking up again at the same time next morning. None lasts for more than three days, even though it does get six hours' sleep. But fresh buds keep coming to the surface.

This splendid, rubbery-stemmed perennial is most at home in shallow, mud-bottomed ponds and the quiet coves of lakes. Old patches of it often cover many yards of water with their curious flat, floating, round leaves, each at the end of a separate stem. Some of these are eight or nine inches wide, and a strong wind often flips their edges up like the brim of a soft hat. But no matter how much the wind and waves may toss them about, they are still afloat and dry when the commotion ends.

The *venus flytrap* really catches flies. And once the jaws of its trap have closed only a very strong insect can possibly escape! Several other kinds of plants, including the *sundew*, also use insects for food. As you can see in the photograph, each leaf has two rounded halves that are hinged together like the shells of a clam. Both halves are covered with tiny hairs, and along their edges are rows of strong bristles. This is the

179

180

181

Unlike most of its orchid cousins, the *yellow ladyslipper* does well in home gardens and even along lawn edges.

The *tiger lily* first came to us from foreign lands, but it is so much at home now that it has spread far and wide.

The *turkey beard*, or *bear grass* is found only in "acid" sandy soil, dry on the surface but moist deep down.

"trap", and the picture shows it "set" and waiting for its prey.

When a *milkweed* seed is ready to take off, it has a sort of parachute made of a great many long, fine silky threads thinner than the smallest hair. The dozen or more dark, irregular spots that you see near the middle of the

85

182

183

In both its all-white and blue-and-white forms, *Rocky Mountain columbine* is one of our finest early summer flowers.

Many people think that the plumy seed heads of *virgin's bower* are even more lovely than its white blossoms.

picture, and in the upper left corner, are the actual seeds. And all the white, fluffy-looking part is the chute which brings them to earth far away.

Most of the *cacti* in the Southwest have brightly colored flowers which pop out unexpectedly in May or June. Like its cousins, *mound cactus* is covered with sharp-pointed spines arranged in groups of six or eight. The purpose of these is quite simple: to protect the plant against desert animals.

Many kinds of wildflowers are very fussy about where they grow, but the *yellow ladyslipper* doesn't seem to care. It will make itself perfectly at home in a garden or among the lawn shrubs. Sometimes a single old plant has thirty or forty blossoms every year.

Tiger lilies do not always produce seeds, but to make up for that they have a curious habit of forming little dark purplish bulbils, like baby bulbs, at the points where the leaves are attached to the stalk. By the end of the summer these are as large as good-sized peas, and after they have fallen to the ground each one sends a single root down into the soil. Gradually each of these roots pulls the bulbil after it, and in three or four years you will find a complete new bulb, growing at the proper depth, big and strong enough to have flowers and bulbils of its own!

Our picture of *turkey-beards* shows only the upper part of the stalks which carry the hundreds of little blossoms in May or June. These flower spikes are five or six inches long, and the stalks hold them four or five feet above the ground. At the bottom is a big clump of long, very thin leaves that often reach halfway up to the flowers. It is such a strange looking plant that you would not expect its blossoms to be fragrant. But they do smell sweet, and their perfume lasts for a long time.

There are nearly a dozen different species of *columbines* that are natives of the United States, and all but one of them come from the West. The flowers of each have the same general shape and way of growing five graceful hollow "spurs" reaching backward from the flaring, open face that you see here. Inside these spurs is the sweetish liquid, or nectar, that hummingbirds, butterflies and moths love.

Generally the blossoms of the *Rocky Mountain columbine,* which is Colorado's state flower, are a mixture of soft blue and white, and about two inches wide. But sometimes you come across the all white variety shown in the photograph.

Plenty of wildflowers are famous for their blossoms, but only a few have equally attractive seeds. *Virgin's bower* is one of this double-feature group. Each of those little curved, plumy tails is fastened to a seed, and when the right time comes they all sail away in the wind so that, when they finally come down to earth again, new virgin's bowers can start growing where they land.

The flowers of *spiderwort* always have three broad petals and grow at the top of stalks one to two feet tall. Their color may be either violet, purple, pink, or white, and the stalks of the stamens in the center are covered with fuzzy hairs. This fuzz is the reason for the "spider" part of the name. Springtime is flower time for this Southern perennial, and the best place to look for it is in wooded regions where the soil is rich.

The general flower shape of all the *ladyslipper orchids* is similar, but the petals on each side of the "heel," as you might say, sometimes make a good deal of difference in the effect. In the queen species they are quite short and broad, as you see, but in the yellow ladyslipper they are long and ribbon-like. It is things like these, as well as the color and size, that are important in learning to know any kind of flower from others that are closely related to it.

Wet meadows and the edges of sunny bogs are the places to find *grass-pink orchids*. Each plant has only a single leaf which looks so much like a broad blade of grass that you would hardly notice it unless the pink flower is there to attract your attention. The plants are quite sure to be widely scattered, too, and they very seldom grow in a thick patch.

This species flowers during the summer. It looks so much more graceful than either the *yellow* or the *queen slipper orchids* that you would hardly think it belonged to the same family. But that's the way it is with *orchids;* many of them are so different from all the rest that only a real expert can be sure of what they are.

In New England they call it *mayflower,* but by whatever name you know it, *trailing arbutus* is the choicest wildflower of early spring. Its white or

Spiderworts have four different colors, depending on the individual plant, and are often seen in southern gardens.

The *queen ladyslipper* is the tallest and showiest of our American members of this *orchid* group, but it is hard to find.

184

185

light pink blossoms often appear while the earth is still frozen hard, and its stems lie flat on the ground often hidden by fallen leaves. The tips of even its largest evergreen leaves seldom reach more than an inch into the air. About two-thirds of the plants in any patch are males and produce no seeds, while the remaining third are females and produce the "berries". These are odd little white fruits with several hundred small seeds scattered over the surface of each one, somewhat like the seeds on a strawberry. The juicy pulp of the fruits is so eagerly eaten by birds as well as ants that most of the seeds never get a chance to grow.

Meadows, marsh edges and open woods where the soil is rich and moist are the haunts of the *sweet white violet.* This is one of the violet species whose regular blossoms never produce seeds. Instead, its seeds are formed inside a set of short-stemmed flowers that never open. Scientists call these "cleisto-gamous" flowers, and they are hidden among the plant's leaves where no one is likely to find them without a careful search.

July is the *butterfly weed's* best flowering month, when the summer heat seems matched by those blazing flowers. Many other plants would wilt and die if they were in its place, but this native American has a long, thick root, somewhat like a giant *carrot,* and it grows straight down into the ground. Maybe this is one reason why high temperature and a scanty water supply don't sem to bother it at all. The name butterfly weed comes from the fact that *monarch butterflies* feed eagerly on the nectar in its blossoms, and *monarch caterpillars* are equally fond of eating its leaves. Perhaps this name fits better than its other one of *orange milkweed,* for the flower color may be anything from light yellow to blood red.

186

The *grass-pink orchid* is so delicate that you'd think it would be lost in the vigorous growth of meadows. 186

Trailing-arbutus, or *mayflower,* is almost worshipped by people who know it well. It is slowly disappearing. 187

You can count yourself lucky when you come upon a *sweet white violet,* one of the choicest of its tribe. 188

187

188

189

Hot weather and a hot spot on a mid-summer day suit the flame colored flowers of the colorful *butterfly-weed.*

190

California poppies grow wild out west, but people elsewhere grow them successfully in their back yard gardens.

The saucer-shaped blossoms of the *California poppy* are two to three inches broad, and their stalks are around twenty inches tall. In some cases the blooms are egg-yolk yellow, while in others they are orange or cream-colored. As you look down on them they seem to be set on a large bluish mat of their own lacy leaves, a sight that will be remembered for a long, long time.

These variations in flower color are hard to explain, for California poppies have a way of breaking the rules in a number of ways that botanists do not fully understand. There is one type of them that blooms in the spring, and another whose flowers appear only in autumn. But you can be very sure of this: they are among the showiest of all our wildflowers.

In its native home this poppy generally behaves like a perennial, but where the winters are really cold it is likely to be killed. That is why, in many gardens, it is advisable to sow fresh seed early every spring as is done with regular annuals.

The stout flower stalks of the *Parry nolina* rise to a height of five or six feet, each one crowded with countless small cream-white blossoms. A strange and very beautiful sight. Nolinas are perennials. They look like some of the *yuccas,* which grow in the same sort of places. One way to tell them apart is by their flowers, which are large in the yuccas and small in the nolinas. Both groups belong to the *lily* family.

There are only two kinds of *partridge berry* in the world—this American one, and another in Japan. Ours grows in rich-soil woods over a large part of the country and sometimes makes almost solid mats a yard or more wide. Its slender green stems wander in all directions, sending roots down into the ground as they grow. The tiny rounded leaves, white fragrant flowers and red berries all grow in pairs, one on each side of the stem. The winter-green-tasting berries are a favorite food of the ruffed grouse or "partridge", and that is the reason for the plant's odd name.

There are nearly three hundred kinds of *lupines* that grow wild in North America. A few either are annuals or grow like shrubs, but in general lupines are perennials and die down to the ground in autumn. Their height is anywhere from three inches to six feet, and the flowers of all species are the same general shape, whether their color is blue, yellow, white or mixed.

Lupines are sun loving plants, and when they find the conditions they like in open fields or mountain meadows they may cover many acres with a perfect sea of color.

The best known is called the *blue bonnet,* of which the people in Texas are so proud. If you look closely you'll discover that the plant really does look as if it is wearing a lot of perky little blue bonnets.

These straight-stalked plants are so good looking that for many years they have been garden favorites in Europe as well as the United States. By crossing different kinds some growers have developed many new sorts, with larger flowers and different colors.

A foot-wide splash of yellow against the dull blacks and browns of a winter-worn swamp—that is the first impression that the *marsh marigold* makes as you see it in the early days of spring. None of the tree leaves are showing, and other plant colors at this season are only faint tints of green or pink. But the marsh marigold glows cheerfully as if to announce the arrival of a new and warmer season. This strong-growing perennial with its roots in the bog mud and its blossoms and smooth, rounded green leaves bright in the pale sunshine, is a favorite among country folk of the Middle Atlantic and New England states and far to the West.

North America has about fifteen species of wild *trilliums,* and an equal number are found in other parts of the world. Their curious name, which means "triple", was given to them because their leaves, petals, and some of the inner parts of the blossoms are always grouped in threes. Wooded slopes and patches of fairly dry ground in shady swamps are the places to find this splendid white perennial. It comes into bloom when the tree leaves are about half grown, and a single plant will live for many years unless some accident occurs. You often see it growing happily in gardens, too, provided they are somewhat shady.

191

The good-natured *moss pink, moss phlox* or *creeping phlox* is an astonishing little plant. In the wild its innumerable half-inch blossoms may be almost any color from white to purple, and nurserymen have pro-

192

Parry nolina, with its massive flower stalk and spears for leaves, likes the rocky slopes of the southwest.

Partridge berry is almost too dainty to be real. Yet many a larger plant would die in its deep woodland home.

90

The *lupine* tribe extends from coast to coast and from Canada to the Gulf. Few wildflowers are as widely known.

Marsh marigolds grow beautiful, round, green leaves as lovely as the golden blossoms that rise above them.

White or *"great" trillium* has made good in hundreds of gardens whose owners never saw it growing wild.

193

194

duced many new pastel shades by hybridizing or crossing different selected plants. The size of the blossoms has been increased, too, so that when they are at their peak they conceal practically all of their unusual foliage. Its leaves are almost as slim and bristly as needles, and they crowd so thickly that they practically hide the stems on which they grow. Most of them stay green through the coldest winters.

Although it grows in dry, sunbaked mountainous places and is only a few inches tall, *bitter root* produces two- or three-inch flowers that look like white or pink waterlilies. The blossoms appear from June to August. Earlier in the season the narrow leaves die down, then suddenly revive as though they decided to make a nice setting for the flowers. This queer habit, together with the fact that the dried

195

roots revive even after years, led to the second half of its scientific name: *rediviva,* which means "living again". The first part, *Lewisia,* is in honor of Meriwether Lewis, co-leader of the Lewis and Clark Expedition to the Northwest in 1804, who first brought the plant to public attention. It's the state flower of Montana. The roots were a favorite Indian food.

Fringed gentians are found only where the soil and moisture conditions are exactly right. The plant is a biennial, and failure of its seed crop for two successive years will completely wipe out a colony. This can easily happen from accidental grass fires in dry weather, or from severe attacks by a tiny fly-like insect whose grubs eat the seeds before they have time to ripen. The name comes from the delicate fringe around the top of its rather tubular flowers. Sometimes it grows only a few inches high and bears a single blossom. Or, if you are very lucky, you may find a strong two-footer with many branches and dozens of superb colorful blossoms.

An *epiphyllum* is a cactus which, believe it or not, doesn't have a single spine! There are a dozen or so species of these plants, most of them found in the region from the Mexican Border southward as far as the Guianas. Nearly all are epiphytes—that is, they are air plants which grow on trees or other natural supports instead of in the ground. For this kind of life they have peculiar roots and leaves that are able to gather nourishment from both air and water. Most of the big-flowered *orchids* which ladies wear on special occasions are another type of air plant.

Goldstar grass isn't a grass at all, even though it does have grass-like leaves! It belongs to the *amaryllis* family, and it grows from a bulb as does the giant amaryllis which has been such a popular house plant for generations. But instead of having a few huge blossoms a year it has many little yellow ones about three-quarters of an inch across.

It is found in the open as well as in the shade of woods, generally where the ground is dry. Goldstar grass is easy to grow in a well-drained garden if its need for acid soil is met. The bulb lives for years, no matter how cold the winters are. And the little black, round seeds which follow some of the flowers often take root where they fall. Thus, after a while, there will be a

Most gardeners do not know that the beautiful *moss pink,* a creeping phlox, is a native American wildflower.

The small *bitter-root* seems to die. Then, all of a sudden, out pop flowers of great beauty and surprising size.

Flecks of deep sky blue massed in a colorful autumn meadow—that is the exquisite *fringed gentian* at its best.

Its stems are leaves, and its leaves serve as stems. Those are two of *epiphyllum cactus's* several oddities.

196

198

197

199

200

201

202

Goldstar grass is small and modest, but it has the strength and courage to keep sending out new flowers for weeks. 200

A shy American cousin of one of our best known garden flowers. Look for the *anemone* deep in the woods. 201

There are many species of wild *irises*, but none of them is neater and more up-standing than the *blue flag*. 202

neat little family that will expand each year instead of just a single plant.

Wood anemones, often known as *windflowers,* grow only six or eight inches high, and their white or lavender-tinted blossoms are no more than an inch across. But their pointed leaves are as pretty as little *ferns,* and the dark, slender stems are so springy that they make you think of finely tempered wire.

The species is perennial and its root system is in two parts: a thickened "stock" that lies horizontally in the ground, and a few slender feeding roots extending downward from it.

Blue flag is a thoroughly dependable perennial wild *iris* that makes itself quite at home in any garden as well as near streams and marshes where the soil is naturally moist. Its deep lavender-blue blossoms, with their yellow centers delicately veined in bronze, are about three inches wide, and the stalks that carry them may reach as high as two feet or more. Like those of most irises, the flowers are not particularly long lived.

In early spring the *bloodroot* spreads its snow white blossoms for everyone to see. Each is about an inch and a half across, and there is only one on a stem. But they are so starry and glistening, and stand out so sharply against the soft gray-green of the leaves beneath them, that you almost hold your breath in sheer admiration. Bloodroot is a perennial and grows from a woody, orange-tinted underground rootstock from which feeding roots strike downward into the soil. In these hard roots, as well as in the stems, is the red sap which gives the flower its name.

Rich, cool, damp woods are the *foam flower's* favorite home. There its cream-white flower spires really make you think of foam as they rise on

203

205

204

206

The many-pointed stars of *bloodroot* are a feature of early spring days. The plants do well in shady gardens, too.

The northern *foam flower* dislikes heat and strong sunshine. This is why you seldom find it except in cool woods.

Long lived and hard to transplant, the low-growing *fringed polygala,* or *gay wings,* spreads in many directions.

Tall as a man and stunning in the beauty of their huge blooms, *rose mallows* are late summer's showiest wildflower.

eight inch stalks above clusters of broad, dull-surfaced leaves that redden prettily in the fall. In spite of their delicacy they are among the most noticeable wildflower blossoms of the welcome spring season.

Foam flower likes to keep cool, and so the place to find it at its best is up toward the Canadian Border or in the mountains farther south where the cooler air found at high altitudes helps to keep the temperature down. It is particular, too, about having plenty of rotted leaves, or "humus", in the soil where its roots are. It is a long lived perennial which northern people like to plant in their shady wildflower gardens, where it looks especially well among trilliums, bloodroot and windflowers.

The foam flower tribe has only about eight species, of which six are North American, one comes from Japan, and one from the Himalayan Mountains.

Many people use the name *gay-wings* for the *fringed polygala,* because it reminds you of a bug with its wings spread. It creeps along close to the ground and seldom grows more than a couple of inches tall. The best place to look for it is in cool, damp woods, although sometimes it grows on hummocks in regular swamps. Generally it is so covered by dead tree leaves that you would not notice it except when its showy flowers are perched at the tops of their short, upright stems like bright little sentinels.

Gay-wings sometimes spreads into large but thin patches by sending its long, branching, underground stems in all directions. Each of these has thin feeding roots scattered along it so that they can reach deeper into the soil for food. The whole system is so rambling and easily injured that digging up the plant and moving it to some other place generally kills it. But when left undisturbed in its natural home Gay-wings will live for many years and never fail to brighten the spring days with its odd "flying flowers".

In August, when the marshes that they love so much are a sea of tall grasses and cat-tails that ripple in the wind, the *rose mallows* spread their great blossoms in the sunshine. Many of them measure six inches across, and some are even larger. The other plants around them show little color except green, so as you look far across the marshes they seem alive with the mallows' lovely saucers.

This strong-growing perennial, whose stiff, straight stalks are often six or seven feet tall, belongs to a large tribe which includes *okra,* a garden vegetable, and the famous *hibiscus* of the South. Some of them are shrubs almost big enough to be called trees; others trail along the ground. One or more of them will be found in such faraway countries as Africa, Asia, Japan, Australia and Hawaii.

Many people have grown rose mallows in gardens, where they seem to be as happy as in their native marshes. Particularly beautiful varieties of them have been developed by seedsmen from the typical pink species.

Next to *goldenrod, Jack-in-the-pulpit* is our best known wildflower. Its peculiar green, brown-striped hood or "pulpit", with "Jack" standing in the middle of it as though ready to deliver a sermon, is a familiar sight in countless woodlands and other shaded places over a large part of the country. Yet, common though it is, a great many people have no idea of the facts behind its strange shape and appearance. What seems to be the flower is not really a blossom, but a sort of roof protecting the true flowers down in the tube at "Jack's" feet. These are small and not much to look at, but without them there would be no seeds and no future generations.

Our woods and fields contain many plant surprises, but few of them are more remarkable than *Jack-in-the-pulpit.*

Black-eyed susans will grow almost anywhere, which is one of the reasons they can be found in so many states.

207

208

In midsummer, when Jack as well as his pulpit has withered away, you will often find a tight cluster of bright green seeds, looking somewhat like a large blackberry, at the top of the stalk from which the hood grew. As the days pass its color changes to a bright scarlet and finally, when all the seeds are fully ripe, they crumble apart and drop to the ground. A year or two later, if you look very closely, you may discover the tiny plants which have grown from them.

Jack-in-the-pulpits will grow almost anywhere as long as they have a good deal of shade. So, if you'd like to have some in your garden, go right ahead. The best time to plant them is when the stalk and leaves are ready to die after the first autumn frost.

The central and midwestern States are probably the original home of *black-eyed Susan,* but today you will find it almost everywhere in the country. It is one of those cheerful showy beauties that don't care a bit whether the soil around them is rich or poor, shaded or sun-baked.

Black-eyed Susans, brilliant "yellow daisies," are not long lived plants, but they produce so many seeds that there is little danger of their disappearing unless they are cut down before they have a chance to finish flowering. Occasionally they behave like annuals—that is, live for only one season. But as a rule they are biennial and flower in their second season. In any case, the first blossoms open fairly early in the summer and others keep on coming for five or six weeks. You may even find a few as late as September, although these are quite sure to be small and poorly colored.

The remarkable *Indian paint brush* plants, of which there are many different species in the West, puzzle even the experts. Their colors are

209

When you examine the *Indian paint brush* you find more striking color in the leaves than in the flower. 209

The giant *saguaro cactus* is the world's strangest tree. It has no leaves and its flowers grow out of its trunk. 210

The strange *Indian pipe* has no real leaves, no green in its stem, no trace of life-giving chlorophyl. 211

210

211

raw, startling and yet perfectly fitted to the mountain country where they are found. The actual flowers are small and rather unexciting. It is the bracts, or little scale-like leaves which surround them, that put on the real show. It is known that some are perennials and others annuals, but nobody seems to know why they will grow in one place and not in another. Strong, healthy ones of different kinds have been planted in many gardens. Practically all have sickened and died. Perhaps the best theory

212

Most yellow *daisies* are just yellow daisies, but *Oregon sunshine* really suggests the sun.

for this behavior is that their roots are more or less parasitic—that is, they must have some other organism in the soil on which they can live. This could explain their failure to grow in gardens, especially when we don't know what the necessary organism is.

The *saguaro*—or sahuaro, to give it its Spanish pronunciation—is the unbelievable *giant cactus,* oldest and largest of the American branch of the family. Sometimes fifty feet high and often up to three hundred years old, it may weigh as much as six tons. Woodpeckers chop their nesting holes in its trunks. Generations of Indians as well as early white settlers used its dead wood to build their homes and its fruit for food and wine-making. It is so prominent in the Southwest desert scenery that its blossom has been understandably chosen as Arizona's state flower. This astonishing plant is a cousin of the old time favorite that we call *night blooming cereus,* but its flowers open in the daytime instead of after dark. There are many other differences, too, such as the singular lengthwise ridges which cover the entire surface of the main trunk and its branches. These raised portions are actual reservoirs, which fill up with water during the rainy season and hold enough to meet the plant's needs for as long as three years in case the weather is so cranky that no more rain falls. As the supply is used the ridges gradually contract, and when the rains come once more they expand and fill up again!

Some midsummer day, deep in the woods where the soil is rich with rotted fallen leaves and branches, you will come upon a ghostly cluster of *Indian pipe,* one of the strangest of wildflowers. Its stems and bent blossoms suggest the shape of a pipe, but that is only the beginning of its oddities.

This shy woodlander has no real leaves like those of other plants—only those little scale-like points along the stems. And its flowers, whether they are white or sometimes pinkish, are the same color as the stalks. Nowhere in the entire plant is there a sign of green, because Indian pipe has no trace of that magical chlorophyl without which almost every wildflower, bush or tree would die. Indian pipes are what is known as *saprophytes,* which means plants that live on decaying leaves, wood or some other kind of organic material. This is probably why they are seldom found anywhere except in woods—indeed they are far from common even there. It is practically impossible to transplant one successfully to a garden, however shady it may be. Apparently the disturbance of being moved upsets the pipe's way of living, and although it may last a short while there is little chance that it will come up again the following year.

In the western mountains where the *Oregon sunshine* yellow *daisy* is at home it is one of the cheeriest of the flower sights. It is one of the *composites,* which are almost the largest of all flower families. Nearly twelve thousand species belong to it, including all of the *daisies, asters, sunflowers,* and many others easy to find. But when you do discover one you can be sure that you have found a plant as singular as any in the whole world.

The wildflowers we have discussed fall into four general classes.

The *annuals.* These sprout from seeds in the spring, grow rapidly, produce flowers and then seeds in summer or early fall. As soon as the seeds are ripe and have fallen the plant starts to die, leaving its seeds on the ground where they can take root the following spring and start the family all over again. California poppies often behave like annuals in regions that are a little too cold for them.

A second class is the *biennials,* whose seeds come up like those of the annuals but grow more slowly and seldom have flowers during their first season. In autumn the stems die, but the roots live through the winter and send up new stems in the spring. These fresh shoots are much stronger than the first ones, and when they are big enough they bear flowers and seeds. After that the whole plant dies, while its seeds wait until the next spring to start a new generation. Black-eyed Susan and fringed gentian are two of the important biennials.

A third group is made up of *perennials.* Most of these die down to the ground in autumn, like the annuals and biennials. However, their roots often live for six years or more and every spring send up new stems which bear flowers and then seeds. The blossoms, though, seldom appear until the plants are one, two, or even three years old. There are a great many kinds of perennial wildflowers, including trillium, spiderwort and turkey-beard.

The fourth general class is the *aquatics* which live in the water of ponds, lakes and slow-running streams. One of the most beautiful of these is the white waterlily. Its roots usually reach down to the mud several feet below the surface, and its long-stemmed leaves float on top while its flowers are often raised still higher. There are some kinds of aquatics that float around loose and never touch bottom with their roots, such as the water-hyacinth. These are able to find all the food they need in the water itself with the help of the air above it.

These are some of the important facts of wildflower life that will help to explain the puzzling things that these plants often do.

213

The South American *callithea butterflies* show a play of iridescent colors that can hardly be matched in jewel-like tones by any other living thing.

BUTTERFLIES AND MOTHS

No MORE beautifully colored things exist than some of the butterflies of the world, and those of the tropics are frequently the most spectacular of all. Especially outstanding are such colors as are shown by the *South American callithea butterflies.* No reproduction can possibly do justice to the jewel-like tones of turquoise and sapphire that adorn the upper sides of their wings. The wings beneath are not as brilliant, but as though to make up for this they are variegated with red in bold contrast. On an actual specimen in flight the most striking thing is the way the colors shift and vary with every change in the angle of the light or of the eye of the viewer. Watching one of the butterflies with the light behind you, and watching it turn and twist, you would see the colors change with every movement. Then, if you were to change your position so that the light were beyond the butterfly, you would see an entirely different set of hues.

Like the callithea butterflies the *urania moth* is a native of the new world tropics. It may surprise many people to see a moth so brilliantly colored, but a part of the answer is that the uranias fly during the daytime. That does not mean that many of the night-flying moths are not brightly colored, too; but the average seems to be higher among the day fliers. Like

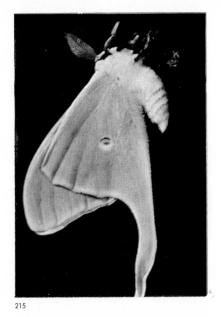

214

The colors of the *urania moth* of the tropics vie with those of butterflies in brilliant changeability.

215

The North American *long-tailed luna moth* often flies to lighted windows during late spring and early summer.

the callitheas, the color of the uranias changes and shifts with every motion.

Our *North American luna moth* proves that the tropics do not by any means have exclusive possession of beautiful things. It is one of our largest moths, having a wing spread of four inches or more. Lunas often fly to lighted places at night during late spring and early summer and circle and blunder around, the helpless victims of this strange instinct.

The larva of the luna is some two and a half inches long when full grown. It is bright yellowish green with a purplish head, and has yellow lines on its sides and three rows of bright red tubercles. It may be found feeding on any one of a number of common trees. Eventually it will spin a silken cocoon around itself, inside which it will change to the pupal stage and later to the adult moth.

Many of our butterflies are so fancifully named that it is sometimes hard to see the application. The *dog face butterfly* does, however, bear on the upper side of the front wings a sort of an animal head in silhouette, with even an eye-like spot. This butterfly ranges widely in the central and southern states and far southward into the tropics. In California occurs an even more striking species which is largely deep orange instead of yellow, and has a purplish iridescence. The larva of the dog face is downy green, sometimes plain but sometimes striped or banded with yellow, orange or black. It feeds on *clover* and on related wild plants such as *false indigo.* The adult butterflies have a quick, strong flight and are not easy to catch except when they are visiting flowers.

The larva of the widespread *viceroy butterfly* is a curiously ornamented creature which may be found feeding on the leaves of *willows, poplars* or *aspens,* or of quite a number of other trees or shrubs. Its bold and contrasting coloration probably helps it escape the notice of birds, which are not likely to pay much attention to a thing that looks like a dead leaf with a piece broken out of it. In the autumn the adult female viceroy lays her eggs singly on the tips of leaves of the proper food plants. The eggs hatch shortly, and the tiny larva eats a bit and then sets about preparing a winter home for itself. It does this by eating away much of the outer part of the leaf, sparing the midrib and the basal parts. It then rolls this basal part into a tube which it lines thoroughly with silk. It also fastens the stem of the leaf securely to the twig, thus insuring that it will stay there all winter, no matter how hard the winds blow and the snow comes down. Inside this silk lined tube, called its hibernaculum, it spends the winter. In the spring, when the warmth comes again and the buds of the food plant break to let green leaves escape, the tiny larva awakens from its torpor, crawls out of its winter home, and sets about the serious business of eating, growing up and going through the changes that will transform it into an adult butterfly.

The adult viceroy is a common butterfly in the eastern and central states. Its orange-brown and black colors and pattern are very similar to those of the famed *monarch,* which it is often considered to "mimic". As we see later, the monarch is definitely distasteful to potential enemies. This idea of mimicry is fortified by the fact that the viceroy is colored very differently from its relatives, the *red spotted purple* and the *white admiral,* which are largely black, iridescent blue and white. According to the theory of mimicry a bird which by eating a few monarchs has learned to leave them alone would thereafter also shun the viceroy. Of late, however, a strong suspicion has arisen that the viceroy is itself distasteful!

In South America there are quite a few species of *agrias butterflies,* their

The male and female *orange sulphur,* or *alfalfa, butterflies* shown resting in this picture are easily distinguishable. The female (right) has light spots on the dark borders of her wings, whereas the male has solid black borders.

216

217

A female *cecropia moth* laying her many eggs on a twig. These eggs are about one-sixteenth of an inch in diameter.

218

The *cecropia* larva, or caterpillar, eats greedily, laying up a store of food that will last its entire life.

colors often a blending of pigment reds and browns with iridescent, structural blues. They are large, stout bodied and strong fliers. Some of the species are really not uncommon, but due to their unusual habitat they are usually very rare in collections. Their whole life cycle is spent in and around the tops of the great forest trees, which may form an almost solid canopy a hundred or two hundred feet above the ground. Here the butterflies lay their eggs on the food plants, the larvae eat and grow and change to pupae, and the next generation of butterflies emerges. No wonder very few specimens were ever caught by man, and that the beauty of these butterflies combined with their rarity make them great collectors' prizes. Wealthy collectors such as Lord Rothschild in England paid hundreds or even thousands of pounds to gather collections of them. Eventually one of the most experienced field collectors of butterflies, a German named Fassl, worked out a method of baiting the butterflies by means of decaying meats or fermenting fruits and thus luring them within the reach of long handled nets or of net traps set high in the tree tops. And later it was found how to induce a female to lay her eggs in captivity, from which many perfect specimens could be reared. So the agrias market took a sharp drop, from which it has never recovered. Some of the species remain great rarities, but others which are just as beautiful can be purchased for comparatively little from dealers.

The *cecropia* cocoon. Inside this structure the caterpillar will change to a pupa and spend the whole winter.

Cocoon cut open to show pupa inside. On its surface are outlines of wings and legs of the future adult.

219

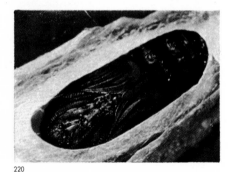

220

Very likely a great deal more has been written about the *North American monarch* than about any of our other butterflies. In the first place it is so big and boldly colored and marked, that even the most confirmed city dweller can hardly fail to see it. And it flies out in the open, slowly and, if we can apply the word to a butterfly, almost majestically, quite as though it had no enemies to worry about, which is actually the case. But the thing that really appeals to the imagination of those of us who are condemned to spend our winters fighting cold and sleet and snow is that it flies south for the winter, as most northerners would like to do themselves. It is not by any means our only migratory butterfly, but its migrations are so regular, and so spectacular, that they have thoroughly caught the public fancy.

Like all of the butterflies, and nearly all, if not all, of our moths, the individual monarch starts life as an egg. This is elongate and sculptured with raised lengthwise ribs and cross lines. Pale greenish in color, it is glued by the mother to a *milkweed.* As the tiny larva develops inside the eggshell its dark head can be seen. Eventually it can be noted to be very actively chewing its way out through the shell. When it first comes out it is pale yellowish green, hairy, and about an eighth of an inch long. Soon, however, it sheds its "skin" in the first of four such molts, and then assumes the bold and showy coloration which it will have for the rest of its larval life. Its appearance, unlike that of most larvae, actually seems to be designed to be plainly seen by birds and instead of hiding itself beneath leaves or in a nest, it feeds calmly out on top of the milkweed leaves in plain sight of every passerby. How can it do this and survive?

The answer lies in the chemistry of the milkweed which has an acrid, burning sap that is poisonous or very distasteful to most animals. The

Wet and helpless, the *cecropia moth* has emerged from the cocoon and hangs up to spread and harden its wings.

Its wings spread and its skeleton hardened and dried, the *cecropia moth* is now ready for its very first flight.

221

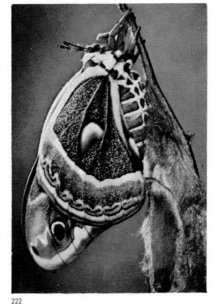

222

223

224

Male and female *io moth*. The male (left) has yellow front wings, while the wings of the female are brown.

The *Baltimore checker spot* is a stay-at-home butterfly that seldom strays an eighth of a mile from its birthplace.

monarch larvae, however, feeds and thrives on this diet. In so doing it apparently takes unto itself something of the nature of the milkweed, for it is shunned by birds that gobble up other caterpillars with dispatch. Of course every bird has to learn to leave monarch larvae alone, usually by a literally bitter experience. But therein lies the usefulness of the distinctive colors of the larva, marking it as bad medicine.

The larva does have some enemies in certain tiny parasitic wasps which may lay their eggs on or in it, although it is freer from this danger than most other caterpillars. The larva of the wasp bores into the body of the monarch larva and lives and grows as a parasite within its host. Eventually the work of the parasite will so weaken the poor monarch that it will not have the strength to transform to an adult butterfly. The long whiplike, black filaments with which the monarch larva is equipped, one pair forward and one pair aft, may serve as a certain protection against such wasps, for the larva thrashes its body around when disturbed, whipping the air with these.

If it escapes such enemies, the larva feeds away on its bitter diet. It grows quickly, shedding its old "skin" (actually its outer skin covering) at intervals as it grows too large for it. In a spirit of true conservation it eats the old shed skin each time. In about two weeks it is full grown, being about two inches long. It then begins preparation for a major change in its way of life.

Seeking a convenient leaf or stem it proceeds to spin a tough, flat button of silk, forming more silk in this process than it has during its whole previous life, for the monarch is not a great silk producer. The silk, like that of all butterfly and moth larvae, is a liquid secretion of glands in the head which hardens into a thread when it is squeezed out into the air from an opening on the lower lip. Meanwhile inside the larva a new shape and new organs are beginning to form. Finally, its spinning finished, the larva grips the silk button with its last pair of prolegs and swings free, head downward. It then sheds its "skin" for the last time as a larva, and is now an entirely different looking object, the pupa. In this stage it continues to hang head downward, held securely to the silk disc by a hook-studded spike at the rear end. This last molt is an acrobatic feat of the first magnitude, for the larva must simultaneously let go with the prolegs, as it sheds the skin over them, and catch the silk with the spike which is inside the skin which it is shedding. If the timing were not perfect the larva would tumble down to the ground and have little chance of surviving.

The pupal stage is sometimes called a "chrysalis" from a Greek word meaning "golden" because many butterfly pupae have metallic looking golden marks on their pupae. The monarch is one of these, and one could easily believe that the markings were really gold. The remainder of the pupa is at first yellowish, but it soon turns to a very beautiful translucent green. It is hard to believe that this mummy-like creature, hanging head downward and almost bereft of the power of motion, is actually the same creature as the active, striped caterpillar that only a day or two ago was eating so avidly. And it is as hard to realize, until one has seen it happen, that out of this object will come the wide-winged Monarch, capable of flying across an ocean.

Inside the pupal shell the organs of the larva break down and rebuild into those of the adult butterfly. If we look closely at the surface of even a newly formed pupa, we can see the outlines of the wings in miniature, and of the long, slender legs and antennae and tongue of the butterfly. As days pass, the black and brown and white pigments of the adult appear and show stronger and stronger through the thin pupal shell. Eventually, in from perhaps as little as four to as many as twelve days, the adult is fully formed. The pupal stage has played its part, undramatic but essential, in the life of the monarch. It has furnished a quiet period when the almost complete reorganization of larva into butterfly could take place, a change so drastic that it could hardly be accomplished while the insect was moving about.

Finally comes the crucial time when the adult monarch is ready to emerge. Struggling with its long legs and pumping the blood madly through its body, it breaks the shell of the pupa and drags itself out. Its wings are tiny miniatures, soft and useless pads, and its skeletal structures are unhardened. Hanging downward for some time, it must pump its wings up to full size and then wait until they and the other parts of its outer shell harden. At last, with perhaps no more than

225

The *painted lady* is the most cosmopolitan butterfly. These specimens rest on thistle, a favorite larva food.

Tropical *zebra butterflies* gather together at night in a favorite bush. This one is poised on oleander shrub.

226

few preliminary waves of its wings, it takes off on its first flight with all the skill of a veteran.

The great autumn broods of monarchs fly, even from Canada, to the southernmost states and Mexico. On the way they sometimes come together at night in great flocks of thousands on certain trees or shrubs, and certain localities are famous for these sleeping assemblies, year after year. The winter is spent in drifting around and luxuriating in the warm climate. Then in the spring, which comes early so far south, the survivors begin a slow northward flight. This is an individual affair, and thus not as spectacular as the autumn migrations. It is doubtful if any of them make the whole trip to the north; instead the females lay eggs after flying some distance, and from these eggs arises another generation which continues the northward flight which may reach as far away as Canada.

It is hardly surprising that an insect with such superb powers of flight attempts even ocean crossings and apparently sometimes succeeds in making them. The monarch seems to have made both the trans-Atlantic and trans-Pacific journeys, being now established widely across the Pacific islands. Truly the monarch is well named.

Not all butterflies are as welcome as the monarch, about which we humans can say nothing but good, although an unwary bird that had tried to eat one might disagree. The *European cabbage butterfly* is very much on the other side of the fence, for it has neither beauty nor salutary habits to recommend it. This undesirable visitor was introduced accidentally into Quebec about 1860 and has since spread over a large part of the continent. its downy green larvae are pests on a great many plants of the cabbage family, attacking *cabbage, mustard* or *watercress* with equal fervor. They

This *southern giant swallowtail butterfly,* found mostly in the tropics, is a very strong flier. The caterpillar of this butterfly is called an "orange dog" in Florida, where it is sometimes destructive to citrus trees.

227

have even been known to eat *nasturtium* plants being grown in a window box ten stories high above the streets of Manhattan. Fortunately for us there are some parasitic wasps, related to those which attack the monarch larvae, which probably play the major part in holding the cabbage butterfly in check.

One of the familiar butterflies over much of the United States and Canada is the *mourning cloak,* so called because of the white-edged black of the under side of its wings. It also occurs widely in Europe. English butterfly collectors, to whom it is known as the "Camberwell beauty", consider it a rare prize, for it does not seem to be able to breed in England and only occasionally flies over from the Continent. The margins of the wings of the mourning cloak, and of its near relative the *Compton tortoiseshell,* are normally irregular and frayed looking. When these butterflies alight on a tree trunk or among dead leaves and fold their wings over their backs, their irregular outlines and dull colors beneath really disguise them, making them resemble flakes of bark or dead, crumpled leaves.

Both the mourning cloak and the Compton tortoiseshell are hardy souls who spend the winter with us in the adult form. Not for them the escape to sunny climes of the monarch. In the autumn the butterflies seek sheltered nooks in the hollows of trees or logs or, since man came along, in barns and sheds or old tin cans or barrels. They have even been found in some numbers inside old abandoned automobiles. Here

228

Tiger swallowtail was first pictured by an associate of Sir Walter Raleigh when latter was governor of Roanoke.

they cling with their wings tight over their backs, stiff and inactive during the cold. They are quick to revive when a bit of warmth comes along, however, so that occasionally a prematurely mild, sunny day in late winter or early spring will awaken them too soon and afford us the curious spectacle of butterflies flying over patches of snow. Since a mourning cloak that emerged from its pupa in late August may still be alive and active as late as the next May, we see the fallacy of the popular idea that all butterflies are ephemeral and fragile things that live for but a few days.

One of the largest and most striking of our North American moths is the *cecropia,* a red, black and white giant whose wings may spread five inches or more. Like its relative the luna moth, the cecropia often flies into lighted places at night in late spring or early summer, and then beats around erratically. Also like the luna, the cecropia has no mouth parts with which to eat or drink. In the adult stage it is able to live only until it has used up the supply of stored foods in its tissues which it accumulated by eating leaves when it was a larva.

The female cecropia lays a great many eggs, usually on one of the

107

The egg of the *monarch butterfly* is laid on a leaf of milkweed, chiefly the common, pink-flowered variety.

chosen food plants of the species, but sometimes quite promiscuously. She thus does not exercise the care that the females of most butterflies do. The eggs are round and somewhat flattened, and about one-sixteenth of an inch in diameter. Like the eggs of most moths, and unlike those of most butterflies, they are smooth and unornamented by sculpture. The list of possible food plants is quite large, including *willow, apple, pear, hawthorn, lilac, privet* and many others.

The newly hatched cecropia larva is a tiny, hairy thing, with little that is distinctive about it. Soon it molts, as it will do several times more, and then begins to assume the characteristic appearance of its species. When it has finished its larval growth, a process that may take six weeks, it is one of the largest and most striking of our caterpillars, combining green, yellow, coral red, blue and black to make an object that is so bizarre that most people think it must be poisonous. Actually, of course, it is dangerous only to the leaves which it eats. If cecropia moths were ever to become really common or abundant, it is perfectly possible that they might be quite a pest because of their appetites. But they are actually not very common, by insect standards at least, being held in check quite effectively by the attacks of parasitic wasps.

When fully grown the cecropia larva begins to prepare for its transformation to the pupal stage. Like the majority, but by no means all, of the moths, it does so by first spinning a silken cocoon. This it fastens lengthwise along a twig so securely that it may remain there for two years or more. The larva spins the cocoon around itself, so that it soon becomes entirely encased and hidden. Inside the outer shell it proceeds to spin a smaller, oval case of closely cemented silk that is proof against the wettest weather. Inside this it molts its larval "skin" for the last time, transforming to the pupa. Like those of most moths the pupa is plain brown, lacking the ornamentation that characterizes the pupae of butterflies. On its surface can be traced the outlines of the wings, antennae and legs of the future adult. The pupa merely lies quiet, while inside is accomplished the reorganization of the structures of the larvae into those of the adult. It is not, incidentally, a good idea to cut open a cocoon to expose the pupa if you

The boldly striped caterpillar of the *monarch butterfly,* completely unconcealed, feeds on milkweed leaves.

231

Attached to a twig, the caterpillar of the *monarch* hangs upside down, preparing to change into pupal form.

want the moth to emerge, for such exposed individuals frequently dry up and die.

Inside its snug cocoon the cecropia pupa rests for the duration of the cold weather. Sometimes, for reasons about which we know very little, it may hold over in the pupa stage for an extra year. It is not until late spring that the adult moth begins to take shape inside the pupal shell. Finally it is fully formed and ready to emerge. At this time it voids a quantity of a rather corrosive liquid which softens and partly dissolves the silk at one end of the cocoon. Through the opening thus formed the moth drags itself, to emerge into the outer world a most wet, flabby and bedraggled looking object. Its wings, like those of the newly emerged monarch, are merely sac-like miniatures, and all of its structures are soft and weak. Crawling upward, it finally comes to rest and hangs for some time while it pumps up its wings and hardens its outer structures. At this time it voids the remainder of the liquid which it has formed within its body during its change to the adult form. It is well to remember that this liquid is not only bright pink but corrosive to many fabrics, so that it is not wise to let the moths hang on curtains or anything else of value while they are finishing their emergence.

Finally the moth is ready for flight. With sometimes no more warning than a little trembling and a few preliminary waves of its wings it takes off. The males are stronger fliers and much more active than the females, which are handicapped by the great weight of their bodies, already swollen with eggs. The antennae ("feelers") of the males are widespreading plumes, while those of the females are smaller. It is largely by means of sense organs in these that the males locate females, sometimes at great distances. At times a veritable swarm of ardent suitors will crawl and fly around a single female, wooing her by we know not what strange rites. Collectors often expose females in screened boxes to lure in males. Sometimes, if conditions are right, dozens will respond.

Since the cecropia cocoons are fastened so securely as to stay up in the trees or shrubs, they are quite conspicuous objects after the leaves fall. The winter, then, is the time to go cocoon hunting. Of course quite a few of the cecropia cocoons found may prove to be those of the year before from which the moth has

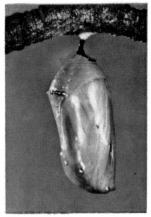

The newly-formed, mummy-like pupa of the *monarch* now hangs where the caterpillar was a few minutes before.

232

109

long ago emerged. These can usually be told by the opening at one end. Still others may have already been found and opened by birds or squirrels; and still others may be those of larvae which had been attacked by parasitic wasps. But enough will be good to make it worthwhile to keep a lookout at all times. Some of the best cocoon hunting is often in city parks. A good cocoon usually gives a dull, heavy thud when shaken gently, whereas an empty

233

234

235

or parasitized one gives either a dry rattle or else no sound at all. The cocoons should be kept in a cold place, preferably outdoors, so that the moths can emerge at the normal season. And it must be remembered that occasionally one will hold over for a second winter.

Each of the giant silkworm moths of North America makes its own distinctive cocoon. Those of the *luna* and *io moths* are merely spun in a leaf, with which they fall to the ground. But those of the *promethea moth,* a common species which feeds chiefly on *spicebush* and *sassafras,* and of the *ailanthus silkworm moth,* which feeds on the *ailanthus* that is so abundant in many Eastern cities, are spun in a leaf which is securely bound to its twig; and so these are especially easy to find.

The great quantity of silk spun by the larvae of such big moths has long interested people as a commercial possibility. To this we owe the introduction into this country of the big, green ailanthus silkworm moth, as well as of the tree on which it feeds. However, no commercially feasible method of loosening and reeling the silk has ever been worked out; and now the cheapness of synthetic fibers like rayon and nylon makes any further attempts unlikely.

Another of our native silkworm moths, and a fairly near relative of cecropia and luna, is the somewhat smaller io moth. Its sexes are quite different from each other, the male being the one with yellow front wings. The enormous

The colors of the *monarch's* wings show through the pupal shell when the adult butterfly is fully formed.

The adult *monarch butterfly* drags itself out of its pupal shell and begins to spread its beautiful wings.

The *monarch* has finished spreading its wings and is ready to take off to spend the winter in the south.

110

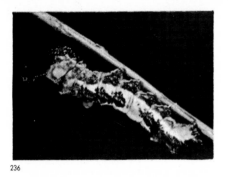

236

237

The caterpillar of the *viceroy butterfly* is a curiously colored and shaped creature that resembles a dead leaf.

This newly-emerged *viceroy* looks more like the unrelated *monarch* than it does like its own close relatives.

black and blue eyespot on each hind wing is kept hidden beneath the front wings while the moth is sleeping during the daytime. In the new world tropics there are dozens of close relatives of the io, some nearly as large as cecropia and others half or less the size of our io. The green larva of the io is covered with clusters of sharp hairs. These are very irritating to the human skin, causing a very painful, burning rash. The poisonous quality does not carry over into the adult stage, however, so that the moths themselves can be handled with impunity. Such poisonous caterpillars are really very exceptional. The only other one in North America that presents a bad problem is that of the *brown tail moth,* occasionally a serious pest on various trees; and it is not a native of this country at all, being an introduction from Europe.

In strong contrast to the big, clumsy and nocturnal moths is one of the most attractive butterflies of the world, the *painted lady* or *cosmopolite.* It is an extremely active, strong flying species, which has spread until it is at home in nearly every continent. It is a very restless creature, seldom spending much time in one spot. Occasionally, after a period when the larvae have been having unusually good success in growing and escaping parasites, a very large population may build up in an area. Then a definite migratory urge strikes the butterflies, which take wing in great migratory streams numbering many thousands. It is not always possible to predict

The *European cabbage butterfly* is an unwelcome visitor which we would like to send back where it came from.

The *mourning cloak* spends the winter snugly tucked in a hollow tree, and is one of spring's first butterflies.

238

239

240

241

The *agrias butterfly* is a famous "high flier" of the South American forest. Collectors prize it greatly.

The *Compton tortoiseshell butterfly* looks like a ragged dead leaf when it folds its wings above its back.

the direction of such a migration, which has the double advantage of relieving the population pressure in the crowded area and of colonizing new places. The whole thing is as unlike the organized and very regular migration of the monarch as anything we can imagine. The larvae of the painted lady feeds on *thistles* as well as on a host of related plants; and the adults are very fond of visiting the flowers of this prickly plant.

In strong contrast to the painted lady is a butterfly of the eastern United States called the *Baltimore.* The name arose from the fact that the butterflies bear on their wings the black and orange colors of Lord Baltimore, the founder of Maryland. The larvae feed chiefly on the leaves of *turtlehead,* a very attractive flowering plant of wet meadows. They live at first in a sort of communal web; but after hibernating when partly grown they scatter and live solitary lives while finishing their growth the next spring. The adult butterflies are great stay-at-homes, seldom straying a couple of hundred yards from the locality where they were reared. They thus tend to occur in small colonies well isolated from one another. It is to the places where the turtlehead grows that we must go if we are to find them.

The tropical *zebra* is very common in some parts of Florida and occurs in other extreme southern states. It shares with the monarch the good fortune of being distasteful to birds, owing to the poisonous nature of the plants (*passion flowers*) on which it feeds as a larva. It can thus afford to have a slow, lazy flight, with shallow wing beats and a great deal of gliding. Zebras have a curious habit of gathering in large numbers in certain bushes and trees, night after night, to sleep companionably. One observer recorded the same individual, recognized by a distinctive tear in one of its wings, returning every night to the same bush for a period of nearly two months. The zebra is a widespread butterfly, occurring as far south as Peru. In Central and South America it has a host of close relatives, other *heliconians,* most of which have scarlet or yellow patches or streaks on the wings, or are iridescent blue or orange brown or black. All are shunned by birds because of their bad taste as well as their tough, rubbery structure. They are one of the favorite groups of tropical butterflies among collectors, but are extremely difficult to classify because of the great amount of mimicry of each other that they appear to have indulged in. This sort of thing, as we have seen in discussing the viceroy, makes it easier for potential enemies to learn to leave the genuinely "protected" butterflies alone. Needless to say quite a lot of other butterflies and even many moths, themselves perfectly good bird food, capitalize on this by mimicking the heliconians, and thus probably gain a certain measure of protection.

The *giant swallowtail*, like the Zebra, is essentially tropical; but it occurs northward to Minnesota and New England, subject to some seasonal fluctuation. In the south its large larvae feed on the leaves of citrus trees, on which they are quite a pest in years of abundance. Known as *"orange dogs"*, they are dark brown with creamy white lines and patches. Like the larvae of other swallowtails (including the *tiger*), they have a Y-shaped scent organ which they thrust out from the front part of their body when they are disturbed. This organ has a very strong, aromatic and unpleasant odor, which must serve as quite an efficient protection to the larvae. The giant swallowtail is a familiar sight in the south but, since it is a strong flier, is not too easy to net and is best caught when visiting flowers.

The *orange sulphur* or *alfalfa butterfly* is now common in every part of the United States, although this was not the case as little as thirty years ago. For some reason the butterfly began extending its range northward and eastward in the early part of the twentieth century. Now it has migrated throughout all of New England and eastern Canada and has been caught in Newfoundland. Its larvae thrive best on *alfalfa*, on which they may become quite a pest. Very closely related is the all-yellow *clouded sulphur* which, except for its color, is almost indistinguishable from the orange sulphur. The clouded sulphur has always, as far as we know, been an

The *dog face butterfly* is well named, bearing on the upper side of its front wings a sort of animal head in silhouette, with eyelike spots. This butterfly is found in central and southern states, and in the tropics.

abundant inhabitant of the northeastern states, as well as of the rest of the country and southern Canada. Its larvae thrive best on *clover*. With the immigration of the orange sulphur into its territory the clouded sulphur has faced some competition from its invading cousin. The two species hybridize with each other so that now one may see in any of the states intermediate specimens that are pale orange, or yellow with orange patches. Both of the sulphurs have a white female variety that is not uncommon. It is not a true albino, for it has the dark pigmented borders of the wings, but it is white where its normal sisters are yellow or orange. Altogether this makes quite a variety of forms of this pair of butterfly species.

Both of the sulphurs are "mud puddle" butterflies, the yellow species more than the orange one. When the butterflies are abundant one can sometimes see flocks of hundreds packed shoulder to shoulder around the edges of mud puddles "taking the waters" together companionably. Apparently these gatherings are all of young males which have recently emerged from the pupal stage. For a few days the young bachelors dissipate mildly at their "clubs" (the butterfly equivalent of the neighborhood soda fountain). Then they scatter in search of mates and the serious business of butterfly life.

The play of colors on a butterfly's wing is characteristic of what the physicist calls "structural color." It is caused, not by actual pigments, but by minute, sometimes almost submicroscopic structures which, in many butterflies, are located in the tiny scales that cover the wings. The blue of the sky and the colors that we see when there is a film of oil on the surface of water are familiar examples of the same sort of thing. The result is the appearance of color when there is no actual coloring matter present. In many birds and insects the structural colors may be backed up by actual pigment colors, too, which modify and sometimes deepen them. A simple test for the presence of structural color is to wet the surface of a dried specimen lightly with alcohol or carbon tetrachloride or some such liquid which will dry quickly completely. If the color is structural it will change its hue, but will regain it on drying out. You can make this simple test the next time you catch and mount a butterfly.

243

American egrets seem at times like fairy visitors from another world, especially when displaying the lacy, delicate plumes for which they are famous, and for which they were almost wiped out years ago.

LIFE IN THE EVERGLADES

THE EVERGLADES—a name to conjure with! Mysterious, remote, almost a legend and one a bit fearsome perhaps, but compellingly fascinating.

What *are* the Everglades? Are they a huge forest through which the sun cannot strike? A vast wilderness where boa constrictors hang from trees, crocodiles lurk in the mud and ferocious animals stalk the night?

Let's call them what they really are, what those who know them best have always called them, those who have lived amid them for generations—the Seminoles who still live there. To them, the Everglades are "Pa-hay-okee"—grassy water! They are a great freshwater marsh stretching to the horizon, dotted here and there with clumps of shrubs, bushes and sometimes trees. Mile after mile of grass, that sharp-bladed, tooth-edged, formidable plant *Cladium effusum—sawgrass*. This is the Everglades.

Grassy glades reach southward from their birthplace, Lake Okeechobee, almost to the very tip of mainland United States, Cape Sable. From Okeechobee, the "Big Water" of the Seminoles, the land slopes gradually southeast and southwest. During past ages the overflow and seepage from the great lake created the Everglades. Roughly, this "grassy water" extends about one hundred miles north and south and fifty miles east and west.

115

Mangrove fox squirrels can be pepper-and-salt gray, reddish or black—but all possess the white nose and ears.

One road crosses the Glades from east to west, the famous Tamiami Trail. Begun in 1916, the two ends crept toward each other with various delays and terrific hardships until 1928; then they finally met and the Trail was done. It is something more than a road; it is an engineering marvel, a monument to a determined endeavor which conquered the unknown.

The Glades teem with life, from minute, ephemeral forms which live but a day to huge throwbacks to the Age of Reptiles. From tiny mice to lumbering manatees; dainty hummingbirds to giant white herons; infinitesimal minnows to great tarpon; and pretty little lizards to deadly rattlesnakes. All these are there, insect, fish, reptile, bird and mammal, but many a visitor, crossing this amazing region on the Tamiami Trail, has returned home to report that "there's nothing there, not a thing but trees and grass and water." To them the Glades seem to be the abomination of desolation, but to others they are a never-ending storehouse and generating plant of multitudinous, swarming life!

The plants of the Everglades differ from those of other parts of the country because of the influence of the tropic zone. Strange trees and shrubs with strange and fascinating names occur; trees covered with great flowers, some studded with thorns, others with poisonous leaves or fruit. Largely West Indian in character, many of these southern Glades plants bear little resemblance to the oaks, maples, elms and spruces so familiar to us in the North.

We find such names as mahogany, tamarind, poison-wood, manchineel and gumbo-limbo! Everything seems foreign, but now and then we do find acquaintances; there are cypresses, gums and bays, and of course, the palm. Florida seems synonymous with palms; the majestic Royal, the slender Thatch, the Silver and the graceful Coconut. The Glades is a botanical wonderland; every visitor should at least see that remarkable cross-section of its trees, shrubs, vines and flowers on the southern edge of Miami—the Fairchild Tropical Garden.

Modern bird protection is so linked in many minds with the *American egret* that it can well be taken as the type of that successful endeavor which was once thought to be little more than the clamor of a few fanatics. This beautiful species, together with the *snowy* and *reddish egrets,* were known under the general term of "plume birds" and furnished the much desired "aigrettes" demanded years ago by fashion. Pluming flourished in the early years of this century, and veritable battles took place between the scattered wardens, who were attempting to protect the birds, and the hunters who were determined to secure the high-priced feathers. The egrets were almost extinct and the reddish egret had vanished from the Glades. However, protection in the field and corrective laws engineered by the Audubon Society and other interested groups finally succeeded in saving these exquisite birds, and in recent years even the reddish egret is reappearing in the Florida Keys.

One of the largest of American squirrels lives in the Everglades, a race known as the *mangrove fox squirrel*. Almost as large as a house cat, a good sized specimen will measure as much as 28 inches, including the tail. The specimens in the Glades are often quite blackish, although in other places they may be red, or pepper-and-salt gray. With white nose and ears, the mangrove is easily identified. It is much more of a ground dweller and feeder than most of the squirrels people are familiar with.

Large birds, or even those of medium size, do not have a monopoly on bright colors. A very small bird which migrates through the Glades and often spends the winter there, is the most brilliantly plumaged bird of the country! Its very name is suggestive—the *painted bunting*. In some parts of its range it is known as the "nonpareil", which means "without an equal." No blending of color takes place, no gradual shading of one color into another. It has a bright blue head, flaming red underparts, brownish wings and a shining yellow-green back patch, all as sharply defined as though painted with a brush! It belongs to the great finch family and has the stout, seed-crushing beak of the sparrows, grosbeaks and other finches.

The female is so different from her gaudy mate that one would never think she belonged to the same species. She is a plain greenish-backed, sparrow-like bird with yellowish underparts. This is nature's plan, for it makes her inconspicuous on the nest. A good place to see this remarkable rainbow of a bird is the Parrot Jungle, just south of Miami, where *parrots, parakeets* and *macaws* are a great tourist attraction. The

This brightly plumaged small bird is the *painted bunting*—it flaunts more colors than any other native bird.

The *manatee* or *sea-cow,* a great lump of shapeless flesh, has flippers instead of legs and is helpless on land.

245

246

117

The little *chameleon lizard* shows its "blanket" when alarmed or excited. It is a valuable insect control.

Along the Tamiami Trail, the peculiar "birds' nests" plants that dot the trees are the wild "pineapple" *air plants.*

The *box turtle* shuts itself up in a tight box so nothing can do it damage. It eats insects but is also fond of vegetable food. Living on land, it rarely enters the water but can swim if it must.

seeds these birds scatter and waste while feeding attract wild specimens; and the nonpareil often appears among them.

Many species of song and insectivorous birds migrate through the Everglades. *Vireos, warblers, swallows, tanagers, thrushes* and *waxwings* all pass through, and some of them remain for the winter. *Robins* are innumerable in winter. Ducks occur in great flocks during late fall, winter and early spring. *Pintails, bald-pates, teal* and *scaup,* together with *shovelers* and *ring-necks* are common. *Coots* swarm in multitudes over ponds, bays and canals. *Marsh hawks* winnow over the sawgrass, *red-tailed* and *red-shouldered hawks* swing high in the sky and *sparrow hawks* are abundant. *Turkey vultures,* universally called *buzzards,* pick up remains of wildlife killed on the roads, or hunt for carrion amid the grasses and hammocks. Graceful *swallow-tailed kites* cruise above the mangroves in spring, catching and eating their insect prey on the wing.

Everywhere are the herons. *Great blues, little blues, greens, night herons, Louisianas* (another badly misnamed bird) and the *egrets.* Now and then in the fall, the largest of all the American herons, the truly majestic *great white,* leaves the Keys and wanders about in the Glades as far as the Tamiami Trail.

The largest of the Everglades' mammals does not seem to be a mammal at all! One of the strangest creatures anywhere is the *manatee,* or *sea cow.*

It is a great, lumbering, almost shapeless blob, and is entirely aquatic like a seal. With its huge, flapping upper lip, it feeds on vegetable matter, submarine grasses and plants. The manatee sometimes reaches tremendous size, well over a thousand pounds; it ranks with the walrus. Living along the coastal rivers, bays and estuaries, it also gets into Whitewater Bay of the southern Glades, and at times is seen far out at sea. Many have been killed for food and furnish a lot of "beef", for their length runs from seven to thirteen feet.

Commonest of the lizards is the familiar *chameleon,* a little green fellow that grows to a length of six inches and feeds almost entirely on insects. The changes in color for which it is famous are caused by light, temperature and the mood of the creature itself. Under ordinary conditions in sunlight it is a dull brown, but if two males meet, an interesting encounter results. The pinkish throat fan or "blanket" is distended, the bodies become ash-gray and the two dart at each other, tangling into rolling balls, until one is the victor. The defeated one scampers off, often minus a tail, and is then a dull yellowish color, while the victor struts about—now vividly green. Soon this fades into the normal brown and the tiny "dinosaur" is ready for an unwary insect to happen along or another encounter with a rival male.

Turtles are very numerous throughout the Glades. Along the Tamiami Trail dozens can be seen atop rocks, logs and snags in the canal; they drop into the water as a car approaches. Evidently the turtle has very keen eyesight in spite of his dull, inactive appearance.

One of the best-known varieties is the *box turtle,* which, when alarmed, closes itself into a veritable armored tank by pulling in head and legs and flexing the hinged shell together. It is a dry land dweller but is found near water most of the time and is able to swim when necessary. It feeds mainly on vegetable matter, but also takes earthworms and insects. When kept as a pet it becomes very tame and will eat from one's hand.

Anhinga Trail is a favorable place from which to watch Glades turtles. Here one can see quite a variety; the large, showy *yellow-bellied turtle;* the fierce *snapper* with its long tail; and the flattened, long-snouted *soft-shelled*

To swim, *alligators* fold their legs along their sides and the great tail works like a boat's propeller.

The *anhinga* or *snakebird* is a grotesque looking creature, half-bird, half-reptile in appearance.

250

251

252

254

253

255

The colorful *roseate spoonbill* might belong in another age, but it lives today and can be seen during the winter.

The *otter* is almost a fish in fur. In the water, it swims, dives, and catches fish as well as a seal.

These strange but beautiful *spider lilies* shine like white stars amid the dark green grasses of river banks.

The *indigo snake* is the biggest snake in the country, but for all its size, it is harmless and usually gentle.

turtle. The little *painted turtle* is one of the most attractive but hard to catch.

Few of the Glades' botanical oddities attract as much attention as the *air plants* and *orchids*. Much confusion exists in visitors' minds as to which is which and many roadside stands in Florida sell air plants for orchids, which they are not. Driving across the Tamiami Trail, the winter visitor sees in the then leafless cypresses what look like great numbers of birds' nests. These are the "wildpines" or air plants. Seen at very close range they look much like a pineapple and indeed, are related to that fruit. They attach themselves to trees, either on limbs or trunks, and live on air, atmospheric dust and water. The widened base, from which the leaves spread, is a veritable reservoir, and even in dry times one can detach an air plant, turn it upside down, and see water run from it. In late winter the bracts of the plant become very red and are often mistaken for the blossom; actually, the small flowers are blue, emerge from the red bracts, and are hard to see at a distance. Certain species show creamy-white flowers rather than blue.

One of the most "desirable" sights for the majority of visitors in Florida is the *alligator!* It is easy to see this great saurian in captivity; there are numerous alligator "farms" all over Florida and many of the roadside "zoos" have specimens. Given time, the visitor can eventually see alligators in the wild as well—though much persecution has reduced the population

considerably. Thoughtless shooting, hide-hunting, and the sale of baby 'gators so depleted this natural asset that, some years ago, protective legislation was instituted. Florida awoke to the fact that the alligator was a drawing-card; now it is possible to see it in many a locality where, a few years ago, it was practically non-existent.

The usual sight of an alligator proves rather disappointing. Seen from a distance when out of the water, it seems hardly more than a black log, and with no more movement than one! When in the water, three dark knobs appear above the surface, the tip of the rounded snout and the eye ridges, with sometimes a small section of armored back. Apathy and inactivity are characteristic of specimens seen in the "farms." However, the alligator is capable of fast movement when occasion warrants, both afloat and ashore. It can and does actually run at times, getting up on its toes and progressing at a surprising rate, like a gigantic lizard.

A large percentage of an alligator's food consists of turtles, which are very detrimental to game fish. So where the alligator occurs there is usually good fishing, for the turtles are kept under some natural control. Dogs sometimes fall victims; pigs, raccoons, deer and birds are taken as well. Alligators are often found hunting in the great heron and ibis rookeries; they prey upon the young birds which fall from the nests. A cornered 'gator is a most formidable antagonist. There is little chance, however, of anyone ever being attacked by one under ordinary circumstances.

People are often surprised to learn that the *crocodile* occurs in the United States. It is rare, found only in the Everglades Park. Though it strongly resembles the far commoner alligator, there is no reason to be confused if a good look is secured. The crocodile is a dweller in salt or brackish water; it has a sharply pointed snout and is definitely greenish in color, while the 'gator is black, has a rounded snout and lives in fresh water. Though more generally aggressive than the alligator, there is nothing to fear regarding attacks by a crocodile unless the reptile is cornered. It has long since learned to avoid man and is one of the most wary of wild creatures today.

The range of the crocodile never extended further north than Palm Beach. It is far more susceptible to cold than the alligator and therefore does not venture much out of tropical waters. It nests on the keys of Florida Bay and parts of the Cape Sable mainland, laying numerous long, hard-shelled eggs. It covers them with a mat of vegetation, which

This big spider, the *silver agriope,* is as harmless as it is handsome. Look for its web on bushes, vines and trees.

256

121

257

258

Wild *flamingoes* do not occur in Florida except as accidental wanderers from the warm tropics.

One of America's strangest animals is the shy *opossum*. Ugly and unattractive, its behavior is always interesting.

eventually hatches the eggs by generating heat through decomposition. Many young crocs are taken by predatory birds and animals; only a small percentage reach adulthood.

A remnant of antiquity is the somber, silent *anhinga, water-turkey* or *snakebird*. It belongs to a tropical family called the *darters* and lives in freshwater swamps and marshes, lakes and streams. The male is jet black with white spangles on the back and wings; the female shows a fawn-colored throat and chest. The only note seems to be a sort of guttural growl, inaudible at any distance. The anhinga swims with the body completely submerged, the long slender neck looping along in strange jerks and strongly resembling a swimming snake, hence one of its names. In flight, the long rounded tail looks much like a turkey's; it is responsible for another name, while *anhinga* is a South American term. This strange bird impresses all who see it as being very reptilian in general appearance. Because of its submarine swimming the plumage becomes soaked, and this is the reason it is so often seen sitting on a rock or branch, with the wings held open—it is drying its plumage. This habit is shared by the *cormorant*, which some people mistake for the snakebird. The anhinga's nest is placed in willows or cypresses, at no great elevation. The newly hatched young, covered with a buffy down, look even more reptilian to the observer than their parents.

In the mangrove lakes of the Cape Sable area, and occasionally in other parts of the Glades, one of the most noteworthy of Florida's avian attractions appears. It is a rival of the *flamingo* in brilliant color and strangeness of beak. This is the *roseate spoonbill,* called by the natives "pink curlew." This remarkable bird seems to belong to a forgotten age; it might be an appropriate companion for dinosaurs and pterodactyls! It is, in fact, a sort of throwback to the Age of Reptiles. The sight of one's first spoonbill is something to remember. Unbelievably pink against the cobalt of the sky, or glowing amid the dark green backdrops of mangrove lagoons, it is

unearthly in its beauty. The queer, spatulate beak gives it a rather awkward look but adds to the prehistoric aspect. In feeding, the beak is swept rapidly from side to side through the water and gathers the bird's food.

The *spoonbill* nests in mid-winter; colonies occupy some of the keys in Florida Bay, or now and then the lakes near Cape Sable. Close protection through recent years is building up the population; the efforts of Audubon wardens in the past, and the rangers of the national park now, are showing results. The sight of spoonbills is always a primary objective on the Audubon Wildlife Tours of Florida Bay, and the birds may at times be seen in the Glades on the tour that penetrates that area.

The *spider lily* gleams white against the somber backgrounds of dark river banks and prairie hammocks. Long filaments of the stamens are connected by a membrane like fine gauze, and from the cup thus formed the filaments extend further outward, giving the flower a spidery appearance.

A familiar water animal in the Glades is the sleek, handsome *otter*. It is almost a fish in fur! Of considerable size—nearly three feet long, exclusive of the foot-long tail—it is dark brown in color, looking black at any distance. The feet are webbed like those of a duck and the animal has great agility in the water. It rolls, dives, swims beneath the surface and otherwise disports itself with all the ease and dexterity of a miniature porpoise. Its food is largely fish, which it catches with ease.

259

Some of the common and harmless serpents of the Everglades are the *blacksnake, king, garter, coachwhip* and *water snakes.* One of the most striking is the big *indigo snake.* It is the largest serpent of the country, attaining a length of nine feet, being blue-black above and below, except the chin and throat which are red. It is completely harmless and very gentle, living on small mammals, birds, frogs and even other snakes.

Of the spiders, always typical of the tropics, the large, showy *silver agriope* is conspicuous in the Everglades. It is silver and yellow in

Tiny suckers on the feet of the *tree frog* enable it to cling to any surface, even upside down.

In time, a key or island grows as the aerial roots of the *red mangrove* catch and collect trash and debris.

260

261

262

Blooming *water hyacinths* are beautiful but interfere with the movement of boats by tangling in propellers.

The shells of the *liguus tree snails* gleam like porcelain. Nature has designed them in a variety of patterns.

color, spinning a web more apt to be seen amid foliage than about buildings. It is perfectly harmless, despite some opinions to the contrary.

The *flamingo* is usually so eagerly anticipated by the Florida visitor that one of his first questions is, "When and where will I see a flamingo?" Strange to say the answer is, "The chances of seeing a wild flamingo in Florida are several hundred thousand to one!" The reason is that the wild bird does not occur in Florida except as an accidental wanderer from the West Indies, Central America and South America.

Years ago, flocks occasionally visited the Florida Keys, and there are scattered records of individuals appearing along the Gulf and south Atlantic coasts, but the flamingo does not belong in the United States and ornithologists never found it nesting in this country. It is of course possible to see it in captivity; many of the zoos, bird "farms" and other tourist attractions display the birds. The best known collection is the flock at the Hialeah race track near Miami. Here, excellent care is taken of them, the correct environment and food provided, and the birds are seen under as near normal conditions as possible, with their natural brilliance of plumage. They have nested there now for several years. Most captive flamingoes are pale, washed-out looking creatures, far removed from the beauty of wild specimens. To see the latter is a feeble hope, but there is always a chance that a fortunate observer may see an accidental straggler; in the bird world, strange things happen.

A familiar but unique animal is the *opossum*. The Glades is its home, along with many other parts of the South. It is ugly, unattractive, scaly-tailed and white-faced. Though widely hunted, the 'possum persists even in towns and cities. It makes a living by eating a wide variety of food. Strange characteristics of this animal are the female's pouch, where she carries her young, and the habit of feigning death when attacked. This trick gives rise to the expression "playing 'possum".

The Everglades is a frog paradise. They exist in uncounted thousands and make the air ring with their varied pipings, chirps and bellowings! They vary in size and vocal power, from the dainty little *tree frog* to the huge *bullfrog*. The small green tree frog, with its yellow side stripe, is often found near dwellings and, after a rain, many appear on the porch screens.

The bullfrog is the basis for a very considerable industry of the Glades. "Frogging" is widely practiced by both the native whites and the Seminoles, and the market for frog legs is a source of income for many. They are hunted at night with strong lights which dazzle the frog's eyes and are taken alive by means of a long pole with a spring clip at the end. Long, narrow skiffs or dug-outs are used, which are poled through the marshes. In recent years the so-called "air-boat" has largely supplanted these ticklish craft. The air-

A cupful of water from a slough (slew) shows a swarming collection of life—some of it microscopic, some of it discernible to the eye—while around the slough live insects, frogs, snakes, birds, mammals.

The only *stork* in this country is the *wood ibis* or *"flinthead"*. His flying feats include soaring upside down.

Sawgrass is a barbed-edged, long-bladed grass and the dominant growth of the Everglades region.

263

264

265

266

Water hyacinths came to this country from South America. They flourish in warm climates—die in the frost.

boats are wide and flat-bottomed, usually with blunt ends. They carry a small airplane motor mounted on a tripod, with a huge, elevated rudder behind it. This rudder works in the slip-stream of the propeller. The craft can navigate in extremely shallow water; it will skim over beds of wet grass! Such craft have opened up regions which were practically inaccessible before.

As the Glades near the coast the vast grassy marsh runs into higher growth. The great walls of green which line the rivers and bays penetrate inland to spread around the many lakes, estuaries and sloughs (pronounced slews). These walls are made up of *mangroves;* queer dense tangles of aerial roots, twisting branches and glossy leaves. Most abundant is the *red mangrove* which, along the southwest border of the Glades, grows larger than anywhere else in the world. There are *black mangroves* too, with heavier trunks, rising higher before they branch. Among them are fewer of the *white mangroves,* with their slender, light colored foliage.

In almost any stretch of open water among the ranks of the *sawgrass,* the surface is apt to be covered with a bright green floating plant with bulbous bladders below the leaves and a trailing mat of fine hairlike "roots". For much of the year it bears a magnificent display of lavender blooms, clustered on a stem and looking much like what it is—the *water hyacinth.* It is not native in Florida or even in the United States. This invader is what is called an "exotic". It is a stranger from South America, brought into Florida during the last of the nineteenth century as a decorative plant. Since then it has spread all over the Gulf Coast and up the Atlantic as far as South Carolina. Its dense mat of floating plants is a menace to navigation in many rivers and waterways, and thousands of dollars are spent every year in clearing it out. On large bodies of water, or long canals, the hyacinths are blown

The empty shell of the *locust* is found clinging to tree trunks—looking like a model of the insect in cellophane.

Exotic *swamp lilies* are characteristic of the Glades. Their white blooms stand out against the darker vegetation.

267

268

126

269

The brilliant *purple gallinule* resembles a chicken which has gone wild and taken to the water. Its beak, forehead and breast glow with color—a marsh bird, its long toes are adapted to walking over lily pads.

about by the wind; where there is a perfect mat of them one day, there may be a complete lack the next, depending on the direction of the wind.

One of the most lowly but startlingly beautiful life forms of the tropic Glades is the brilliant *tree snail.* Though only of two species, the genus *liguus* and *oxystyla,* there are numerous hybrids, many of them very restricted in their range, so much so as to occupy but a single hummock, or one key in Florida Bay. It is generally supposed that they travelled to Florida in hurricane debris from Cuba and other islands in the West Indies; some of the palms came the same way. At any rate, these delightfully colored tree snails became established in the tropic zone and do not occur outside its limits.

Some years ago a very marked fad for collecting the handsome shells developed, and great inroads were made on the snail population. During the late 1930's, there was a frantic endeavor on the part of certain collectors to out-do others. Many went to extreme lengths to secure hybrids of unusual beauty, and some collectors, finding a hitherto unknown hybrid, would take all they could find and then set fire to the hummock so that no one else would have that particular form! The establishment of the Everglades National Park has gone far toward preserving these unique forms of life. Much of its present area was a hunting ground for "lig" collectors (short for *liguus*) but is so no longer. What was once Royal Palm Park (Paradise Key) is now one of the ranger stations of the National Park, and the visitor can see tree snails in the growth there.

Everglades creatures take varied forms and range from the tiny to the huge. A cupful of water from one of the numerous sloughs will be found swarming with tiny bits of busy life, while about the edges of the slough larger forms occur; many an insect, reptile, bird or mammal.

Upright projections around the base of each water-growing *cypress* are called the "knees" of the tree. These swollen trunks permit the cypress to breathe. In the Everglades this tree is the outstanding species.

A characteristic bird in the Everglades is the solemn-looking *wood ibis,* sometimes called "flinthead" or "ironhead". Actually, it is not an ibis but a *stork,* the only one in the country. This wood ibis is one of the flocking birds and is seen in large numbers along the Tamiami Trail and throughout the Glades generally. The white body plumage is set off in flight by wide, black-edged wings, and the bare, dark head is extended at full length. The bird nests in large colonies in the mangroves and cypresses, many nests being in the same bush or tree. A very accomplished flier, it sometimes circles in the air at great elevations, swinging around on motionless wings for long periods. Often seen in company with egrets and other herons, it feeds in mixed flocks close to roads and canals, where it may be easily watched.

Everywhere, amid the vast stillness, stand the serried ranks of *sawgrass.* It is the grass of the River of Grass, a savage, uncompromising plant, with a rough stem covered with multitudinous barbs that bite, cut and slice like myriad knives. It was sawgrass that helped the Seminoles stand off the U.S. Army—it was and is the plant that only an alligator can touch without getting cut!

The *locust,* or *cicada,* is a familiar insect, related to our grasshopper. The high, shrilling note of the locust is a typical summer sound in numerous places and the empty shell, or skin after shedding, is frequently found on tree trunks.

Lilies are general favorites everywhere and the Glades are dotted with these lovely flowers. Typical of them is the bautiful *swamp lily* sometimes known as *St. John's lily.* Though flowering mainly in spring and summer, occasional blooms can be seen in mid-winter. The contrast between the pure white petals and red stamens against the flat green leaves is very striking.

Though Anhinga Trail seems particularly connected with the snakebird, another species is seen there and greatly admired. This is the resplendent *purple gallinule.* Gallinules (there are two of them, the Florida and purple) are chicken-like birds with very long toes (not webbed) adapted to walking over floating vegetation. True to its name, the purple gallinule's breast glows with brilliance and the highly colored beak and frontal plate enhance the exotic appearance. It is partial to the *pickerel-weed* or "wampee", and in most of its range will not be found where this plant is lacking.

At Anhinga Trail the bird has become almost domesticated; it is accustomed to people and approaches them without fear. Its more soberly attired relative, the *Florida gallinule,* is far more common and wide-spread in range. It is one of the most sadly misnamed of birds, for it occurs north into Canada and west into California! A good description of gallinules might be that they are chickens gone wild and aquatic! They have a wide variety of clacking, clucking calls, squawks and chuckles, sounding much like barnyard fowls.

Of all the trees of the Everglades the outstanding species is the *cypress.* One can hardly think of the region without this tree; in fact, the great swamp that borders the Glades on the west has long been known as the Big Cypress. Two kinds occur, the *bald* and *pond cypress.* The former is much the larger of the two and grows to tremendous size, though most of the big ones have long since been cut for lumber.

The delicate, fern-like foliage, buttressed trunks and numerous "knees" make it easy to recognize. With its leaves lost in winter, few trees can look as "dead", but spring brings out the beautiful feathery green. As one goes westward on the Tamiami Trail and comes to the Loop (40 miles from Miami) pond cypress is abundant and merges further on into the big cypress area.

The most deadly creature on the North American continent is the great *diamond-backed rattlesnake.* It is a fearsome but handsome thing. An untreated bite from a large specimen can cause death in twenty minutes. It attains great size, though very large ones are seldom seen now. The largest

North America's most dangerous form of life—the *diamondback rattlesnake*—can cause death in twenty minutes.

The eastern *brown pelican* is a ponderous but spectacular fisherman and a typical part of the Florida scene.

271

272

diamond-back reported measured 8 feet, 3 inches in length and weighed 16 pounds. The track of this snake in sandy areas makes a perfectly straight line, like that of a cart wheel, with none of the sinuous twisting which characterizes trails of other serpents. The rattlesnake should be watched for when one is in the field; nothing can be said to minimize its death-dealing powers, but chances of encountering it are small.

Moving toward the coasts from the interior Glades, the ponderous, dignified *brown pelicans* begin to show themselves. Serio-comic in expression, the pelican stares with apparent disapproval on anyone coming into close range—except when fish are offered! About some of the docks where fishermen gather, they are almost domesticated and will all but take fish from one's hand. The great pouch under the lower mandible is the pelican's outstanding physical feature and is thought by many to be a sort of market basket in which the bird carries fish. This is not true. When the bird is feeding its young, pre-digested fish are coughed up into the pouch. The little pelicans reach into the bag-like receptacle to secure their nourishment. The great stick nests of the pelicans are placed in mangroves, close together.

To watch pelicans at their fishing is to witness a spectacular performance. Diving from considerable heights, they hit the water with a tremendous splash and nearly disappear beneath the surface. Most of the fish they catch are not desirable from man's standpoint and the pelican is not the competitor that some fishermen think. Now and then, high over the Glades, one may see a flock of the splendid *white pelicans,* drifting along on air currents on their huge wings. They spread as much as nine feet, and are edged with black. It is a much larger bird than the brown pelican and spends the winter in parts of Florida, nesting far out west. Its manner of fishing differs completely also, for the birds swim along, herding schools of fish in front of them until a shallow bank is reached, or some corner in a bay or pond. There the fish mill about and are seized by the great yellow beaks of these spectacular birds.

Occasionally one looks up against the towering thunderheads out over the Gulf Stream to see, swinging in magnificent circles, a great dark-bodied, white-headed, white-tailed bird ascending ever higher until he is all but lost from earthly view. It is the *bald eagle,* emblem of the United States, a fitting avian crown for that avian paradise, the Everglades.

273

Small birds that prey on butterflies are afraid of owls. The *caligo butterfly* is protected from some of these enemies by the "owl eyes" on its wings.

CAMOUFLAGE IN NATURE

IN WARTIME both soldiers and civilians will attempt to hide themselves, their equipment and factories from the eyes of their enemies by means of what we call "camouflage". Army encampments may have their permanent and temporary buildings, as well as individual tents, painted brown, green, or variegated to resemble more closely the immediate surroundings. Gun emplacements and machine-gun batteries may be covered with netting on which real or artificial leaves and branches are spread. Ships sailing over submarine-infested seas are painted with zigzag lines and bands of contrasting colors to break their recognizable outlines. You may remember that Malcolm's men, when attacking Macbeth in Shakespeare's play, carried branches of the trees of Birnam Wood as camouflage.

We might be tempted to say that if man would learn to live in peace with his fellow men, camouflage would not be needed. Yet it is used also in our peacetime activities. In everyday life some of us disguise our garbage pails with shrubbery; we hide unsightly spots on our property with trailing vines. Piles of broken rock are often made into lovely rock gardens. In our homes we arrange handsome screens to hide doorways or less attractive parts of a room. A beautiful picture may hide an unsightly stain on a wall or conceal

131

274

275

When danger is sensed, the *least bittern* raises its bill and stands rigid, blending with its background.

Cottontails escape enemies because nature has endowed them with a coat closely matching their environment.

the baleful eye of a television set. Locks, buttons, and bells may be disguised to look like the wood in which or on which they are placed.

In Hollywood and elsewhere photographers use cleverly painted screens as imitation backgrounds, and thus often deceive the moviegoer.

American Indians, when hunting deer or antelope, would sometimes wear the skin of one of these animals, and by means of this camouflage could often creep within arrow-shooting range. Before the Spanish explorers brought the horse to our continent, the plains Indians stalked buffalo in antelope skins. Primitive races in various parts of the world even today employ this method of disguise freely in their hunting.

But don't think from this that man invented camouflage! Much for which men in their egotism take credit has simply been copied from Nature. In the living plant and animal world about us camouflage plays a tremendously important role. Many kinds of humble creatures actually depend for their physical survival on the perfection of their camouflage, because predators ready and anxious to devour them are all around. Many insects, for instance, which spend most of their lives on green leaves, are similarly green in color and on this account are much more difficult to find, not only by us, but, what is more important to them, by their natural enemies. Well known examples are the little green plant lice or aphids which live on our garden *nasturtiums,* the *green stinkbug* which crawls about on the grape leaves in our vineyard, and the grotesque *praying mantis* which lies in wait for unwary flies among the leaves of our shrubbery.

In the *crab spiders* this principle is carried a step further. Species which live in the yellow plumes of goldenrod are usually yellow in color. Thus they are practically invisible to the large and small bees which visit the flowers for pollen and nectar. When the bee alights, engrossed in her busy activities so essential both to her hive and to the plants which she services,

132

out jumps the spider from his ambush, lassoing her with silken threads hurled speedily over her wings to hogtie her, to be quickly followed by more strands to stop the thrashing of her legs. When she is securely bound in what is equivalent to a prisoner's straitjacket, the spider injects his venom into the still-living bee's body—and then begins his meal! Species of crab spider which set their ambush in flowers of other colors usually match the color of the blossom selected.

Is there a trap door leading to your attic or cellar? Nowhere will you find more perfectly constructed ones than over the homes of our southwestern *trap door spider*. These big hairy spiders sink tunnels almost vertically into the ground, cement the inner sides with glue (thus preventing miniature cave-ins), cover the walls with a carefully spun silken tapestry, and close the entrance with a perfectly hinged camouflaged trap door. Holding this door open with their hind legs they may lie in ambush here, ready to pounce upon an unwary approaching insect traveler.

The little green or brownish *measuring worms* which we sometimes find, to our discomfiture, crawling over our coats or dresses after a short walk through the woods spend most of their time on green leaves, which they devour hungrily, or on the brown twigs and branches en route from leaf to leaf. So Mother Nature, in her wisdom, has given them a coat which in color renders them inconspicuous in such surroundings. But sometimes they inch their way over the creamy white flowers of *yarrow* or the yellow petals of *black-eyed Susans*. Against such backgrounds they would be as conspicuous as a khaki-clad soldier walking over a snowfield. So, like our alpine sol-diers, the measuring worms put on a suit of camouflage.

A *bumblebee moth* (top) and a true *bumblebee* (bottom) here are visiting a petunia plant together. Most insect-eating birds, afraid of being stung, leave bumblebees alone. Resembling the bee, the stingless moth is avoided.

276

In summer the arctic tundra home of the *snowshoe rabbit* is brownish. The animal's coat is brown, too.

In autumn the first snows change the landscape to one of mixed brown and white. Notice the *rabbit's* coat now.

Our soldiers in alpine and arctic regions put on suits of white. The measuring worms bite off little pieces of the flowers on which they are crawling and glue these pieces all over their tiny bodies. When they are completely covered, their natural enemies—like insect-eating songbirds looking for a juicy meal, or certain female wasps in search of a fat caterpillar body in which to lay their eggs—will mostly overlook them.

We have probably all noticed and wondered at the peculiar markings to be seen on the skins of many of our snakes. The *milk snake,* for instance, is grayish with three series of rounded brown blotches bordered with black. The *timber rattlesnake* is yellowish-brown with three rows of more or less confluent and irregular brown spots which form zigzag-shaped crosspatches. Such snakes as these, when lying on the fallen leaves in a forest or among the grass, moss and weeds along a roadside, are so effectively disguised as to be almost indistinguishable. The hazel-brown *copperhead,* with its coppery red head and its 15 to 25 V-shaped blotches in hourglass design on its back, blends perfectly with its surroundings when coiled on a bed of fallen leaves or when sunning itself on an exposed traprock ledge. The 5-foot-long *pine snake* is glistening enamel-white, with chestnut-brown blotches margined with black. On the floor of a room in our house or on a classroom table its remarkable coloration causes it to stand out like a man in full dress would in a streetcar—But just try to see this creature in its natural habitat in the pine barrens of southern New Jersey, lying motionless on the white sand, among the fallen pieces of black pine bark! You would surely pass it by unnoticed! The deadly *bushmaster* in South America is so dangerous to man and beast alike chiefly because its coloration blends so perfectly with its jungle surroundings.

Do you know why it is fortunate that female birds are so very often plain-colored, drab or brown, while their mates may be dazzling yellow, red, or blue? To find the answer to this we need only recall that it is usually the female bird that sits on the eggs and patiently hatches them while they are in the nest. Sometimes this incubation takes many days or even weeks. During that time she huddles down in the recesses of the nest and her dark colors render her far less conspicuous. Hawks, owls, snakes, weasels, and the many other predators including man are much more likely to overlook

279

In winter the *snowshoe rabbit* becomes white—completing an excellent example of camouflage by protective coloring.

her and her nest because of this natural blending of her colors with those of the nest, and, in turn, those of the nest with its immediate surroundings. Some *hummingbirds* cover the sides of their nests with bits of lichens, thus causing them to look still more like the lichen-covered branch on which the tiny nest is built. Birds that nest on the ground, like certain *ducks, grouse* and *pheasants,* will often cover their eggs with leaves, grass or other nearby fallen vegetation when they have occasion to depart from the nest for a while, thus more effectively hiding both nest and eggs. Sometimes, as in the case of the *yellow-headed blackbird* and *ruby-throated hummingbird,* the showy males will take no part in the making of the nest, and may even avoid helping in the feeding of the young while the latter are still in the nest. Thus they will never betray by their bright plumage the location of the nest, eggs or young. The young are usually protectively colored, or are hidden by the mother.

The bright colors of the male birds serve to protect the females and young by contrast. Often, if a male bird sees an enemy approaching his nest, he will fly immediately in front of the marauder, thus drawing his attention. The marauder may then turn and follow the male, and the crafty male will lead him on, by flying a few feet at a time, until he has led him far away from the endangered nest.

Cottontail rabbits, living in the brier thickets along the edges of our fields and meadows, wear a brown suit of camouflage, and so do the *moose, elk* and *deer* of our forests. They can stand very still in the semi-darkness of a dense forest or thicket and be indistinguishable from their surroundings. Then, if discovered, they can be off like a shot. Baby deer—or *fawns*—however, lie helpless for a time on the soft forest floor where the sunlight, seeping through the tangled foliage overhead, makes a mottled design of sun and shadow. So Nature has given to the fawn a similarly mottled coat. Many other forest creatures all over the world show this mottled design on their coats. *Giraffes,* browsing on the leaves of lofty branches on the African veld, blend perfectly with their surroundings because of the broken blotches of their coats. Even the amazing color pattern of *zebras* renders them almost invisible on the African plains, because it so effectively breaks their outline from a distance.

The *measuring worm* wears protective clothing—bits of *black-eyed Susan* petals hide him in this picture.

280

135

Certain *whales* and *dolphins* are marked with contrasting blotches of white and black, and are thus protected as effectively as our camouflaged battle-ships. Our native *bitterns* have many brownish lines in the coloration of their feathers. When frightened by a sudden strange noise in the marshes where bitterns live, these birds will raise their long pointed bills to point at the sky directly overhead. The parallel vertical lines thus produced by the markings of the plumage and the shape of the bills and legs combine to cause these heron-like birds to blend perfectly with their surroundings of *cattails, reeds* and *marsh grasses.*

Our soldiers have their heavily armored tanks to protect them from enemy fire as they invade no-man's-land. These ungainly tanks find almost perfect counterparts in the scaly coats of *armadillos* and the hard shells of *turtles*—and turtle shells are often also camouflaged by being of a dark inconspicuous ground-color, by having bright lines to break their outline, or by flecks of color to blend with the mottled forest floor.

In the waters of our vast oceans are more beautiful examples of nature's art of camouflage. Most surface fish have their scales of pastel hues which blend with the diffused light in the water about them. *Speckled trout* are practically invisible against the sun- and pebble-speckled bottoms of clear mountain streams. The *flounder,* moving along lazily or resting on the

Swallowtail larvae are nearly defenseless, but dragon-like imitation eyes often frighten away hungry birds.

If you look closely, you'll see a dangerous *copperhead* hidden among fallen leaves, and ready to strike!

Old wife moths have brightly colored lower wings hidden under bark-colored upper wings when the insect rests.

The *tree hopper* resembles a thorn as he rests on the stem of this bush, effectively hidden from garden birds.

281

283

282

284

285

The slender *chameleon* can change his colors to match the surroundings as
he waits motionless on a twig, leaf, or rock to trap some unwary insect.
Many fish change their colors too, blending with different hues of the sea.

bottom of the sea, changes his colors to match those of the terrain immediately beneath him. His original left side becomes "top deck" with dark coloring. His original right side becomes "bottom deck" with all color gone and
with its rightful eye and nostril actually migrating over to "topside"! The
mackerel, on the other hand, swimming rapidly just beneath the surface of
the deep sea, has a back of shimmering iridescent blue, like sunlight reflected
from the waves about him. The *chameleon,* sunning himself on a leaf, stem
or rock may take on a green, brown, or gray color.

In the famous Sargasso Sea—that huge aggregation of seaweed which
floats in an isolated portion of the South Atlantic—live several small *mouse-
fish* so marvelously camouflaged as to be virtually invisible. Yet there is actually more surface to them than there is to many of their plainer relatives
in other waters. Not only does their color match that of the seaweeds perfectly, but nature has given them all manner of curious finger-like fins which
project from their bodies in various directions like the leaves of the *sar-
gassum* about them! Little *sea-horses* often encircle the seaweed stems with
their tiny prehensile tails and are most difficult to distinguish as they sway
in rhythm with the plants. Some species of these enchanting creatures even
have irregular leaf-like fins which effectively break their outlines and make
them look just like a piece of the waving seaweed! An Australian species,
living in coral-reefs, is red in color and has scores of leafy appendages like
the red coral and algae around it.

Some fish of the shape which we usually regard as "normal" for a fish
live in stagnant waters under overhanging trees. Leaves and branches break
or fall from the trees and float on or are suspended in the water beneath.
Nature has given to these leaf fish a flat elliptical shape strongly simulating

137

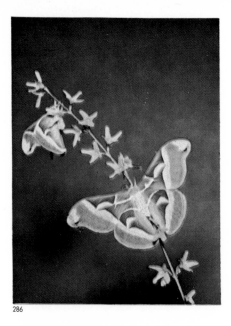

286

Brilliantly and beautifully colored, the *cynthia moth* is not noticeable when seen against bright flowers.

the waterlogged leaves about them. Even the teeth on the leaf margins are imitated on the dorsal fins of the fishy masqueraders!

Certain butterflies, known as *leaf butterflies,* when they perch on a twig and fold their wings above their back, take on an amazingly leaf-like appearance. Sometimes they resemble a living leaf, more often a dead one. In at least one case, "tails" on the under wings form the imitation stalk of the counterfeit leaf, points at the top of the upper wings form the midrib and side veins of the leaf! A large mantis-like insect in Ceylon, known as the *walking leaf,* is not only completely green in color, but has a flat leaf-like body, green leaf-like wings, and large flat leaf-like expansions on its legs, each with markings like the veins of a leaf! A tropical *mantis* wears imitation flowers and thus actually attracts insects.

Many moths and butterflies resemble the bark of trees on which they normally rest. In the group of moths called *underwings* the lower wings are often brightly colored, but are completely hidden by the bark-colored upper wings as soon as the insects alight. In the case of the *questionmark* and related butterflies it is the lower surface of all the wings which simulates the bark of the tree on which the creature lands with folded wings.

Walking sticks are flightless insects with extremely slender stick-like greenish or brownish bodies and long slender legs and antennae. They are very slow-moving and are extremely difficult to distinguish when they are resting on leaves or branches. In some species their body even gives the appearanc of being covered with moss or lichens.

In our ponds and streams live the larvae, or young, of *caddis flies.* Only an inch or so in length, these plump little creatures would make delectable eating for many larger water creatures. In fact, their name is derived from a German word for "bait", because they were formerly so much used for this purpose. In these present days of artificial bait the adult caddis flies serve as the models for many favorite baits used by fishermen, among them the arti-

Here, for one unguarded moment, the usually-cautious *measuring worms* can be seen on these white flowers.

287

138

ficial fishing lure called the "dun". To protect themselves from their many enemies, the caddis fly larvae build houses—much as we also build strong homes for ourselves to protect us against the weather and against potential enemies like burglars. Some caddis fly houses are built by clipping pieces of leaves found at the stream bottom and neatly fastening the edges together with silk, forming a narrow tube about the length of the creature's body. This is carried about as it wanders along the stream bottom, with only its head and legs protruding, but on the approach of danger the little "worm" quickly retreats into its snug shelter. Other species of this fascinating group of animals cut small twigs into tiny bits and arrange them in crosswise fashion over their bodies. Still others, living in running rather than in still water, build cone-shaped houses of sand. Sometimes they must weight down these stick-covered homes with tiny stones and shells embedded in silk. In all these cases the resulting home is beautifully disguised and is universally overlooked by all except those enemies who have had experience in hunting for them.

Many moth larvae, called *bagworms*, when spinning their cocoon shelters, will hang on the outside little bits of leaves or twigs from the tree or shrub giving them shelter. This, again, helps to hide the cocoon among the foliage during the summer and early fall and even renders it less conspicuous on the leafless tree or shrub in late autumn and winter.

Related to the measuring worms is the *stick caterpillar*. It is brownish in color, and when at rest, or when suddenly frightened, will assume a rigid position at a sharp angle to the branch on which it happens to be at the moment. At such times it will fool most of its many enemies into mistaking it for a little stumpy twig or spine. A similar trick is played by the *treehoppers*. Some of these resemble little buds or bumps on a twig, or the scars left by falling leaves, or even thorns. One, most frequently found on the thorny stems of locusts or rosebushes, almost perfectly simulates a thorn and thereby escapes many of the birds which would otherwise delight in feasting on it. Related to these curious insects are the *frog-hoppers,* whose tender, wingless, and totally defenseless young expel a sticky whitish liquid which they promptly beat into a meringue-like froth by a constant whisking about of their body. This froth soon completely envelops them like a mass of white

Alarmed, the tiny creatures begin to bite off small pieces of the petals, gluing them to their bodies.

Here the *measuring worms* are almost entirely invisible—disguised by their own instinctive camouflage.

288

289

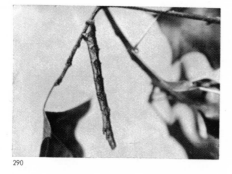

290

291

The *stick caterpillar* is well named, as he imitates a twig at the approach of danger. Many caterpillars do this.

If hungry enemies mistake these *leaf fish* for waterlogged leaves, the amazing little creatures may survive.

spittle and thus effectively hides them from their enemies. Some caterpillars when resting quietly on a leaf look like an inedible slug or, in the case of the *banded purple* and *giant swallowtail butterflies,* like some nauseating brown-and-white bird droppings!

Many butterflies are extremely showy when the upper surface of the wings is viewed. Alighting on a branch or tree trunk, or on the ground, they will at once fold their wings and hold them, pressed tightly together, vertically above their backs. The under surface is much duller in coloration. Birds which may have been chasing the little insects in the hope of getting lunch from them, are understandably surprised suddenly to have the butterfly apparently disappear before their eyes. He was there a second ago—now he is gone! Similar "surprise value" is found in the white tail of the *cottontail rabbit,* the white underside of the tail of the *Virginia deer,* raised in flight, and the white rump of the *flicker.* Dogs following a rabbit or deer will often become so engrossed with the white tail which waves before them like a banner—as a red flag before a bull—that they neglect to follow the scent with their noses. When the white banner suddenly disappears from view the surprise and shock to the pursuer are so great that some minutes may elapse before he recovers himself sufficiently to take up the scent. By that time the rabbit or deer may be safely away.

Mountain goats live among snow and ice, and their white coats blend in perfectly with this background.

Caddis-fly larvae build camouflaged houses into which they can retreat when approached by hungry enemies.

292

293

In arctic regions, or high up on mountains where similar cold and snowy conditions prevail, many animals wear white overcoats in the winter. *Weasels* and *snowshoe rabbits,* normally brownish in the snow-free summer months, become pure white in the winter. *Polar bears, mountain goats,* and *white whales,* living in regions of perpetual snow and ice, are always garbed in white. Indeed, some of these creatures, like the snowshoe rabbit and the *ptarmigans,* have three suits of clothes. For the summer, when the arctic tundra is uniformly grayish-brown with *reindeer-lichen* and *sedge,* they have a brown suit; for the winter, when the ground is deeply covered with snow, they have a white one; and for the autumn and spring, when the surface of the ground is merely flecked here and there with snow, they have a brown-and-white mottled ensemble. These outfits are changed by the simple phenomenon of growth of different colored hairs or feathers.

Primitive tribes of men often don horrifyingly painted or grimacing masks during their various war or rain dances, or when attempting to exorcise disease "devils", or they may hideously paint their faces. In some of our own North American parades and festive celebrations we also don masks of various sorts. Surely you have been to a Philadelphia Mummers' Parade, a New Orleans Mardi Gras, a Mexican fiesta, or a plain old country masquerade ball. Our detectives may disguise themselves to look like traveling salesmen, Western Union messengers, or repairmen. Plainclothes policemen, dressed to blend with the surrounding crowds, mingle unobtrusively on bustling city streets. Our animal friends do much of the same thing.

The famous *lantern fly* of the American tropics wears a hideous mask resembling the head of a young alligator. He is even said to have the power of making this head glow weirdly in the dark on the approach of danger. Many naked caterpillars,

294

295

When danger threatens, this *tomato sphinx caterpillar* rears up, and his bright horn looks menacing.

Among the seaweed, this *weed fish* is indistinguishable because of plant-like outgrowths on its fins.

The *dead leaf butterfly* folds its brilliantly-colored wings and is "invisible" among the dry leaves.

296

unprotected by the bristly or stinging hairs which make some of their cousins so undesirable as food for insect-eating birds, have developed large imitation "eyes" on the forward portions of their bodies. These often give them a dragon-like appearance well calculated to scare away potential enemies. The *giant click beetle* of our northeastern states has two such huge "eyes" on its wing-covers when it is adult. In the tropics there are species where these eyespots are actually luminous!

The green larva of the *tiger swallowtail butterfly,* like that of some of its relatives, such as the common *spicebush swallowtail,* has two black and yellow spots on the front of its body which bear an amazing resemblance to a pair of large, staring eyes. Since this larva lies in a nest made of a folded leaf, enemies are likely to see only the front end, which looks for all the world like the head of a menacing green snake. This fortunate little larva is endowed with yet another protective camouflage. Its brilliant, leaf-green body blends in perfectly with the color of its home.

Many moths have eyespots on their wings, but the world championship in this respect is held by the *owl's-head butterfly* of South America. The "eyes" on its wings are almost exactly the size, shape, and color of the true eyes of a small owl. Small insect-eating birds are usually very much afraid of owls, so the value of these markings to the insect is obvious.

Some of the *sphinx moths* fly in the daytime and hover about long-tubed flowers in exactly the fashion of hummingbirds. Others have much the shape and colors of bumblebees. In both cases their mimicry protects them from at least some of their hungry enemies. A certain *clearwing moth* resembles a common wasp so closely that when both are resting together on a flower they are almost indistinguishable from each other. Most insect-eating birds avoid wasps, bees and hornets, apparently for fear of being stung in the

How many insects can you see below? There are ten *moths* in this mountain-laurel bush. Note their colors and patterns blended with leaves and stems. The large moth at the left is a *luna;* the large one at right, a *cecropia.*

298

299

A *hummingbird's* nest is so small it can be covered by a quarter, yet it too is camouflaged, with *lichens*.

The *horned lark's* colors protect it. Its breast matches the sand, and its back is the same color as the plants.

mouth, throat, or stomach. Non-stinging moths which resemble bees or wasps therefore are also relatively safe from such birds.

In a number of cases a perfectly harmless animal so closely imitates a poisonous or otherwise dangerous one that it, too, is left strictly alone by creatures which may have had sad experiences with its counterpart. For instance, the *coral snake* of our southeastern states is deadly venomous. The *scarlet snake*, not at all closely related, closely resembles it in size, shape and coloration, but is harmless. Yet it is left quite alone like its venomous cousin! The *monarch butterfly* in its immature or caterpillar stage eats greedily of the leaves of milkweeds. The bitter substance characteristic of these leaves is transmitted to the insect's body and renders it decidedly unpalatable. As a caterpillar it has bright bands of yellow, green and black, which effectively "warn" birds not to try to eat it! The same birds also soon learn, after, perhaps, one or two attempts, not to try to eat the gaudily colored adult monarch either, for it possesses the same sharp taste! The *viceroy butterfly* lives in the same area as the monarch, but is not at all bitter-tasting. Yet since it so closely resembles the monarch in size, shape and coloration, birds also avoid it. Other pairs of butterflies exhibit similar mimicry.

And now here is an excerpt from an article by Dr. Arthur A. Allen, Professor Emeritus of Ornithology at Cornell University, that describes how various species of birds survive by means of protective coloration.

In thinking over the birds with which we are familiar we soon discover that brilliant colors, in almost every species, are restricted wholly to the males, and a moment's reflection suggests to us that the law of "the survival of the fittest" would soon weed out any bright-colored females, should they arise, by drawing attention to their nests and inviting the destruction of their offspring. The very exceptions to the rule fur-

Many *caterpillars* look like inedible *slugs*. This one has a chance of surviving long enough to become a *moth*.

300

143

ther substantiate it, for when bright colors are normal to the female, as in the *kingfisher* and *red-headed woodpecker,* nature protects the offspring by causing the eggs to be laid in holes in trees or in tunnels in the bank where the female is entirely hidden from sight while incubating.

Another method of protecting conspicuously colored birds is by endowing them with extreme wariness, and it is seldom that any of them will allow as close an approach as do their dull-colored mates or relatives. They seem to realize that they are conspicuous and rely upon their alertness to escape. Moreover, is it not of direct benefit to the species that there should be a conspicuous decoy to lure away from the vicinity of the nest any enemy that passes that way? For even should the male be seen and captured, the offspring might still persist.

Brilliancy of plumage probably originates, we are told, because of an excess of strength and bodily vigor, and this fact undoubtedly tends to perpetuate and increase the brilliancy, whenever the bright colors are not directly disadvantageous to the species, because the vigorous bird is most likely to secure the best mate and have the strongest offspring. It may well be asked, then, why the males of all species are not conspicuously colored and able to rely upon their wits to escape their enemies. But think for a moment of the environments which birds are called upon to fill. There are the treetops and the great open spaces where enemies cannot lurk unseen, and here it is that we find the conspicuous *tanager, trogons,* and *honey creepers,* the *gulls, terns, herons,* and *flamingoes.* On the other hand, there are the thickets and dense coverts near the ground where enemies can approach closely or lie concealed, and here it is that we find our most protectively colored *grouse, woodcocks, sparrows,* etc. Thus it is clear why the gaudy tanager is confined to the treetops and why streaked sparrow must simulate its dry grass haunts if it would persist. Birds dwelling within reach of skulking enemies seldom wear brilliant colors or bear feathers that are continuously conspicuous. Their coloration often fits their environment so well that it hides them.

In discussing brilliant colors we should remember that very few birds wear the bright colors throughout the year, the kingfisher and the red-headed woodpecker being notable exceptions. The vast majority shed their bright

The *hog-nosed snake* plays dead. He lies on his back, opens his mouth, protrudes his tongue, becomes limp.

But he can carry this ruse too far. Turned "right side up", he rolls over into the "dead" position again!

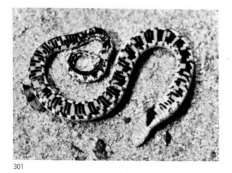

301

302

303

The *purple gallinule* is always associated with water. Its purple hues fade
nicely into its environment. But other birds, endowed with bright plumage,
know they are conspicuous, and are compensated by an extreme alertness.

colors after the breeding season and do not don them again until the following spring. With many of the *ducks,* however, this change from a brilliant to an obscure plumage in the male occurs as early as June or July and
by the time most birds are ready to take on their obscure plumage in August
and September, they are ready to assume their brilliant feathers once more.
It will be remembered that after the breeding season all birds molt every
feather on the body, including the wings. In the spring the molt of the *tanagers* and *indigo bunting* is incomplete, as the old feathers of the wings and tail
are retained.

It is interesting to examine the young of these birds in their first plumage, which in the male is brighter than the female, for almost invariably
they resemble the female, or when there is a difference, the male in winter
plumage. It is a well-known fact that the young of animals often summar-
ize in their development the steps through which their ancestors have passed
in the course of their evolution. The plumage of the young birds, therefore,
or the winter plumages of the males, may often show relationships that one
could never guess by examining the breeding plumages. Thus, the immature and winter plumages of the *blackpoll* and *bay-breasted warblers* are
almost indistinguishable, although the adults are so different in the spring.
The spotted breasts of the young *robins* and *bluebirds* indicate their relationship to the *thrushes,* and the streaked breasts of the young *chipping* and
field sparrows show the typical sparrow coloration from which the adults
have departed. With a very few species, the young in their juvenal plumage
are just as bright as the males or even brighter. Young kingfishers, for example, can scarcely be distinguished from the adults except by the rufous
feathers in the band across the breast, and young *downy woodpeckers* tend

to have the whole top of the head reddish rather than a mere crescent of red on the nape.

Most of the larger predatory animals will avoid contact with dead animals and will not attempt to eat the dead bodies of animals found in their wanderings. So pronounced is this instinct that zoo-keepers usually have to feed living mice or other rodents to their caged snakes. Taking advantage of this habit, numerous animals will feign death if danger threatens. So famous is the *opossum* for this habit that the expression "playing 'possum" when one simulates death is a well known part of our language. Several common snakes in eastern and southeastern North America, including the common *spreading adder* and the *hog-nose snake,* will feign death if the elaborate show of bluff which they put on by hissing and puffing does not drive away the potential danger. They will then flatten out, turn over on their back, and become perfectly limp. No amount of pushing or shaking will "revive" them, and if you should turn them over into the normal position they will promptly turn back over again.

In fact, it must be emphasized that most, if not all, of the animal actions described in this book are instinctive. The instinct resulting in the protective behavior has apparently been built up through countless ages through the elimination by enemies of those that did not so behave.

Many shorebirds, as well as land birds such as the *horned lark* and *whip-poorwill,* are protectively colored in such a way that they blend perfectly with their nesting habitat. Many a bird student has had the experience of nearly stepping on the female of one of these species because she was not discernible while sitting on her nest on the ground. Finally she "bursts" from almost underfoot and gives the observer still more reasons to marvel at the variety of ways in which nature protects her own.

Our *leopard frog,* living so much in the moist grass along the edge of ponds and streams, not only wears a green coat to blend with the grass about him, but there are many irregular blotches of brown on his back which perfectly simulate the small spots of shadow among the green grass.

One could continue almost indefinitely to enumerate the ways in which the animals about us use camouflage in their struggles for existence in the cutthroat competition which helps to bring about evolution of new forms through a survival of the fittest. The examples cited are just a very few that come quickly to mind. The pictures used here, while authentic and carefully chosen, could easily be supplemented by a host of others. Some might even show nature so successful in her camouflaging that one would be hard put to discern the animal in the photograph! Many pictures of *horned toads,* for instance, have been taken in our southwestern deserts, where the animals blend so perfectly with their surroundings that, try as one may, it is not possible definitely to discern them on the photograph—and one has only the photographer's word as proof that they are there!

As you walk through the woods and fields, along a country roadside, or by some peaceful pond or stream, you will be surprised how many examples of nature's camouflage you can find!

Unerringly guided by instinct, with only feet and beak as tools, the *barn swallow* fashions a nest peculiar to its own species.

NATURE'S ARCHITECTS

IN THE HUMAN WORLD, buildings are designed by architects and constructed by craftsmen. Yet despite intelligent designs, the pooling of many skills, and the utilization of different materials, results still may be unsatisfactory. In contrast, nature's architects, without training, usually working alone, and with no tools except their own bodies, have produced structures so remarkable that man often has copied them.

Furthermore, nature has already solved many of the architectural and engineering problems of home-building. Wild creatures have softened the rigors of extreme temperatures with insulation and air conditioning. They use natural building materials and have invented silk, wax, glue, paper, and cement. Drainage problems have been solved by underground dwellers, while homes in the treetops often are more storm-proof than the trees themselves. Nature's builders have constructed almost every type of home imaginable from cliff dwellings and moated castles, to penthouses and skyscrapers. Some, like the *yellow-jacket's* subterranean home, are so secret that their occupational routine has never been observed. Others, like an *osprey's* nest on a telephone pole, are wide open to public view.

305

306

Mounds of *Allegheny* or *wood ants,* the largest ants in this country, may be occupied for several human generations.

Bush-tits, inconspicuous little birds of the west, build a giant nest and swing this pendulous home from twigs.

Birds which nest in colonies are confronted by much greater hazards than those whose nests are dispersed and harder to find. Generally, colonial birds like those dwelling on barren, rocky, or sandy islands, or along the ledges of sea cliffs, find protection through their very isolation. Among song birds and other creatures as well, the danger of wholesale destruction is largely eliminated during nesting by the fact that they must scatter considerably to find suitable living quarters.

Actually, housing shortages play little part in limiting animal populations when each creature is his own builder. Each species knows instinctively where to locate its home, and each individual knows precisely how to build it. In the case of *honey bees* each worker bee "graduates" from being a construction engineer. But in the event of an emergency, such as the destruction of part of the hive and its building corps, older bees recall the construction skills of their youth and even reactivate the wax-producing glands. When colonial species like the *paper wasp* find their aerial apartment house fully tenanted they simply enlarge it. This is done by removing the inner walls and building up new layers on the outside. More cells and even tiers may then be added to each floor.

House hunting of a familiar type is practiced by the *hermit crab.* When growth makes the crab uncomfortable in its appropriated snail shell it must abandon this protection while it goes looking for larger quarters. Molluscs of all kinds, from snails to clams, steadily add to the size of the shell that constitutes the only "home" that most of them ever possess.

Like the hermit crab, other creatures take up quarters abandoned by the original tenants. *Woodpeckers, badgers,* and *woodchucks* are the chief building contractors of the natural world, providing homes for many birds and mammals less equipped for burrowing. In taking over abandoned nests, some new tenants do a good bit of renovating. For instance, when the *deer mouse* takes possession of an old bird nest, it gathers up the softest mate-

148

rials available, lines the nest with fine grasses or shredded bark fibers, and covers it over completely. Instead of picking some open, sandy or rocky site for its nest, as most shore birds do, the solitary sandpiper goes to the woods to occupy the abandoned home of a song bird. *Horned owls* will appropriate a *hawk's* old nest or a *crow's* platform of sticks.

The majority of warm blooded creatures and many insects build nests. Several purposes are served by these homes. Often they enable the parents, immobilized by nesting duties, to escape notice by enemies. Primarily, of course, the nest is an incubator. Usually it is insulated. By controlling temperature and moisture, it prevents sudden changes which would be harmful, even fatal, to newborn, naked young. Feathers or fur in the lining insure against chilling, but many homes are endangered more by heat than cold. The platform nest of a *hawk* or a *heron* or *eagle* may be perched on a treetop in blistering sunshine. For weeks the infant occupants are subject to sunstroke. Only the parent bird, making a parasol with its body or outstretched wings, can shield the young from the merciless sun.

Immature, soft-bodied *leaf hoppers* enjoy the comfort of an air-cooled bubble bath. This they provide by sucking juices from plants, then blowing bubbles with the liquid. You can readily discover this *"spittlebug"* buried in froth, but enemies pass by unknowingly.

Bees, too, air-condition their hives in summer. Gathering outside, they hover near the entrance beating their wings so vigorously that they blow cooling air throughout the hive. Similar behavior has been observed among the *polistes wasps*. When the sun's rays get too hot the wasps fan violently. If this isn't enough, some of the insects carry water inside, dropping it into the cells. Evaporation cools the nest so effectively that the temperature may drop as much as 18 degrees.

Tree trunks, fenceposts, and timbers in homes are sometimes riddled by the tunnels of the *black carpenter ant.*

An insect's egg laid in a *willow* bud leads to the production of this conelike *gall*— a home for the young insect.

Wood piddocks bore with long, elastic "feet". The split wood proves the clams have grown since entering it.

307

308

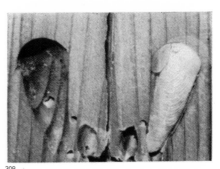
309

149

310

312

311

313

The *trap-door spider's* nest is hard to open, because the spider hangs to it with strong front legs and fangs.

American Museum of Natural History exhibit shows the *peregrine* bringing food to its young on a lofty ledge.

Very much like the moated and guarded castle of the Middle Ages, the *beaver's* lodge home is virtually impregnable.

Unlike many amphibians, the *dusky salamander* lays her eggs on land and stays in the nest until her young hatch.

If you discover the nest of any wild creature, the builder is not far away. True, an eagle or a hawk may forage fairly far afield because it can travel easily and swiftly, but most animals make their homes as close to their sources of food as is safe and practical. The *scarlet tanager,* for instance, feeds on insects that live in treetops. *Woodpeckers* extract insects from the trunks of trees. *Moles* ferret out grubs underground.

Each creature instinctively builds its home in a habitat where there is an ample supply of food for itself and its expected family. This territory it will defend against its own kind. Generally other species are not competitors for the same food and will be ignored or at least tolerated.

Both the *fox* and *gray squirrel* build summer homes that might be mistaken for the nests of crows or hawks. The squirrel's "dray", as the nest is called, generally is round, about the size of a basketball or larger. Even at a great height a hawk's nest looks flat, with conspicuous large sticks protruding. The squirrel's nest has more dead leaves, twigs, and bark strips. Dead sticks broken from nearby limbs or green branches as thick as a man's thumb may be gnawed through and used to form the framework. Then the squirrel goes to the ends of the branches and cuts off twigs and bunches of leaves. These are fashioned into a compact mass, so well thatched over that most nests must be waterproof. The walls are 3 to 6 inches

150

thick, surrounding an inner chamber 5 to 6 inches across. This is lined with moss extracted from the bark of the tree, or chewed-up bark strips.

Red squirrels build their nests in a *pine, spruce, hemlock,* or *fir.* The winter nest generally is located in an abandoned *flicker* hole or in some other hollow in a tree or large branch, much like the home nests of the larger squirrels. The summer nest is a globular mass of bark strips, roots, grass, and moss. It may be built on a firm platform of sticks, or supported by a number of ascending smaller branches. In areas where no holes are available, red squirrels use these nests the year 'round.

The native American *packrat* or *wood rat* is sometimes a tree dweller. One of nature's most versatile architects, the packrat may erect a six foot mound on the ground, secrete its home in a cave, dig and roof over a trench in the earth, or build a globular house in a tangle of brush and vines or in a mul-

tiple-stemmed tree. In any case the rat contrives to have a soft, grass-lined inner chamber for his nest.

While birds of many species nest in trees, few live in the treetops. The brilliant scarlet tanager is one of the highest home builders. So are the *grackle* and the *blue jay.* The rough platform of the jay's nest may appear to be of haphazard construction, but each stick was chosen with care. The birds scorn dead sticks that may litter the ground, preferring green twigs which they seize with their bills and break off. With these they construct a strong framework, eventually adding a softer lining to the shallow cup.

With the exception of the hawks, owls, and eagles which make very large nests, virtually all birds build a new nest each year, and generally for each brood if they have more than one. The nest of a bird of prey, however, represents such a big construction job that customarily it is used year after year. Some nests of *bald eagles* have been occupied for 30 years or more, but as a rule they become so heavy in a few years that they place a great strain on the tree. Often a main supporting branch gives way or the whole tree may go down in a storm. The "Great Eyrie"

Snail shells are never outgrown. Snails and other molluscs add to the size of their homes as long as they live.

Flickers excavate nest holes. A chisel-like bill, driven by a powerful neck, can build a home in a very few days.

314

315

151

of the bald eagle at Vermillion, Ohio, was 12 feet tall and nearly 9 feet across its flattened top when it was destroyed in a storm in 1926, after 36 years of continuous use. The total accumulation weighed 4,000 pounds!

In contrast to the eagle's mighty rampart of sticks is the minute lichen-covered cup of the *ruby-throated hummingbird.* So tiny that a half-dollar will cover it, the nest is saddled to a branch with a spider web or with silk from a *tent caterpillar* nest. The female hummingbird gathers soft down from ferns and milkweed and from young oak leaves. Like a *chimney swift,* she may use saliva to glue the nest to its support. The soft materials are built gradually into a cup, which she shapes with her body as she sits inside. It takes her about a week to build a nest, and longer if rainy.

Quite different from the treetop platform of sticks or the little cup balanced on a branch is the deep, purse-like nest of the *Baltimore oriole.* Dangling lightly from the descending outermost twigs of an *elm* branch, this nest is among the most complicated known to man. Many thousands of shuttlelike movements of the oriole's bill are needed to produce the thousands of stitches, knots, and loops found in an average nest.

The necessity of a bird finding a particular nesting situation is well illustrated by the diminutive *parula warbler.* Scarcely five inches long, the *usnea warbler,* as it is sometimes known, nests in northern regions only where the *usnea* or *old-man's-beard lichen* grows. Weaving together the gray strands from the branches, the birds fashion a nest which they can enter through an inconspicuous opening on the side. Equally well hidden are the nests of parula warblers which live in the south. They are more abundant than the northern birds because their nesting site is in *Spanish moss,* widespread in the southern swamps and among the numerous *live oaks.* While seen commonly enough in migration, parula warblers rarely nest except where one or the other of these superficially similar plants grow.

As you will find if you go exploring more bird nests per acre are built

Once living only in the wild, many *phoebes* now build their moss-covered homes around bridges and buildings.

Thousands of stitches, innumerable loops and knots went into the making of this *Baltimore oriole's* hanging nest.

316

317

318

A *blue jay's* nest of sticks is lined with grasses. Every stick that goes into this rugged, platform-like nest is tested by the *jays.* Weak, dead sticks are discarded. Both sexes share in the nest building and incubation of eggs.

in dense thickets and shrubbery than in any other type of habitat with the possible exception of a good cat-tail marsh. The obvious attractions of these areas are (1) excellent "cover", (2) fine foundations for building and (3) an abundance of food.

One of the largest and most remarkable thicket homes is found in Western North America. It is fabricated by the *bush-tit,* a cousin of the more familiar *chickadee* and *tufted titmouse.* Constructed of soft material, it is woven together with spider webs and swung from slender twigs. Considering the minute size of the birds—only slightly larger than a *hummingbird*—the nest is gigantic. Some measure twelve inches in length!

Certain *western thrashers* and smaller birds like the *cactus wren* and the *desert sparrow* build their nests among the *cholla* and other varieties of *cactus.* As effective as a barbed wire entanglement in repelling enemies, the sharp spines are not a hazard to the birds that dwell among them.

Frustrating as it is to try to locate nests in a thicket, it is even more baffling to look for them in a marsh without wading into the water. The strange sounds of *rails* and *bitterns,* the gurgling calls of *red-winged blackbirds,* and the chatter of *long-billed marsh wrens* prove that most marshes really are well populated.

Not all marshes, however, provide good nesting sites. Stands of the giant reed, *phragmites,* are like a barren desert. The bare stems stand too far apart to permit small birds to harness several of them to support a nest. Other plants may be too short-stemmed to keep homes safely above the high-water line. Cat-tails, *wild rice,* and certain *bullrushes* provide ideal foundation for suspending nesting platforms. They are utilized by *least bitterns,* by the *yellow-headed* and *red-winged blackbirds,* and by the most energetic builder in

153

this habitat, the long-billed marsh wren who constructs a globular hut.

While creatures that make their homes in trees and bushes still can be preyed upon, they are relatively safer than those which nest on the ground. Concealment then becomes especially important. But even a well hidden nest may be detected by four-footed predators, or by snakes, prowling incessantly, or may be crushed underfoot. The large nests of game birds run a greater chance of being stepped on. Of course, nature compensates for these additional hazards. Ground-nesting birds generally have larger families than birds which live in less vulnerable situations, so they are able consequently to sustain greater losses.

The *bob-white* or *quail* may lay up to 17 eggs in its nest in a field or at the edge of the woods. Such large clutches of eggs can be found also in the saucer-like, leaf-lined depression which is the nest of the *ruffed grouse.* Located in the woods but not far from a clearing where bushes provide tender buds, the home of this game bird is hard to find.

Some of the smaller ground-nesting birds build a dome shaped nest with the opening on the side. The *ovenbird* on the woods floor, the *northern water thrush* along some wooded watercourse, and in many cases, the *meadowlark* live in little "ovens" which cannot be spotted from directly overhead.

A few birds go underground. The smallest member of its family, the brown and glittering white *bank swallow,* is an accomplished excavator. Found in Europe, Asia, and North Africa as well as in North America, it migrates north along coastlines, then follows up river valleys until it finds steep, sandy or clay banks. Clinging to the bank, the swallows peck the dirt with their bills. Once they deepen a hole enough to get inside they use both bills and feet. At first they kick out the loose dirt; finally they must carry it out in their mouths. Most burrows are 2 to 3 feet long, but some 8 and 9 feet long have been reported. Another bank dweller is the *belted kingfisher.* Its nest is an enlargement at the end of a burrow 4 to 15 feet long. It is unlined except for a pile of regurgitated fish bones, upon which the pure white eggs are laid and incubated.

Carpenter bees occupy plant stems. This species produces no wax, so they substitute dry stems for waxen cells.

Tunnels mark a *mole's* journey. They dig beneath surface for insects; the nest is also underground, near supply.

319

320

One of the most extraordinary of underground nesters is *Leach's petrel.* At nesting time these seabirds make their sole annual pilgrimage to land. Their arrival is known to almost no one, because they quickly dig an un-

154

derground nest, a burrow beneath root or rock. So vulnerable to enemies are the petrels that breeding colonies have survived only on isolated islands uninhabited by burrowing native animals or by man's camp followers—rats, cats, dogs, or hogs. The *burrowing owl* is better able to take care of itself. This little nine-inch-tall bird is familiar in many parts of the west. In the east it nests only in south-central Florida.

Surprisingly little is known about the behavior underground of many creatures that nest or hibernate there. Only a few scientists have ever fully investigated a *prairie dog's* amazing engineering accomplishments, for the rodent's "plunge hole" is a vertical chimney as much as 16 feet deep! How he disposes of the soil from the depths of his plunge hole and from the extensive tunnel that continues on horizontally remains a mystery. It is a puzzle, since he kicks loose earth behind him instead of carrying it out.

321

Insect *galls* on *goldenrod*. A larval fly occupies the center of this stem gall, shown cut open at the right.

The sharp, long claws on this rodent's front feet make possible extensive tunneling operations. Commonly a second vertical shaft is started from below, and may run all the way to the surface, serving as a back door. Though often incomplete, such a shaft would be useful if the nest were to become partly flooded.

Apparently well counseled by instinct, the prairie dog builds a flood-control dam around his burrow entrance. Inattention to this flood-control work might be costly since midsummer cloudbursts can create lakes 2 to 3 inches

Nest of *queen yellow-jacket*. Smaller than a hen's egg, this home will eventually be the size of a basketball.

Spiders spin a web of silk. Wheel-like perfection of the *orb-weaver's* design is one of nature's wonders.

322

323

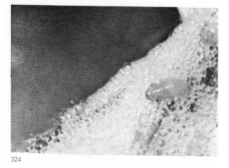

324

325

Young *spittlebugs* live in froth. Vulnerable to heat, this insect nymph blows itself a cooling bubble-bath.

Although it has a listening post near the entrance, a *prairie dog's* nest may be sixteen feet down.

deep on the nearly impervious hard ground. A serious breach in the "dike" would send a flood pouring down the plunge hole.

In contrast to the prairie dog's deep but relatively simple tunnels, the passageways of the *mountain beaver* are intricate indeed, and they are excavated only a few inches below the surface. Careful excavations in California some 40 years ago revealed the remarkable ramifications of the system of burrows. Near Point Reyes the burrows extended for 2 miles or more. In one area of less than 3 acres there were at least 100 burrow entrances, possibly the work of no more than a dozen beavers. The doorways appear to be located largely by chance, wherever the miner feels an urge to dig.

Patiently studying the animals and following up their tunnels, scientists have found that while the systems interconnect, the number of adult animals living together is never more than two. Each tunnel system has one or more nest chambers, about a foot and a half in diameter. Globular in shape, they are located under stumps or logs for security reasons, and contain dried grasses, leafy twigs, or, sometimes, leaflets stripped from the fronds of the *sword-fern.* In digging out the beaver tunnel described here, the investigators uncovered two *salamander* nests beneath the rodent's nest. This was truly a chance discovery, but then so are most similar "finds", so secretive are these amphibians. Some, like the *spotted* and *tiger salamanders,* lay fist-sized egg masses in ponds, but "terrestrial" species hide them in some tiny cavity in or under a log or beneath a flat stone. Most often discovered are the eggs of the *dusky salamander.* Commonly found under stones along streams, these four-inch-long creatures seek out a flat stone in moist soil. Burrowing beneath the stone in midsummer, the female enlarges a tiny room and lays 15 to 35 eggs.

Unlike those salamanders which lay their eggs in ponds and then immediately leave the water, land-dwelling salamanders guard theirs until they hatch, two months later. Possibly it is only in this way that the eggs can be kept free of mold or fungus growth. Eggs that are deserted by the parents always seem to be destroyed by an enveloping plant growth.

The life history of many species of *bumblebees* has been worked out because their homes often have been found in abandoned nests of *field mice, chipmunks,* or other small mammals not far beneath the surface. The queen bee makes the selection, choosing a soft, dry protected location. Within the nest she makes a thimble-like, waxen honey pot and a thin-walled nursery about the size of her own body, and then begins to lay eggs. Within three weeks the first adults emerge and the hive is in operation.

Still largely a mystery is the pattern of activity within an underground *yellow-jacket* nest. It is known, through excavation and study of abandoned nests, that species of this group (*vespula*) begin to build in tunnels formerly occupied by *ground squirrels, gophers,* and other digging mammals. The yellow-jackets presumably enlarge the original chambers at a steady rate until the nest is the size of a football or larger.

The combs of yellow-jacket nests are composed of hexagonal cells like those in the hive of a *honey bee,* but the tiers are arranged horizontally instead of vertically. Also there is but a single layer of cells instead of two layers, and the cells are used only for rearing the brood, never for storing food as bees do with their honey.

Probably the most abundant and ubiquitous of underground dwellers are the multitudinous kinds of *ants.* Few forms of life offer more opportunities for fascinating, first hand observations than do these well organized social insects. Once you start to notice ants you will find them in almost every imaginable place. Look for their pathways cutting through the grass on a lawn like a super-highway through the forest. Find where the *pavemnt ants* descend between chinks in the bricks or concrete. Turn over a stone in the woods and observe the home life of an ant colony, or split a log and discover the labyrinth of galleries tunneled out by *carpenter ants.*

Ants clearly exhibit the characteristics and advantages of group life: (1) active, beneficial cooperation, (2) continuation of the group beyond the life of the individual, (3) family life involving special care of the young and (4) pro-

With *cat-tails* for support and the slender leaves of dry *sedges* for weaving, the *long-billed marsh wren* builds a coconut-shaped nest. Boundless energy and an urge to be busy make this wren construction king of the bird world.

326

327

328

Familiar to all who hike through the woods, the *gray squirrel's* tree-top nest is occupied only in summertime.

Landslides, undercutting by streams and excavation by man threaten *bank swallow* colonies such as this one.

vision for extensive and available food supply.

In providing for a constant food supply some species of ants have become farmers, raising mushrooms; others have become herders or dairymen, with "herds" of aphids that have been domesticated.

Largest of our ants is the *Allegheny* or *mound-builder ant.* Its hills are found chiefly on wooded slopes, often among *pines,* and average 2 to 3 feet tall. If left undisturbed these nests may remain tenanted for 20, 40, or even 80 years. The large mounds are composed of soil excavated from underground, mixed with pine needles, twigs, straw, and other debris. They are honeycombed with passages which continue below the ground level in a vast network of intercommunicating chambers. Some students estimate that perhaps 100,-000,000 ants occupy one of the larger nests!

Most skillfully hidden and most intriguing of spider homes are those of the *trapdoor spiders* found in the southern California foothills and the South Atlantic states. The "trapdoor" is not excavated in one piece, as might be imagined, but built bit by bit after the vertical burrow has been dug. This tube is first tamped hard with the spider's heavy fangs and later is lined with silk webbing. In building the ingenious lid for her nest she first neatly trims the edges of the opening and then gradually builds out a "roof" composed of damp earth and silk.

When it reaches one-third of the way across the opening, the partly formed door is raised and bent back. The completed door fits so perfectly that the spider must hang on to the inner edge of the burrow with her hind feet when she springs out and seizes some unwary passerby.

Many insects spend most of their lives out of sight inside the stems or leaves of plants. The *solitary* or *carpenter bee,* unable to produce wax, excavates chambers in pithy plant stems, and in each lays an egg and stores a supply of "bee-bread"—pollen soaked with honey—for the young bees.

Almost everyone at some time has seen erratic, thread-like, pale green patterns on leaves. Under close scrutiny it can be seen that they consist of tunnels completely within the leaf itself. Starting as a delicate line, from the point where an insect egg hatched within the leaf, they wander crazily, growing ever wider as the *leaf miner* feeds and continues to grow. Even less suspected by most observers are the insects which spend their larval lives within amazing plant structures known as *galls*. Most plentiful are the *"oak-apples"*, caused by punctures made by *gall-wasps*.

It is believed that the gall is produced by the plant's reaction to the irritating presence of an insect egg or larva. Many species of wasps, flies, and aphids, and even some beetles, caterpillars, and mites are responsible for the growth of galls. Each species singles out a particular variety of plants, and deposits an egg which produces a gall unlike that of any other gall-maker.

If you cut a gall in half you may find a tiny cavity occupied by an egg, or by the larval insect. As it grows, it is likely to eat out the spongy plant tissue, making a hole to the outside for later use. When fully fed it emerges to form its cocoon in the soil or perhaps on the bark of a tree.

Many birds conceal their nests quite successfully within the branches or trunks of trees. Except for an innocent looking hole there may be no evidence that birds are living inside. Amazingly diverse bird families are included among the hole-nesters: *wood duck, sparrow hawk, house wren, crested flycatcher, bluebird, nuthatches, chickadees,* and preeminently, of course, *woodpeckers.*

Unlike most songbirds, woodpeckers may use the same nest hole for years. Chickadees, house wrens and bluebirds often move into abandoned woodpecker holes, which are also the favorite homes of *flying squirrels, screech* and *saw-whet owls,* as well as other wildlife. Trees with big hollow limbs, or with cavities in the trunk, provide winter dens for *squirrels* of almost every variety and homes for *opossums* and *raccoons.*

Species like *chimney swifts, barn swallows,* and *purple martins* have completely forsaken their ancestral

Utilizing the same design as a Quonset hut, *mud-dauber wasps* build nests with clay which hardens as it dries.

Unlike combs of bees, *yellow-jacket* cells have open ends facing downward. They are used only for rearing young.

329

330

159

331

332

Deer mice improve a bird's nest. Remodeling jobs, with roof and better insulation, makes snug winter quarters.

A *bagworm* case contains eggs. Spun and carried about by a *caterpillar,* it later serves as a cocoon for a while.

types of nesting sites in favor of man-made quarters. All three of these species formerly lived in hollow trees. The *phoebe* is one species which appears to be in the process of abandoning natural home sites. If we may judge from the phobe's present choice of nesting places, the switch-over to porches, bridges, etc., may not proceed steadily. After every hurricane we find porches and other man-made sites deserted in favor of cavities among the roots of upturned trees. Cliffs and cave entrances also seem to have their regular customers plastering their moss-covered nests to the rocky walls.

Not all creatures raise their families in secret. Some establish their domiciles where they are readily observed, but nearly impossible to reach. On precipitous, rocky cliffs along the west coast, hundreds of nests of *cliff swallows* can be seen. The nests are jug-like structures made up of a great number of mud pellets and lined with grass and feathers.

Some bird-banders disagree with the statement that "once you have visited three *duck hawk* nests you are living on borrowed time". Nevertheless, it suggests the inaccessible nesting sites chosen by the *peregrine,* the name by which this lordly *falcon* is known the world over. While a few have come to nest on skyscrapers and bridge towers, their nesting along the Palisades, above the Hudson River, is more typical.

Enemies may be discouraged by the nature of the material of which a nest is constructed. For example: the homes of the *tent caterpillar* and the *fall web-worm* may be swarming with edible caterpillars, yet the entangling nature of the webs repels even the hungriest birds, unless they be *black-billed* or *yellow-billed cuckoos.*

Spider webs, too, are sticky enough to deter predators. They have one other great advantage. They can be repaired quickly or even replaced completely if necessary. Economical of weight and material, spider webs are still surprisingly strong. The wheel-like design of the *orb-weavers,* familiar in most gardens, is spun upon a basic, square framework and secured by stout guy lines.

160

Few human construction operations are half as absorbing to watch as the web-weaving of the *golden garden spider.*

Some nests are not what they seem. Take the camouflaged domicile of the *bag-worm,* for example. If its presence near the tip of a *red cedar* or other evergreen tree is detected, it probably would be dismissed as just another cocoon. But actually it is the home of an active caterpillar. Soon after birth the little "worms" begin to spin around themselves a ring of silk. As they feed and grow they increase the size of the ring, adding leaves or small twigs to the outside. When the bags have become too big and heavy to hold upright, they let them drop to a hanging position. When full grown they may travel to another tree, carrying their enveloping home with them. Finally, instinct directs them to fasten themselves permanently to a twig. In late summer, winged male moths emerge from some bags, while in others the wingless female nearly fills the bag with a cluster of 300 eggs. She dies, but the eggs survive.

A *cocoon* is waterproof. The tough, impervious outer walls and soft inside are silk, spun by the caterpillar.

Very light-weight for its large size, this *wasp's* nest utilizes the strength of paper, made from wood pulp.

Just as on land, homes in the water world may be exposed or out of sight. They may be quite accessible, or they may stand isolated, protected by an unbridged moat. Some are so well disguised by the builder that it takes an experienced eye to find them.

Completely hidden from sight, and detected only through the presence of the tiny holes through which they entered their hiding place, are certain species of boring *clams,* known as *piddocks.* Many of these secretive molluscs live in mud or clay. Some bore into wood, coral, limestone, or even concrete, gradually carving out larger and larger cavities as they grow. Tunnels of the *wood piddock* and of *teredo worms* sometimes can be found in timbers that have been washed up on the beach.

More remarkable are the walnut-sized nests constructed by small fishes called *sticklebacks.* Defending a nesting territory, the male fish first hollows out a shallow pit by carrying out mouthfuls of sand which are dropped 5 to 6 inches away. Then he gathers threads of algae and other

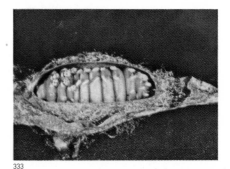

333

334

161

fine plant material, pressing them down into the pit. Next he pastes this material together with a glue-like secretion, and finally he bores a passage by wriggling right through the mass.

Lying on the bottoms of ponds and streams are countless inconspicuous little tubes composed of bits of leaves and twigs, or sometimes of sand grains or tiny shells. These are the work of some of nature's most skilled home builders, the aquatic larvae of the *caddis fly.*

Gathering specific materials to which each species is partial, the "worms" weave them into long, slim tubes. Inside they then lie in wait for food particles to be carried within reach. They even build nets at the mouths of the tubes and stir up currents that propel food into their jaws.

But the greatest construction engineer of all is the *beaver.* Its dam-building feats are fabulous—one dam on the Jefferson River in Montana measured 2,140 feet in length! Dams as high as 11 or 12 feet have been found, with bases which may have measured 15 or 20 feet in thickness.

A dam apparently is worth all the effort. The pond it forms provides the beaver with a refuge from its enemies, transportation for food and lumber, and a pantry for its food supply.

While some beavers burrow into banks of streams, especially if water levels fluctuate widely, the lodge is the classical home. A natural island, or an artificial one built by the beavers, is the usual foundation for the lodge. It must be close to deep water so that one or more tunnels will remain open under the ice. Sometimes the lodge is the home of only one animal but generally it represents the work and home of a group.

A rough circle of sticks marks the beginning, just a few inches above water level. Stones and branches, as well as logs, comprise the walls which gradually lean inward, until at a height of perhaps three feet the structure is roofed over. More sticks and mud are added from time to time as long as the lodge is occupied.

The babies, born in late spring, lie on a bed of grass, leaves, and twigs, but the adults sleep on the bare floor. Food in summer is quite varied, but in winter it consists largely of the bark of poplar, from poles cut in fall and rammed into the mud of the underwater pantry.

The beaver was America's first conservationist. At lease 60,000,000 strong when the Pilgrims landed at Plymouth Rock, these capable dam-builders impounded the waters of a million little streams. By slowing the runoff of stormwaters and fast-melting snows upstream, they prevented or reduced flood damage downstream. What little topsoil was washed from the forested slopes mostly settled in the quiet beaver ponds.

Only recently, conservationists have won support for inexpensive, upstream beaver-dam type flood control structures instead of costly, mammoth dams constructed downstream. And beavers, once exterminated in many states, are again building their moated castles on many a watershed.

335

Yew fruits are interesting and lovely.
Most American yews are descendants of
English and Japanese types.

FLOWERING TREES
AND SHRUBS

IF SOMEONE were to ask you to describe the difference between a tree and
a shrub you would probably reply that a tree is tall and has only one
main stem or trunk, while a shrub is low and has several stems that come
out of the ground close to each other.

This would be a good general answer, although it tells only part of the
story. The fact is that the line of difference between shrubs and trees is often
narrow and crooked. Some species of plants grow into regular trees in one
part of the country but are shrub-like in others, while certain well known
shrubs occasionally turn into trees. Also, many true trees are dwarfs and
not nearly as tall as a good sized shrub. All this probably sounds rather
confusing, so let's forget the differences and look closely at some of the typical trees and shrubs that follow.

A *yew* may be either a low shrub or a sixty foot tree, but it is always an
evergreen and, no matter how it grows or what size it reaches, its fruits are
always much prettier than its flowers! That is one reason we are showing the

163

336

337

Most of the *acacia* species with their splendid golden plumes are famed ornamental trees in their native regions.

Blueberry blossoms create the small, nearly black berries used in making millions of luscious pies.

"berries" here, and another is that they are among the strangest fruits in the world. When you look closely at the quarter-inch red globular fruit you will notice a round, darker spot on several of them. This is really a shallow hole, like a little well, and in it is a single bony, dark gray nut or seed. Only its tip shows through an opening in the juicy red pulp. If you were to plant one of these it would not even sprout for two or perhaps three years. Yet when it did it would start right in to make another perfect yew. The wood of the yew is hard and stringy and for ages men have used it for making bows.

The deep south and southern California are rich in handsome flowering trees, but many people think that *acacias* are the showiest of all. These smallish trees put on a spectacular display of yellow blossoms in late winter or spring, depending on the species, the condition of the soil and amount of rain. In addition, their feathery evergreen foliage is lovely at all seasons.

The tropical parts of both hemispheres are the native home of the 400-odd kinds which make up the acacia clan. In those regions they go under the general name of *wattle,* particularly in South Africa. They are between ten and fifty feet tall. Some kinds grow six or eight feet in a single year. Acacias could not stand the outdoor cold of a northern winter, but they are so beautiful that people as far north as Boston grow them in large greenhouses.

Do you like blueberry pie or blueberry muffins? Well, the *lowbush blueberry* is the plant from which these treats usually come—that is, if you buy them in a bakery. Its smallish berries are shipped to cities all over the country for cooking purposes, and they cost much less than the larger kind that fruit stores sell in separate boxes.

The lowbush blueberry plant is seldom more than fifteen inches tall. In certain parts of the northeastern states, particularly Maine, it covers many acres of high, dry sunny ground with its almost solid thickets.

During the winter you probably would not pay much attention to a lowbush blueberry, because at that season it is a rather messy-looking little shrub. But when spring days have warmed it up its flower buds swell and soon its twigs are strung with odd little urn-shaped blossoms that are beautifully colored. Each flower is replaced by a berry that turns blue-black when it ripens in July or August. You will have another surprise in the frosty days of early fall when those small leaves that looked so dull through the summer become a brilliant scarlet.

The *flame buckeye* is only a shrub from eight to a dozen feet tall, but its May blossoms are the brightest to be found in the whole *horse-chestnut* tribe. When the sun strikes its seven-inch flower clusters, they really seem like red flames.

Flame buckeye is a native southerner with big, coarse leaves that look rather like half-closed umbrellas when they first come out in the spring. It makes a broad, rounded bush that is not especially good-looking until the flower spires form at the twig tips. Then, for a few days, the whole shrub is transformed into a living mound of remarkable beauty.

A buckeye seed is as solid as a marble and has nothing but a smooth, shiny skin to cover it. While these seeds or fruits are growing on the tree they are protected by tough, green, spiny husks. But when they are ripe the husks dry and split, and then the size and color of the fallen seeds resemble the eyes of a buck.

338

The flaring blossoms of the *catalpa tree* do not open until June or July, but when they finally unfold they put on a tremendous show. Each is about two inches wide, and they crowd together to make a solid pyramid of color six or seven inches high. Hundreds of these marvelous groups may be found on a single tree.

Our two American species of catalpa are much alike except that one grows to be eighty feet tall while the other gets only half as big. They are grown in most states, except along the Canadian border where the winters are too cold for them. Their seeds have ragged, hairy wings on

Buckeyes, or *horse-chestnut*, get their odd name from their seeds or "nuts"—which aren't real nuts at all!

Note the lovely fluted, curled petals and odd, spotted interior of the beautiful *catalpa* blossom.

339

165

340

342

341

343

When a *cottonwood's* seeds are ripe and the day is breezy the air is filled with wisps of snowy white.

Goldenbell is another name for the popular *forsythia.* It blossoms early in spring; sometimes a little in fall.

Witch-hazel flowers twist oddly like legs of an insect, and never bloom until after the autumnal frosts.

A *willow* catkin carries flowers so tiny that you'd hardly know they are blossoms. But its seed may become a great tree.

which to sail through the air, and they grow in a slim, round pod from eight to eighteen inches long. The pods look a good deal like gigantic *string beans,* so it's no wonder catalpas are known as bean or *cigar trees.*

The word "catalpa" is the Indians' name for this queer but handsome flowering tree. As a matter of fact, the names that we use today for many other native American plants are the same as those used by the Indians.

One glance at the photograph of *cottonwood* catkins and you know where this tree's name comes from. Those white, cottony puffs are parachutes, to which the tiny seeds are attached. When the time comes, they sail lightly away for maybe a mile before landing and perhaps starting new trees.

Cottonwoods are among the biggest of our native American trees; an especially large one may reach a height of 100 feet. They belong to the *poplar* tribe, and are terrifically fast growers.

The stems of the leaves, instead of being round like those of most other trees, have their lower halves flattened in one direction and their upper halves in another. So, whenever the wind comes from the side, one half of a cottonwood leaf-stem bends and lets the wind slide off the broad part of the leaf without harming it. And if the gale blows from below or above, the other half of the stem does the same thing!

The *forsythia* or *goldenbell* is so covered with graceful, narrow-petalled flowers that you can scarcely see their stems. Each blossom is an inch or more long and wide, and its rich yellow seems to turn the cloudiest day into a bright one. In favorable weather the big show often lasts for two weeks, and then comes the season-long beauty of the shrub's narrow, pointed, deep green leaves which appear after the flowers.

There are four forsythia species, and all of them came to us from China, Japan or southeastern Europe. One kind, the *drooping forsythia,* has many branches which arch out and down until their tips touch the ground and soon take root. This starts a new plant, and in a few years you may have a forsythia thicket twenty feet or more across, instead of the single bush which you planted originally.

Forsythias are named after William Forsyth, a British plant expert who lived more than 150 years ago. In addition to their beauty they are long lived and will grow happily almost anywhere.

The *common witch-hazel* is one of the plant world's surprises! Its squirmy yellow flowers never appear until October or even November. Stranger still, one of its close relatives, *vernal witch-hazel,* often blooms right in the middle of winter and its flowers have a way of opening on warm days and closing on cold ones!

Common witch-hazels are woodland plants, usually growing as shrubs but sometimes becoming 25 foot trees. Very often they live near streams or in other damp places, but once in a while you will find them on higher, drier ground. (If you were to plant one in an open, sunny place it would slowly become more dense and better shaped.)

344

Those spidery, ribbon-like strands in the photograph are really the petals of the blossoms—four of them for each flower. The center part, where the petals are attached, slowly develops into an odd, woody lump divided into two compartments, each of which contains a shiny black seed. When these seeds are ripe a built-in spring arrangement fires them into the air! The photograph shows not

Many northerners go south in early spring just to see the blazing *azalea* gardens which are so breathtaking.

A ripe *persimmon* is a real delicacy to eat, but you will be sorry if you ever bite into a green one!

345

167

only flowers, but also the empty seed pods of the preceding year. The name witch-hazel probably came from a very old English word meaning weak, which certainly fits the straggly way the plants look when you meet them in the woods.

Everyone likes *pussy willows* with their furry, silver-gray little "pussies" that make you think of kittens' toes. But has anyone ever told you that this favorite springtime shrub has at least 300 cousins, some of them huge trees and others that just creep along the ground and are only an inch or two high? The *willow* tribe is one of the largest in the plant world, covering the northern hemisphere and even the equator.

The flowers of all willows are small and grow in slender tassels called "catkins". These first appear as buds along the twigs, grow longer quite rapidly until the tiny flowers themselves can be seen. Some of them will have pistils and can produce seeds, while others have only stamens which release yellow pollen when the time comes. You can see all these things happening if you keep a few sprays indoors in early spring.

Willow seeds are very small and each of them has a white, down-like tuft attached to it so that it can sail through the air, sometimes for a long distance. Most of them never get the chance to take root and grow, but now and then a lucky one comes to earth in a favorable spot and there, in a few years, you might find a new young willow which soon will send its own airborne seeds out into the world to possibly root and grow.

Most willows grow near fresh water, or in rather marshy places.

For a gorgeous display of well shaped and brightly colored flowers, well grown *azalea* shrubs are hard to beat. Many millions of them are raised in greenhouses all over this country and sold for Easter gifts while in full bloom.

346

347

Most of these greenhouse kinds came originally from Japan and cannot stand the cold of northern winters outdoors. But many private and public gardens in the south, where it is warmer, are filled with them.

Azaleas are a type of *rhododendron*. The seeds of all the different kinds are so small that you wonder how they can possibly grow into shrubs that may be twice as tall as you are. The two best known American species are the *pinxter* and the *flame azalea.* The first grows wild in woods and fields along the Atlantic

Any garden without a *weigela* bush is missing one of the finest flowering shrubs of the spring season.

Mountain-ash isn't an *ash,* despite its deceptive leaves. True ashes have winged seeds—not berries.

348

350

349

351

The big, showy blossoms of the *hobble-bush* are males which supply pollen to the smaller fruit-bearing female flowers.

Not all *honeysuckles* are vines. Most of this large tribe never climb, but grow like regular bushes.

Hundreds of these huge, colorful blooms may be found on a single plant of our southern-grown *hibiscus* shrubs.

Rhododendron flowers grow in clusters which, when open, make almost complete balls that are several inches thick.

seaboard, and opens its pretty pink blossoms in May. And the second is native in the southern Appalachian Mountains. It is called "flame" because of the amazing color and brightness of its yellow to orange and red flowers. Large numbers of new azaleas have been created in the past thirty years by crossing different species and varieties, so don't be surprised if you see an azalea some day that is far finer than all its tribe.

You would be entirely right to call the *common persimmon* a surprise tree. It has small greenish flowers that don't look like much, but in the fall its straggly branches are strung with orange and red fruits more than an inch thick, which make you think of Christmas tree ornaments. Besides this, it is a close relative of the *ebony,* that precious lumber tree of the tropics whose wood is absolutely black.

In the middle and southern parts of the United States, where it grows wild, the persimmon is famous for its plum-shaped fruits which you see in the photograph. After there have been a few frosts those fruits will be as sweet, juicy and good to eat as anybody could wish. The persimmon or ebony tribe has nearly two hundred members, most of which live only in the tropical parts of the world and are valued highly for carving. In Japan and parts of our southern states one kind, known as *kaki,* is grown for its very large, fine-tasting fruit. Kaki may reach a height of about forty feet—

352

353

Pear and *apple* blossoms have the same general form. But most of the pear's flowers form no fruit.

Cranberry-bushes are not even distantly related to real *cranberries,* although their fruits look quite alike.

perhaps half as tall as an especially old, healthy common persimmon.

The *weigela* is another of those fine flowering shrubs brought long ago to America from foreign lands. Its remote ancestors grew in China, but most weigelas that you see today are hybrids and different from those old-timers. There are more than fifty kinds, all of the same general type and growing in the same way. You will see at least one weigela bush in almost every fair-sized garden, for they are strong and healthy, grow fast and live for many years. Most reach a height of ten to twelve feet and have so many stems rising from the same root base that you can't see through them after the curving, four-inch leaves and colorful blossoms have come out.

The weigela flower show begins in mid-spring and continues into June as the later varieties come into bloom. Most have pink or red flowers, and there are also whites and purples. The oddest species is the *Chinese weigela* which has differently colored blossoms, white and red, or yellowish and red, on the same plant.

Like the American *cranberry bush* the *mountain-ash* has large clusters of bright red berries that are much more colorful than the little white blossoms from which they develop.

In most other ways, however, cranberry bushes and mountain-ashes are different. The mountain-ash is a regular tree, not a bush, and it may reach a height of thirty or forty feet. Each leaf has a long central stem with leaflets strung along both sides of it. This gives the whole tree a pretty, feathery appearance.

Favorite species are the *European mountain-ash,* or *rowan tree,* and the *American mountain-ash.* The European species is the one you are likely to see growing on lawns, for it was brought to this country in colonial days and has been planted in many different places. But if you see a mountain-ash growing wild in the woods you can be pretty sure that it is our own American kind.

354

Splendid fruits from splendid flowers—that's the way it is with *apples*. No other food tree is so widely grown or enjoyed.

Several of North America's fine flowering shrubs grow best in shady places. One of these is the *hobblebush,* a particularly interesting species because it has two types of white blossoms in the same broad, flat cluster. Around the rim of this flower "platter" the blooms are very large and showy but never produce seeds. Inside this circle are many little fellows only one-tenth the size of their big companions. It is from these midgets that the handsome dark purple fruits develop in autumn, each one containing a single seed. In the damp, cool, northern woods, where it sometimes reaches a height of fifteen or twenty feet, the hobblebush begins its show early in May. When fall days ripen the shrub's fruits, its deep leaves turn to claret red.

Gardeners in Florida and other subtropical parts of the south have many flowering shrubs to be proud of, and one of the finest is the *Chinese hibiscus.* There are several varieties, each with a special color such as red, pink or white, and blossoms up to six inches wide.

This southern beauty came from China, and it has been in this country for about a hundred years. Often it grows like a big shrub, with several main stems and many branches. But where the soil and temperature are just right it may turn into a tree thirty feet high. There are nearly 200 different species of hibiscus. Most of the very showy kinds grow outdoors only in warm climates.

For at least a hundred years *bush honeysuckles* have been favorite garden shrubs here in the United States. They are nicely shaped, live for a long time, and have tremendous numbers of small white, yellow, pink or red flowers. When these blossoms have faded their places are taken by bright yellow, shining red or sometimes blue berries that last all summer and often

171

355

356

The *red maple* with its fuzzy little flowers shows a tinge of scarlet somewhere every month in the year.

Camellias are beautiful shrubs, and there are hundreds of varieties. All have very attractive leaves.

into the fall. There are nearly two hundred species of these fine shrubs. Most of those which you see in this country came originally from China, Japan and that part of the world. The dozen or so kinds which are natives of North America usually have smaller, less attractive flowers than those from the far east.

Bush honeysuckles grow from four to fifteen feet tall and most are about as broad as they are high. A few keep their leaves all winter, especially in the south, while the rest lose theirs by the time really cold weather comes. Some of the best kinds have flowers which, besides being lovely to look at, are very fragrant.

The honeysuckle tribe is really a remarkable one, for it contains vines as well as shrubs. The best known of them all is *Hall's honeysuckle,* a twining climber with delightfully fragrant white blossoms and almost evergreen leaves. Its blackish berries last until midwinter unless they are eaten by various kinds of wild birds.

357

Rhododendrons are world famous for the beauty of their flowers and their number of different kinds— nearly 400 true species plus very many hybrids.

These spectacular plants grow wild over a large part of the northern hemisphere, too, with a few sorts crossing the equator to New Guinea

Bougainvillea blossoms are tropical climbing vines that are most surprising for their immense color variety.

358

Lilacs have been favorite shrubs for hundreds of years, for their beauty is exciting in spring's last weeks.

and Australia. In those regions some develop into regular trees, and a few live among the branches of other trees the way many *orchids* do. Nearly all, though, are bushes from a few inches to several yards tall.

Rhododendrons get their name from two Greek words meaning rose and tree. The depicted American species, the *rosebay* or *great rhododendron,* bears its clusters of white to rose-colored blossoms in late June or July. A very old rosebay may be as much as thirty feet tall, though the usual height is around fifteen.

The *rose* family is one of the largest in the whole plant kingdom. It contains not only those wonderful flowering bushes that we call roses, but also a lot of unexpected members such as *strawberries, almonds, mountain-ash* and, most surprising of all, *pear trees!*

Everyone knows what a ripe pear looks and tastes like, but have you ever seen the little flowers which produce them? Their five petals are pure white, as the picture shows, and they grow in so many clusters of four to ten that sometimes the branches and twigs are almost hidden.

Pear trees have been grown in this country since early colonial times, and it is not unusual to see one that is fifty or sixty feet tall and more than a hundred years old.

American cranberry-bush is one of those plants whose name could easily fool you, for it isn't a cranberry at all—not even a distant cousin of one. Just the same, its fruits look a good deal like ripe cranberries, and people who live in the north country where the shrub grows wild often make jam or jelly out of them.

The American cranberry-bush is a strong, good-looking shrub at all times of the year. In May or June many of its larger twigs are tipped with hand-

The *saucer magnolia* isn't a big tree, but when its flowers come into bloom before the leaves, the whole neighborhood knows about it. Flowers are more than six inches wide, and there are hundreds of them.

359

173

360

361

Many strange plants grow in our U.S. deserts, but none has the queer habits of the brilliant *ocotillo*.

The hard cones which slowly develop from the *jack pine's* softly colored flowers take years to ripen.

some, four-inch platters of white blossoms, and by August or September these have been replaced by the scarlet berries you see in the photograph. Cranberry-bushes specialize in red, for their thick, sturdy leaves turn that color every autumn. Some are nearly four inches long, and together with the brilliant berries they almost make you think that the whole bush is on fire.

The *apple* is one of those trees whose blossoms are almost as pleasing as its fruit. As spring gets under way their swelling buds sprinkle the twigs with a soft pink which often remains after the rounded petals have fully opened. There is no more delightful sight at this season than an apple orchard where each row of trees is a billow of blended white and pink tinted with the fresh green of baby leaves.

Late spring brings the first sign of fruit—little green swellings with traces of the withered blossoms still clinging to them. They are not too attractive at this stage, yet week by week they grow larger and more shapely until, by late July or early August, they are big and plump and round. Then their colors begin to show, a hundred different reds and yellows, some solid, others striped, many blended together in a single fruit. Rather surprisingly, some of the least showy ones have the finest taste and are the juiciest!

Blossoms of the *red maple,* like those of many other species in this famous tree tribe, look like tufts of colored fuzz instead of regular flowers. They grow from such tight clusters of fat little buds that when they open they are crowded together in an almost perfect ball.

All this happens in early spring long before the many-pointed leaves appear, and from a little distance the branches seem to make a lovely network of rich red. Red maples often grow wild in such wet places that they are sometimes called *swamp maples.*

There are well over a hundred different species of maples, some of which are natives of central and eastern Asia, Europe or North Africa. Many of these have been planted in this country, particularly those that come from

174

Japan. Nearly all make handsome ornamental trees from fifteen to almost a hundred feet tall.

Camellias, azaleas and *hibiscus* are the Big Three among the famous flowering shrubs of the south. All are magnificent when in bloom, and the camellia has the special advantage of bearing shining, handsome evergreen leaves as well as flowers that sometimes measure five inches across. Also, the *common camellia*, which is the species pictured here, blossoms from October to April, a period when most shrubs are flowerless.

Several hundred varieties of this outstanding shrub bear white, pink or red blooms that may be either single, half-double, or full double. In many cases you will find two colors, such as white and pink, or light red and dark red, in the same blossom. Camellias grew originally in China and Japan and were brought to our own country long ago. Today, on the west coast as well as from North Carolina to Florida and along the Gulf, their popularity is still growing steadily, largely due to the gardens of the devotees.

When you see a *bougainvillea* in full bloom you can hardly believe that none of that wonderful color comes from the blossoms. The actual flowers are small and far from bright. All that astonishing beauty is in the large, gaudy "bracts" which surround them. Bougainvilleas came to us from Brazil, and are killed quickly by frost. That is why you seldom find them anywhere in the north except in greenhouses. There is much variation in the color of the flower bracts on these odd shrubs. In general they are either a dull or a bright rose red, which may be either light or dark. But in the tallest growing species, which climbs by grasping its support with strong, hooked spines, the color is purple, greenish, or even brick red.

Many tropical plants need plenty of moisture in the soil where they

362

363

No other tree flower has the soft colors and perfect blending of the *tulip trees.* Seeds form in the center cone.

Crab-apple trees don't mind the cold. They have grown wild in severe northern climates for centuries.

The *silverbell,* often called the *snowdrop tree,* has thousands of these small, swinging, splendid blossoms.

364

365

366

When the "keys" or winged seeds of a *maple* are ripe they spin rapidly to the ground like arboreal helicopters.

The *mountain lilac* is not a *lilac* but it is one of the handsomest flowering shrubs found anywhere in the west.

grow, but bougainvilleas are perfectly happy where it's sunny, hot and dry.

Lilacs reached this country in early colonial times. Many of the colonists had grown and loved these fine shrubs in their old European gardens, and so they brought young ones with them to plant around the new homes they planned to build in the American wilderness. Ever since, the popularity of the lilac has steadily increased, for it is an unusually attractive and reliable shrub that flowers splendidly.

The blossoms of many modern lilacs are much larger than were their distant ancestors, because expert growers have spent years in crossing different kinds so as to improve on them. Along with this increased size and number of the flowers in each cluster the growers developed new colors, too. You can get them in whites, violets, purples, dark and light blues, pinks and magentas. The original home of the lilac tribe was southeast Europe, northeast Asia and Japan. One of the best things about these flowers is their wonderful fragrance.

The blossoming of the *saucer magnolias* is an important spring event in most states whose climates are like that of southern New York. Many thousands of people have planted these European trees on their lawns where their big flowers appear before the leaves and, for a time, put on a tremendous show. Even a baby one only four feet tall often has a few blossoms, and when it reaches its full height of twenty-odd feet there will be hundreds of magnificent blooms.

There are dozens of closely related kinds today, with flowers that range from six to ten inches in width. Some are pure white, others pink and white, purple and white, rose and white, and so on. There is even one that stays in bloom for nearly six weeks!

This splendid half-tree, half-shrub finishes its growing season with an autumn display of bright red seeds that dangle from their pods on thread-like fibers for several days before dropping to the ground.

The *ocotillo* is a queer shrub. Though not a *cactus,* it is covered with sharp spines, and has wedge-shaped leaves that fall off in dry weather. Some people call it *coach-whip* because its branches are so long and upright, while others think that *Jacob's staff* describes it better. It lives in the deserts of the Southwest, has white seeds with hairy fringes on them, and the Mexicans plant it in hedges so dense and thorny that no man or beast can get through them. Its tubular blossoms are either scarlet or brick red and there are so many of them that, as you can tell from the photograph, they almost dazzle you. Each of them is more than an inch long, and the whole effect is as spectacular as an Indian blanket.

The rugged *jack pine* is not handsome. Its branches are scraggly and its short, twisted needles are yellowish in winter instead of a good, healthy green. But in the spring its twigs are tipped with oddly shaped flowers of great beauty. Practically all pines have clustered blossoms of the same general type, and it is from these groups that the cones themselves are formed. A few kinds of cones open up and spill their seeds when only a year and a half old, but those of the jack pine cling to the tree for fifteen years before they let their seeds escape! The jack pine is also known as gray pine and black jack.

The reason why nine people out of ten do not know that a *tulip tree* has lovely flowers is very simple: its blossoms are usually so high up, and so hidden by big, broad leaves, that they are hard to see. The moment you get a good view of one you will know from its shape and size where the "tulip" part of the name comes from.

What is the difference between an *apple* and a *crab-apple?* An apple is large and good to eat raw, and a crab-apple is sour, much smaller and harder, and is used mostly for making jelly. As for the trees on which they grow, most regular apples are larger and less wiry than the closely related "crabs".

There are only two *silverbell* species, and both of them come from the south. One, the *mountain,* sometimes grows ninety feet tall among the

367

A universal spring favorite is the *Japanese cherry* tree which blossoms before most other fruit trees.

Juniper trees look much like other evergreens that produce cones, but instead they raise blue berries.

368

177

mountains of Tennessee and North Carolina. The other, known as the *Carolina silverbell,* grows only half that size and lives more in the low country than in the mountains. Often it is a shrub rather than a tree, particularly after it has been transplanted to the north.

The idea of providing wings for seeds to help them travel may sound too astonishing to be true, but that is exactly what certain flowering trees do. Almost any *maple* tree in late summer or early fall will demonstrate exactly how it's done. As you look up into the tree at this season you will see many drooping clusters shaped more or less like those in the photograph. These are called "keys" or "samaras", and they always grow in pairs. If you look closely you will see that where a pair is attached to its stem there are two swellings, one on each side. These are the actual seeds, and every seed has its own thin "wing", shaped like the blade of a canoe paddle.

In California the words *"mountain lilac"* may mean any one of thirty-odd species of handsome flowering shrubs that grow wild in the hills and valleys. But they're not really lilacs at all, for they belong to the *ceanothus* tribe! They do not have the fragrance of a lilac. In fact some kinds have no scent at all.

The most beautiful of the *cherry* trees, from the standpoint of its blossoms, is the *oriental cherry,* which grows from twenty to seventy feet tall and has many varieties. About fifty of these different forms are grown in the United States under the title of *flowering cherries.* Some bear no fruit.

The seeds of the evergreen *junipers* look exactly like bluish or sometimes silvery berries about the size of small peas. Inside each are from one to several hard little seeds, and birds are fond of eating the whole thing. After the soft part has been digested the actual seeds may be dropped far away, and grow into brand new junipers!

All flowers, big and little, grow for the same purpose: to produce seeds which, when ripe, will sprout and become new plants just like their parents. The full story of how this works is much too long to tell here, but you will be interested to know that it begins deep down in the center or "throat" of each blossom. As soon as the seeds have formed there the rest of the flower begins to fade and dry up, leaving the seeds to ripen by themselves. You can see how important all this is when you remember that without flowers there would be no seeds, and if there were no seeds there might be no new plants to replace the old ones when they die.

Numerous plants like *milkweeds, dandelions, dogbanes* and *salsifies* have parachutes on their seeds, which fly them great distances on the wind.

INVENTIONS
IN NATURE

IN MANY, MANY WAYS, nature has long anticipated the vaunted "inventions" of man. Most flowers that depend on insects or birds for pollination "advertise" their sweet tasting pollens with color and perfume. Furthermore, the showy parts of the flowers are usually in a position where they will be most easily seen by the passing birds or insects on which they depend. For example, the *cardinal flower,* pollinated by *hummingbirds,* has its stamens and pistil at a level where they will contact the head of the bird.

Often when soldiers want to protect their front-line trenches, they erect barbed wire. But barbed wire entanglements are used widely in nature. Countless plants have hairy stems or branches, to discourage pilfering ants and beetles. Our *robin's-plantain* and *great mullen* are splendid examples of this. Two *caterpillars,* the *saddleback* and the larvae of the *io moth,* have even more effective "barbed wire" bristles on their backs. Hungry birds are repelled and persons "stung" by the well armed insects, for the spines break off in the skin and inject enough acid to create a burning sensation for many minutes. Other bristly caterpillars like *wooly bears* and *tent caterpillars* are shunned by birds. They sometimes cause a rash if handled. Tent caterpillars

370

371

have the added protection of sticky silk with which they construct tents. Adhesive to the bills of birds, it discourages all but *black-billed* and *yellow-billed* cuckoos, who have learned to rip the tents apart without their bills becoming hopelessly enmeshed.

Have you ever seen the bands of sticky "tanglefoot" painted around the trunks to prevent larvae of *gypsy moths* and *codling moths* from climbing and eventually injuring the tree? Certain plants have used this principle for millions of years. The *clammy ground-cherry,* for instance, has tiny droplets of mucilage on myriad hairs covering its stems. The *wild pink* has these sticky hairs concentrated on the calyx and flower-stalks, while the sleepy *catchfly* has little bands of "tanglefoot" around the stem at each leaf-bearing node or joint. Certain plants like our *milkweeds, dandelions,* and *wild lettuce,* have a sticky, white milky sap. Ants and beetles, climbing a smooth surface like one of these plant stems, pierce the tender plant epidermis with pick-like claws—and a tiny droplet of sticky "milk" will gush out. Soon their legs are covered with adhesive and further progress becomes difficult, if not impossible.

The safety belts which window cleaners use to hold themselves were employed by butterfly pupae for millions of years. Before the larva of a *cabbage butterfly* changes to a pupa it fastens a band of silk around its body with each end firmly attached to the supporting leaf under which it hangs. With the back end of its body also attached by a knob of silk, the pupa hangs in the same position as does our window cleaner.

Hard-shelled turtles are the original armored tanks, although *armadillos* also have a claim to this title.

A proficient carpenter, the *woodpecker* uses a natural "chisel" to carve his home in a dead limb or tree-trunk.

Our *common mole* can dig tunnels at the amazing rate of a foot in three minutes. One mole was actually observed digging a tunnel sixty-eight feet long in twenty-five hours! *Gophers, prairie-dogs, chipmunks,* certain insects, certain snakes, *armadillos,* and members of almost every animal group—even birds—are expert tunnel-makers. The *long clam* and *razor clam* even use streams of water under pressure with which to dig into the mud or sand.

Pockets were "invented" by animals like the *pocket-gophers* and *chipmunks* and are located in their cheeks. In pocket-gophers they are fur-lined, reversible, and open externally, while they are capable of stretching to such an extent that each may contain two hickory nuts the size of the animal's own head!

Woodpeckers use chisels to build homes in tree-trunks. The *hairy woodpecker,* uses the principle of the harpoon in his hunting. The long, narrow tongue has backward-pointing barbs at its tip. Finding larva in some crevice of a tree trunk, the woodpecker merely shoots his sharp-pointed tongue into the insect's body.

Bats use sonar to avoid buildings, trees, or stalactites in a cave. They do it by sending out "radar beams"—bursts of high frequency sounds—higher than are audible to human ears. *Porpoises* and *dolphins* emit sounds which are echoed back to them by other objects in the water and thus help them to avoid collisions. And when it comes to submarines, the *blue whale* is able to swim at fourteen knots, submerge quickly and dive to tremendous depths, remain under water twelve minutes, and surface half a mile away. He is warm blooded and is provided with a thick layer of blubber which conserves body heat, while a huge reservoir of oil in his head is thought to serve as a cushion for his brain against the tremendous water pressure and thus prevent him from "blacking-out" on a deep dive.

Certain *moths* and *butterflies* have been using "drinking straws" for millions of years. They have a proboscis consisting of two slender tubes welded together and diminishing in size toward the apex. It enables the insect to suck up nectar. When not in use the insect rolls up her "straw", storing it in a special carrying case alongside her head.

The *beaver* shows amazing engineering skill in felling trees, often transporting them to his pond by canal, building a dam which surrounds his homesite like a Medieval moat, and then building a castle-like lodge.

372

The *great blue heron* carries a comb with him at all times. The claw on the middle toe of each of his feet is broken up on its lower edge into a series of parallel teeth very similar to those on our pocket comb, to clean and smooth his feathers.

Hypodermic needles, used so often by our physicians to alleviate pain, were "invented" by *bees, wasps, hornets, scorpions,* and venomous *serpents.*

Many insects react to temperature changes as accurately as a thermometer. At about forty degrees Fahrenheit, for instance, all common insects are silent; at fifty degrees *house flies* seek shelter; at fifty-five degrees *honey bees* collect inside their hive and *ants* stop work. At about sixty degrees the *katydid* says only "Kate"; at about sixty-five to seventy degrees she says "she did" and "she didn't"; at seventy-five degrees she says "Katy didn't"; and at eighty degrees she says "Katy-did-it". At about eighty-five degrees honeybees are busy and gentle; between ninety and ninety-five degrees *cicadas* "sing"; between ninety-five and a hundred degrees *grasshoppers* are noisiest; at 105 degrees honeybees cluster outside the hive; between 105 and 110 degrees ants stay in their underground home; and at about 110 degrees most insects are again completely silent.

373

Instead of using a toothbrush, the African *crocodile* lies on the banks of streams with his mouth partly open. Little *crocodile-birds* pick out particles of food from between his teeth.

Many creatures have developed food storage and preserving units that rival man's. Our *gray squirrel* and *chipmunk* cache nuts in winter quarters, *field mice* store seeds in hiding places beneath the snow, while the *pika* dries grasses and other green vegetation on hot flat rocks in late summer and stores the hay in caves for winter use. The *migrant shrike* has a "pantry" in which he hangs surplus food, such as large insects, mice, small birds, frogs, snakes, and shrews. Favorite "pantries" for him are spiny

374

Using the same principle as our mousetrap, this *venus-flytrap* catches insects and other small creatures.

The *skunk* "invented" chemical warfare. A gland at the base of the tail secretes its dreaded liquid defense.

Fangs of venomous snakes, like this *copperhead,* and the stings of bees, are miniature hypodermic needles.

375

branches and the strands of barbed wire fences.

The *spring-peeper* and other climbing frogs have large suction cups on their fingers and toes, enabling them to climb rapidly. Many insects, like our *common house fly,* have similar suction pads enabling them to walk on windows, walls and even on ceilings. Some insects are equipped with both suction pads for smooth surfaces and claws for rough terrain.

The real "inventor" of poison gas and chemical warfare is surely the *skunk.* Possessing a pair of scent glands, the skunk is able to send a twin jet of "tear gas" as far as ten feet. Often the enemy is temporarily blinded. *Guiana termites* use a flit-gun technique. Members of a soldier-like caste among them, called *nasuti,* have "squirt-guns" on their heads.

376

The exploding *witch-hazel* has little "rifles" that hurl the seeds as much as 45 feet away from the parent plant.

Through these they squirt a sticky liquid over raiding ants that have invaded their colonies.

Squids have employed a smoke-screen technique for countless eons. A squid, facing attack, will eject a jet black india-ink into the water about him. Hidden by this "blackout curtain", he may be able to swim to safety before the cloud has dissipated sufficiently, or the ink may form a squid-like blob in the water, distracting his enemy.

The *four-eyed fish* of northern South America is equipped with a perfect pair of built-in bifocals. His eyes are large and protrude like those of a crocodile. When at rest this fish floats motionless, the upper half of each eye above the surface of the water, the lower half submerged. Thus he is able to watch the air above the stream for insects and still keep an eye on the water beneath him for the possible approach of a stalking enemy!

Arrow-shaped squids, called *sea-arrows,* have used jet propulsion for ages. Water is taken into the body near its front end. Contraction of the body suddenly compresses this water and forces it out of a tube-like funnel, pushing the animal in the opposite direction. When the tip of the funnel is bent backward, the squid darts quickly forward to seize its prey; when it is directed forward, the animal shoots backward to escape an enemy.

Most frogs and toads lay their eggs in ponds or streams. Certain tropical *tree-frogs,* however, lay their eggs in the water-filled pitchers of pineapple-like *bromeliads* or *airplants* high on forest trees. The *Faber tree-frog* of South America makes small artificial lakes by constructing dams of mud which, when flooded, provide a safe swimming pool. The *Amazonian tree-frog* raids wild bee colonies for wax and fashions bowls in crotches of tree trunks. These

377

Female *grasshoppers* dig holes in the ground resembling miniature post-holes. In these they deposit their eggs.

378

Tree-frogs have tiny suction cups on their feet, enabling them to climb with ease up walls and tree-trunks.

bowls soon fill with rain water, and form secluded indoor swimming pools in which infant pollywogs mature.

Our *cottontail rabbit* uses telephones and telegraph. When a rabbit sees an enemy approach, he pounds the ground with powerful hind legs. The sound is carried by the ground, as a conductor, to all parts of the field or woods, much as the sound of the human voice is carried by the wires of the telephone. Not only other rabbits, but most of the other wild creatures that live close enough to the ground to hear these sounds, make good use of this original "telegraph" and scamper to safety.

The original billboards were those of plants like our *flowering dogwood* and *hobblebush.* In these plants the actual flowers are so small and inconspicuously colored that they might very well be overlooked by passing insects. With special sterile flower-like structures crowded around the periphery of the inflorescence, as in hobblebush, or with four showy bracts subtending the tiny florets, in dogwoods, the eye of the passer-by is caught and attention called to the wares thus advertised.

Instead of ending in a tail, the body of the South American *armadillo* comes to a very blunt distal end. The armor plating of his back, which protects him from attack from above while he is out-of-doors, extends down to his rear. When pursued he dives headlong into his tunnel, which is of almost exactly the same diameter as his body. Standing still and bracing himself against its walls, his rear end makes a perfect reinforced door, blocking the entrance. Many *snails* carry a circular horny "door" attached to their bodies near the foot. With this they tightly close the narrow entrance to their shell after they have withdrawn behind it. Certain *carpenter ant* colonies have large-headed "doormen", whose hard, square heads close the tiny doorways to their homes. Each ant, seeking entrance, is forced to "identify" herself by touching this living "door" with her antennae.

Our *otter* really "invented" the playground slide. He builds his of mud along the side of a quiet stream. He derives much enjoyment from plunging headlong down this slide and into the water.

Nature's original snowshoe models make their appearance each winter. Our *ruffed grouse's* three toes grow little side appendages which spread the weight of the bird much as a pair of snowshoes enables a man to walk on loose snow. Similarly, the wide hind feet of the *snowshoe hare* help to support it on winter snows. Some marsh birds, like the *gallinules* and the *Mexican jacana,* exhibit an application of this same principle of spread weight. Their toes and/or claws are extremely long and slender—the hind claw of the jacana being as much as one and a half inches in length. This enables him to walk or run over waterlily leaves and other aquatic vegetation, sometimes giving the appearance of actually walking on the surface of the water.

Armadillos of tropical and South America have their backs covered by suits of armor, consisting of small, close-fitting, bony scales. Some species, like the *nine-banded armadillo,* are able to roll themselves into a ball on the approach of danger and thus present a continuous armored surface on all sides. The *pangolins* of Asia and Africa are scaly ant-eaters whose bony scales overlap like shingles on a roof and resemble some of the coats of mail of medieval Europe. The spiny armatures on the leaves, stems, and involucres of thistles, cacti and other plants, like the *devil-walkingstick,* are counterparts of these protective suits of armor found in many parts of the plant world.

Our champion hydraulic engineer is the *beaver.* Building a dam of wood, mud, and stone across some small stream, he is able to hold back sufficient water to form a moat around his castle-like home or lodge. The doorway to his lodge is underwater, although his living quarters are above water level, so he is effectively protected against most of his potential enemies. The beaver, also, seems to be the inventor of canals. He builds these waterways to float logs and branches to his lake from more distant localities.

Nature's original snare was probably built by the *triangle spider.* She makes a triangular-shaped web out of four threads of silk, with numerous sticky cross-threads. The far corner of this web is a very long single thread, which, if left alone, would be

379

380

Bats find their way between tree branches and other obstacles by means of a highly efficient radar system.

Sundews are nature's original flypaper. Sticky hairs entangle insects, which are then enveloped.

Flies have vibrating structures that exert a stabilizing effect similar to that produced by modern gyroscopes.

381

185

382

Nothing woven by humans is more wonderful, considering the equipment available, than the swinging sac-like nest of our *Baltimore oriole,* or the basket nest of the *blue-headed vireo,* shown above.

extremely loose. The spider, however, takes up a position on this thread and pulls in the slack, making the snare taut. When an insect gets close to this web the spider snaps the web by releasing the slack held by her legs. She may do this repeatedly until the victim is hopelessly ensnared. The lasso was used by spiders for millions of years. Approaching an insect enmeshed in her web, a spider will spin strands of silky, sticky thread and hurl these over the struggling insect, quickly drawing them tight and thus gradually immobilizing the flailing legs and wings. Certain *crab-spiders* have carried this lassoing technique further. They hurl their silken strands across the gap between a flower or branch on which they are sitting and an adjacent one. After the far end has been successfully snagged they walk over their new suspension bridge.

Our little cobweb-building *house spider* is a fisherman, but she fishes for insects. In her irregular web are long lines which lead from her tunnel or tent to every corner. She hides in her tunnel with each of her eight legs resting lightly upon one of these "fish-lines". As soon as an insect falls into her web his struggles will cause a tug on one or more of these lines and she will know not only that something has been caught, but also the approximate position of the victim in the web.

Some psychologists have stated that only primates know how to use tools, yet the *golden digger wasp* picks up a pebble of just the right size and closes the entrance to her nursery with it, or even uses a pebble in her mandibles to tamp down sand or earth when sealing the door of her home. The *woodpecker-finch* of the Galápagos picks up a long, thin, cactus thorn in its short bill and with it pokes out insects hiding in crevices of bark and wood. When the insect runs out of hiding, the spine is dropped and the insect devoured.

Then the tool is picked up to repeat the spear-fishing process all over again.

Frogs use solar energy quite regularly. Their hundreds of eggs are each enclosed in transparent jelly. The convexity of this mass acts much like a magnifying glass and concentrates the sun's rays, focusing them on the embryo within the egg. The frog's "incubator" is, therefore, run directly by solar energy. *Opossums* and *kangaroos* have built-in "incubators" in the form of external pouches in which they carry and nourish their very tiny young. Certain antarctic *penguins* have similar external fat-lined pouches which cover their eggs.

The young of alligators, crocodiles, and most birds have a "glasscutter" on the top of their upper jaw. With this they cut through the eggshell before hatching. The *long-tailed ichneumon-fly* has a "drill" about four and a half inches long. A marine snail is able to bore holes into oyster shells, using its rasping tongue as the penetrating instrument.

Quite a few different kinds of plants eject seeds so forcefully as to resemble the action of rifles or cannons. Our *common witch-hazel* is one of these, and the *squirting cucumber,* is another. The seeds of the witch-hazel may actually be hurled fifteen to forty-five feet through the air! *Brookside jewelweeds* use a sling-shot method for hurling their seeds from the pods on the parent plant.

Nature even has her "anti-aircraft" weapons in the form of the *archer fish.* This is a small fish with a flashing yellow- and black-barred body, living in Siam and the East Indies. When an insect flies near to the surface of the water in which he lives, the fish ejects a stream of water with uncanny accuracy.

The ability to emit tiny flashes of light is possessed by both sexes of *fireflies.* By means of these signals they find their mates. A more steady type of light is given off by the microscopic organisms which impart luminescence to certain types of *moss, rotting wood, fungi,* and *plankton.* Certain squids and deep-sea fish exhibit luminescence in definite patterns on their bodies. The *three-starred angler fish,* living about twenty-four hun-

Box-elder, maples, ashes, and other trees use the principle of the helicopter in distributing their seeds.

The *pitcher plant* has hollow leaves, partly filled with liquid, in which it traps hapless insects that enter.

383

384

187

385

386

Show windows to attract attention are bright wild flowers which depend on birds or insects for pollination.

Frogs and *toads* have third eyelids, moving horizontally, which are like water-goggles to a pearl-diver.

dred feet below the surface of the sea, in a region of eternal blackness, carries three "lanterns" at the ends of erect backward-pointing "masts". The so-called "burning of the sea" at night is brought about mostly by luminous *protozoons,* chiefly *flagellates.* Numerous *jellyfish, hydroids, gorgonians, sea-combs, worms, brittle-stars,* and *crustaceans* emit light.

Actual electricity is used by the *electric ray,* which has two "storage batteries" on either side of its head. Here electric energy is generated and stored. One discharge is sufficient to paralyze large sea animals. The *electric eel* of freshwater streams in South America is able to send out discharges of five hundred or more volts many times per minute.

The very long and sensitive ears of many animals, like those of the famous Texas *jackrabbit,* serve them like the antennas on our radio and television sets, effectively picking up even the slightest of sounds.

The branches of bird feathers are fastened to each other by hooks very much like the parts of a zipper. If they become un-zipped, many birds are able to pass them between their mandibles to re-zipper them.

Common *rainbarrel mosquito* larvae have been using snorkels for untold ages. A breathing-tube enables them to hang entirely under water and yet obtain air. Water plants, like *waterlilies* and *pondlilies,* have snorkel-like air-conducting tubes in their leaf-stalks, which conduct air to the underwater parts of the plant.

Stony *coral polyps* build elaborate and beautiful apartment houses, sometimes so extensive as to form reefs or atolls in the sea. The *sea-fan,* of tropic oceans, forms a colony shaped like a netted fan or flattened tree often as much as twenty inches high, with the individual "meshes" up to a quarter of an inch across.

Glue is used in many places in nature. *Honeybees* glue together cracks or other openings in their home with a special glue made from the sticky coverings of certain buds. Our *chimney swift* glues its nest to the walls inside of chimneys. The *gray-rumped swiftlet* of the Malay area is famous for the edible nests it builds against the walls of caverns. These nests are made entirely of a glue-like mucous secreted by large glands in the parents' throats only at nesting time.

The tightly overlapping petals of our *field lily* form a perfect umbrella, protecting the stamens, pistil and nectaries from injury in showers. Certain weaverbirds in Africa build huge hat-like structures of grass and twigs, under which they then place their colonial nests.

Many animals post sentries. *Brown pelican* rookeries in the coastal mangrove thickets of Florida usually are guarded by an old bird on some vantage point. *Prairie-dogs* regularly post sentries to guard their underground cities.

The principle of the floating buoy is used in the leaves of the tropical *water-hyacinth*. This plant produces a rosette of three or more fleshy leaves on a much abbreviated stem. The leaves have long stalks which are swollen and inflated at the center. Containing a large quantity of air, these leaf-stalks act as buoys, keeping the plant afloat on the water, where it swims about with the current. From the apex of the stem issues the hyacinth-like flower cluster, while from the base of the stem many feathery roots extend downward into the water, serving to balance the plant and help keep it erect.

Many of our musical instruments find their counterparts in nature. *Woodpeckers,* like our big *pileated,* drum on dead branches or hollow tree-trunks in their spring courting. The *flicker* will even utilize tin roofs of houses for his drumming. Violins were "invented" by the short-horned *grasshoppers* or *locusts.* These insects rub the upper surface of one margin of their hind wings (like a violin bow) over the lower surface of the thickened veins of the front wings (serving as the strings), thus producing their well-known "song" Other locusts rub the inner surface of their rear femora (corresponding to our thighs) against the outer surface of the front wings. In the crickets the sound is produced by rubbing together the two front wings, each of which has a

The *burdock* is a "hitch-hiker," its fruits being carried from place to place on the coats of passing animals.

Suits of armor, like those worn by knights of old, protect the *armadillo* and *pangolin* from their many enemies.

387

388

189

389

391

390

392

With front feet thickened like spades, the *mole* is able to dig the vast underground tunnels in which he lives.

The original pottery-makers were the *potter wasps*. Their individual homes of mud are shaped like water-jugs.

Mountain-laurel flowers have their stamens bent back and caught in notches, creating a trigger mechanism.

Long before Egyptians made papyrus, these *wasps* made their homes and nurseries of wood-pulp paper.

rasping organ and vibrating areas or tympana like miniature kettle drums.

Grasshoppers are sometimes described as nature's original posthole-diggers. When egg-laying time comes around, the female grasshopper uses the short, stiff, sharp ovipositor at the far end of her body much as we would use a spade. With it she digs a somewhat curved hole about the diameter and shape of her own abdomen, in which she then lays from twenty to one hundred eggs as she gradually withdraws her body.

The question is often asked, "How do perching birds remain on their perch when asleep"? This is brought about by a natural safety lock mechanism in the leg. A tendon passes over the joints of the leg in such a way that when a bird settles down on a branch and the legs are drawn up against the body, the tendon is put under strain and the toes automatically are flexed. The bird's feet thus automatically clutch the branch and lock in that position. To release the lock, the bird must awaken and rise up.

Traps are also used in the plant world. A counterpart to the sticky fly paper that we formerly employed to catch the house fly is seen in the leaves of the *sundew*. The leaves have on their upper surface a thin scattering of erect hairs, each of which is tipped with a tiny droplet of a pink sticky substance. Small insects, landing on the leaves to investigate the attractive droplets, are soon enmeshed. As they struggle to free themselves, the leaf begins to roll inwards from the margins. It engulfs the helpless trapped insects. A digestive juice is then secreted which reduces the softer parts of the insect's body to a form that is usable by the plant. The leaf then opens up, the undigested parts of the insect are dropped off, it turns right-side-up again, and is then ready for another "meal". The dew-threads have their leaves very long and thread-like, covered with pink sticky hairs for their entire length. When sufficient insects have been trapped the leaf rolls inward from the apex to the base. Botanists have discovered a microscopic *fungus* which catches tiny cavorting *springtails* by means of sticky adhesive organs, and then consumes their bodies as food.

Even more like our flypaper are the leaves of the *butterworts*. These plants live in mountainous areas in far northern regions, each producing about eight, rather thick oblong, light green leaves on the surface of the ground. A full grown leaf is about one and a half inches long and three-quarters of an inch wide. Its margins are somewhat in-curved and the upper surface is completely covered with tiny hairs secreting colorless sticky material so very viscid that a droplet can be drawn out into a fine thread as much as eighteen inches long. When insects are caught by these leaves the leaf-margins fold inward to engulf and digest them.

Mouse- and rat-traps find their counterparts in the leaves of the *venus flytrap*. Here the upper portion of the leaf is divided into two similar halves which can close together against each other by means of a hinge-like midrib. The margins of the blades are armed with a close series of stiffy erect pines. Between them and the midrib are two or three small and weak but very sensitive hairs. An insect, alighting on this trap and bumping against at least two of these trigger-like hairs, will cause the two halves of the leaf to snap shut. The marginal spines will interlock and effectively prevent his escape should his body be large enough to prevent the tight closure of the two halves. Bottle-

"Advertising billboards" of white or pink are put up by the *flowering dogwood* trees around their tiny greenish flowers, thus attracting the attention of passing insects to pollen ware which might have been overlooked.

393

394

395

Spanish-needles have spear-like points on their seeds. With these they ride to new territory on passing animals.

The *cicada-killer* stings her victim, then transports its paralyzed body to her underground nursery as food.

traps are produced by the *bladderworts*. These are mostly aquatic plants with the leaves borne entirely beneath the surface of the water and finely dissected into hair-like divisions. Each leaf bears two or three greenish bladders, each about one-tenth of an inch long. The mouth of the trap is very small and is margined with long, stiff, forward-pointing hairs. A colorless, highly transparent, flexible and elastic valve projects diagonally into the bladder at the mouth. Tiny aquatic creatures are able to swim easily into the trap, pushing inward the free edge of the valve, but once in they are trapped because the valve, being highly elastic, snaps shut behind them.

In *sphagnum* bogs we find *pitcherplants*. In these plants the leaves are four to twelve inches long and curve upward. The leaf-stalk is greatly expanded and inflated in pitcher-like fashion. Its inner surface is covered with stiff bristles pointing downwards and is about half filled with a mixture of water and a sweet gummy secretion. Insects start down the pitcher and progress easily because of the position of the bristles, but this same position effectively prevents their turning around and climbing out again. Reaching the liquid, they drown and are soon digested.

Big game hunters dig pitfalls along jungle trails to catch tigers, but the *ant-lion* "invented" this contraption. The female lays her eggs in sand. It hatches into a small, oval, extraordinarily long-jawed larva known as a *doodlebug*, which at once proceeds to dig a funnel-form pit in the sand. At its base the larva buries itself except for its head. When an ant slips into the pit the doodlebug bombards it with sand and undermines its footing as it tries to escape. Eventually, exhausted, the ant slips to the bottom.

Counterparts to our pins and needles are found widely in nature; for instance, in the stiff spurs of the *pin oak*, the quills of the *porcupine*, the spines and bristles of many *cacti*, the stinging hairs of *nettles*, the spines of *sea-urchins*, and the spicules of hard *sponges*. Perfect daggers are carried by the *trigger fish* of the Caribbean. On the approach of a larger fish which might be tempted to devour him, the dorsal fin is erected and a very long, stiff, sharp-pointed spine snaps into an upright position. If the trigger fish is swallowed, this dagger-like spine neatly slits the throat and gullet of the larger fish! Swordfish have their upper jaw prolonged into a sharp pointed sword with

192

which they fight. So powerful are these fish that their swords have been found deeply embedded in the wooden bottoms of boats! The *northern shrike* has a "blackjack" in the form of his bill. He regularly kills mice and small birds by means of a sudden blow on the back of the head.

The *beggar-ticks* and *Spanish-needles* employ barbed spears on their seeds to attach them to passing animals. The *unicorn-plant* of our western plains uses "handcuffs" which snap into place around the feet of passing cattle, sheep, or horses and are carried away. Sometimes they snap into the septum between the nostrils of grazing cattle, like nose-rings. *Milkweeds, dandelions, dogbanes* and *salsifies* have miniature parachutes attached to their seeds,

396

Our radio and television antennas find their counterpart in the "feelers" of the *red admiral butterfly*.

which may carry them for miles. *Balloon spiders* also spin parachutes of silk which may carry them across a field or a hundred miles away.

The lateral fins of *flying-fish* serve as ailerons and were in use eons before airplanes. The tail of a flying bird serves both as rudder and brake. The *sailfish* and *basking shark* have sail-like dorsal fins. Mute *swans* will sometimes partly raise their huge wings while swimming. The wind may strike these and thus help the birds get up speed on the water.

By means of sticky threads which harden in the air like cement and stick fast to anything with which they come in contact, *mussels* anchor themselves to tidal rocks and piers. Rafts are built regularly by *water spiders*. Water spiders construct floating rafts, held together by silk, on which they sail over the surfaces of ponds or calm streams.

Camels and *dromedaries* have built-in canteens. They may drink as much

This *saddleback caterpillar* has bristles serving as "barbed-wire entanglements" to discourage potential enemies.

"Drinking straws" were used by *moths* and *butterflies* to sip nectar from flowers long before man used them.

397

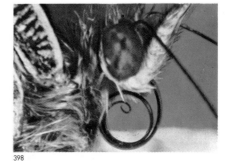
398

as sixteen gallons of water at a time and then go for ten days without another drink. The *Galapagos tortoise* carries its canteens alongside its neck in extensible pouches. Some desert animals are able to make water chemically from vegetable foods available to them. The giant *barrel cactus* has its interior composed of a mass of spongy tissue which absorbs and holds every drop of moisture collected by the shallowly spreading root system during rare rainstorms.

Several reputable naturalists have reported that anesthetics are used by some animals. The blood-drinking *vampire bats* of the tropics are believed to inject a local anesthetic into the shallow wound which they inflict when they bite a victim and begin to lap its blood. Testimony of human victims is almost unanimous that such bites would not awaken a sleeper.

The *jumping jerboa* has skid-chains in the form of stiff hairs which cover his feet and help to keep him from skidding on loose sand. *Slugs* and certain *land snails* should get credit for the "invention" of railroad tracks, for they lay down slippery mucous tracks over which they push themselves as they travel from place to place. *Tent caterpillars* use guide-lines which they spin and lay down as they travel from branch to branch on an *apple tree.* By following these lines in the evening they find their way back to the nest.

Many ants use some flat board or rock on which the winged males and females stage their pre-nuptial "dance" and from which they eventually hurl themselves into the air. Certain tropical *termites,* however, actually build "take-off platforms" by their homes for the convenience of these members of their community. A certain *Palestine ant* builds barns for the shelter of the *aphids* which serve her as cows.

Of all of his inventions, man is probably proudest of his mastery of the air, but many birds, insects and bats, to say nothing of the ancient *pterodactyls,* were sailing through the air long before the days of Orville and Wilbur Wright.

Modern science is giving man tools with which he can study nature's inventions more effectively—high speed and stroboscopic photography as well as ultra-violet, infra-red, and color photography, telescopes and microscopes of increasing power, and new techniques of analytical chemistry and spectroscopy. To a greater extent than ever before the structure and behavior of plants and animals is being studied by engineers, scientists and inventors. Living things have mastered water, land and air; have become perfectly adapted in almost every conceivable environment. It isn't unreasonable to think that we still have much to learn from nature's inventors.

399

Here is an underwater scene of a *coral* reef. Almost all of the organisms in this picture are animals. They include *sponges, anemones, sea squirts, coral, starfish* and *sea urchin.* Can you find them all?

LIFE IN SHALLOW SEA WATER

ALONG THE SHORE at low tide, a group of *barnacles* attached to a rock would not seem very interesting; just some small white shell-like creatures sticking to the surface. But after the tide has come in, these strange animals come to life and begin to feed.

The barnacle has a "sliding door" which keeps it covered and protects it from drying up when the tide is out. But when the tide comes in, the door opens and delicate feathery feet come out and beat a regular rhythm through the water; raking in food—the microscopic creatures that swim past. Although related to the *crab* and *lobster,* which can walk, it has learned to live while stuck fast to a rock, a shell, or even the bottom of a ship.

Its eggs are laid in the water, and after they hatch the young go through a free-swimming stage. This way they find new homes; once on a ship's bottom they secrete a heavy shell for protection and can no longer move.

Barnacles aren't popular with shipowners. As more shells become attached to the ship, they increase its weight and resistance in water. A shipowner may take his ship into fresh water where the barnacles die and drop off for lack of food, or put the hull in drydock and have the shells scraped off.

Since the tide changes twice every 24 hours, animals and plants must learn

400

A group of *anemones* wave their tentacles in a rocky pool. Living under a wharf, they are almost white. When they grow in the light they may take on a green color due to the presence of algae which live in their cells.

to live part of the time covered with sea water and the rest of the time exposed to the air and all the changes that take place.

Animals hide themselves under great mats of seaweed which cluster closely over the surface of the rocks. They are thus kept moist by the seaweeds which protect them from the drying effects of the sun.

A single strand of seaweed may become the home of many clustering tiny animals that attach themselves to the plant and may also be protected by it from the violence of the waves. Tiny strands of *hydroids,* whose beauty and complexity can be seen only under a microscope, or flat colonies of lacelike moss animals or *bryozoans,* often occur in the hundreds.

And there are billions of tiny organisms, both plant and animal, which, because they have limited swimming ability or none at all, are classified as floating life or *plankton.* Most are of microscopic size, with a few larger forms such as jellyfish. Their greatest importance lies in the fact that they form the base of the great food chain of life in the sea. The chain is quite long, one animal preying on another and in turn being eaten by a still larger form. The beginning of any such food chain must be some sort of plant life, for plants are the only living things that can capture the energy of sunlight and transform it into some form of nutrition.

In tide pools can be seen the small animals which crawl and swim, the great festoons of seaweed waving their long, frond-like stalks, and schools of small fish. At first glance the seaweeds dominate the scene, some, like the *kelp,* waving great banners through the water as much as 15 or 20 feet long and attached to the rocks at their base by a tough holdfast structure. Extending from this is a round tough tube about the size of a garden hose in large specimens, and then the great wide frond with its center rib and heavy, rubbery "leaf" as much as two feet wide with a strangely ruffled edge. It is called "devil's apron"! Other varieties of this largest marine plant branch into flat, finger-like projections, have feathery fronds along the side of the tube, or simply long filaments of plant tissue floating for 25 or 30 feet. These are members of a group known as the *brown algae* for their color is predominantly brownish, shading into olive green.

Hanging from the sides of the pool and covering the rocks are thick mats of *beaded rockweed* and *bladderwrack,* both brown algae and the most common of seaweeds. Even along sandy beaches great heaps are washed up by the surf, torn loose from their anchorage on the rocks by storms. Children, finding these, take great delight in squeezing the air-bladders and making them pop. The air-bladders serve a useful purpose, holding the plant upright in the water when the tide is in and helping to protect it from the force of the waves. Since these plants form the greatest bulk of the seaweed in the inter-tidal zone, they shelter innumerable tiny animals in their fronds.

Smaller and beautifully delicate algae grow in clusters on the bottom of the pool, exhibiting all manner of delicacy in their fronds and branches. The *Irish moss* has long been known as the source of seaweed pudding because of the gelatinous material contained in the plant body. There are other forms of *red algae* noteworthy for their beauty. In general, they are more apt to be found in deeper water than the other groups. They are able to absorb sunlight at deeper levels than the brown or green types. The *green algae* are frequently found in the highest tide pools where they may endure rather extreme conditions. In rainy weather these pools may become almost entirely fresh-water due to the run-off from rocks above the tide level, and in hot weather the temperature of these pools may be over 80 degrees.

A large and rather primitive group of animals called the *coelenterates* include not only the hydroids but also the *jellyfish,* the *sea anemones,* and the *corals* of the tropical seas. The scientific name "coelenterates" comes from two Greek words: *koilos* (hollow), and *enteron* (intestine). They are well named, for the largest part of their cup-shaped bodies is a single digestive cavity. Attached to the wood of wharves and pilings or to rocks or seaweeds,

Barnacles growing on the rocks. When the tide is in they feed actively by waving their feet in the water.

An underneath view of the *horseshoe crab.* The gill-books between the walking legs and the tail are used for breathing.

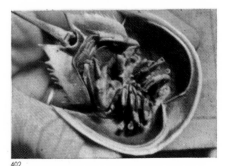

401

402

197

403

404

Snail looking for food on a *sponge*. The eyespots on base of tentacles are the only departure from its yellow color.

The *horseshoe crab,* armored like a tank, has eyes near the front of the shell and a tail of sharp spines.

the hydroids are usually small and inconspicuous and would be mistaken for strands of seaweed since they look so much like plants. They are delicate animals which attach themselves to a base by a stalk. At the tip of the stalk and often branching out in fern-like patterns, are the hydranths. These are cup-shaped bodies surrounded by a row or more of tentacles. When alarmed, they withdraw the tentacles close to the cup, but when feeding, the tentacles are stretched out into the water.

Many are equipped with stinging cells in the tentacles, to harpoon their prey. In the special cell is a minute dart to which is attached a coiled thread. When irritated, this dart is released by a sort of spring and penetrates the prey. It contains enough poison to paralyze a small captive. This serves as a method of capturing food and fighting enemies.

In the hydroid stage they reproduce by forming special bodies like buds which eventually break off and float away and then appear to be small jellyfish with an umbrella-shaped form and a ring of tentacles around the rim. They swim through the water by folding and unfolding this umbrella rhythmically. These tiny "jellyfish" produce male and female cells which unite, attach themselves to a base and begin another hydroid generation.

A second group comprises the true *jellyfish* and these often grow to be quite large. The most common is the *moon jellyfish.* It grows to be as much as a foot in diameter and often occurs in tremendous floating schools. They can cover several acres of the surface of the sea, packed together closely, totaling millions of individuals! Great wind-rows of them may be washed up on the beach and left helplessly stranded there as the tide goes out. Then just as suddenly they all disappear. Having completed their mission of egg-laying, they disintegrate or are sliced to ribbons by voracious schools of fish. As they float in the water they are almost entirely transparent except for the whitish canals radiating from the center and the eggs hanging in pinkish masses from the underside of the mature individuals.

The *red jellyfish,* or *lion's mane,* attains a diameter of several feet and has long strings of tentacles stretching for 10 or 12 feet from the lower side. This and the *Portuguese man-o'-war* of tropical waters can inflict painful wounds with their stinging cells on the unwary swimmer.

The *sea anemones* and *corals* make up the last group. They bear some resemblance to the hydroids in that they have a cylindrical body surrounded at the mouth end by rows of tentacles. Most of the anemones are sessile like the hydroids, which means that they attach themselves to a base and remain pretty much in one place although some of them are able to move slowly about. A few are long and tubular and burrow in the mud on the bottom instead of attaching themselves to rocks or pilings. Others anchor onto the shell of a *hermit crab* and travel to new food supplies. Their radial patterns, in which the tentacles form an encircling fringe at the upper end of the cylinder, resemble the petals of a flower—hence the name anemone.

In the tropical waters of Florida and the Gulf of Mexico live the corals, a group closely related to the sea anemones. They are much smaller but have the same general pattern of structure. They secrete a limy skeleton about their bodies. This skeleton continues to enlarge as the colony grows and divides, so that large structures of coral result. Therefore most of the coral is not living, but the structural remains of innumerable animals very slowly build up the coral in intricate designs of great beauty and remarkable color. Because of their innumerable holes and crevices they become the dwelling place of many bottom-living sea creatures.

405

With the exception of the single-celled *protozoa,* which are too small to be seen, the most primitive group is the *sponges.* Almost entirely a marine group, a few small species occur in fresh water. These creatures are animals although they look like

406

Top view of a large *sea anemone* brought up from deep water. The thick tentacles are armed with stinging cells.

Goose barnacles growing on a stalk. Its resemblance to the head and neck of a goose gives rise to the name.

Rockweeds are attached to rocks, but air bladders keep the fronds floating and they move gently with the tide.

407

408

409

410

The *sand worm* burrows or swims with ease. To each of the segments in its body is attached a fin-like swimming organ.

An unusual relative of the starfish, this *sea cucumber* derives his name from the shape of the body.

The *soft-shelled clam* lives in mud flats. From under the mud it squirts water out of the siphon when disturbed.

plants. They appear as a flat spongy mat growing on rocks or shells and showing on the upper side a few openings, called "chimneys", through which they take water into their bodies. They have no real body structure but are made up of groups of cells which take up the various functions of survival. The body is strengthened internally by structures called spicules, usually composed of silica, or calcium, and shaped in a variety of thin spines or triangles. The openings to the outside are surrounded by tiny waving hairlike projections called cilia, whose rapid motions cause food-carrying water to flow through the body.

Another group of animals along the shore is the *snails*. The most common are the *periwinkles* occurring in countless millions. They climb right up to the upper limit of the tidal zone, protected from drying out by the hard shell and a tough, leathery covering of the opening, called the operculum, with which they can seal enough water into the shell between the tides to keep themselves alive. In some tide pools they cover the bottom several layers deep. They appear to feed entirely on seaweed.

The snails are members of the division or "phylum" of animals called the *mollusca,* which is subdivided into several important groups. The group to which the snails belong is known as *univalves,* since they usually have one shell or valve. The commonest form of this shell is a twisted coil, tapering to a spire at one end and with a large opening at the base from which the living parts of the body can be extended in order to move or eat. They move about on the fleshy foot at a deliberate pace. The colors of the shells often blend with the background on which they live, such as that of the *yellow snail,* which duplicates the color of the sponge on which it often lives.

Many of the snails which live along the coast where they are exposed to the action of the waves have their shells flattened in order to lower their resistance to the rush of water. Examples of this are the *limpets* and the *boat shells,* which attach themselves to the rocks so tightly with their muscular feet that it is almost impossible to pry them loose.

The *rock purple,* a carnivorous snail, feeds to a large extent on barnacles and sometimes on other snails. Slightly larger than the periwinkle's, the tip of the shell is higher and more pointed. Some are pure white while others are variously banded with stripes of brown or purple. Under rocks are found the egg clusters of these animals, tiny capsules attached to the rock by a thread. The foot of these and other carnivorous snails contains a horny tooth called a "radula" which acts like a rasp in scraping a small hole in the shell of the victim. After this has been done, the snail sucks out the meat from inside the shell and moves on to attack another.

A small group of snails is the *nudibranchs* or *sea slugs.* Somewhere along the path of evolution they have lost the shell, although it is present in the early stages of their life. But the adults are soft-bodied and quite small. They crawl about over seaweeds or the sides of pilings and feed on small organisms. Some of them are quite handsome, though they may need to be magnified to be seen well. Other slugs may have many branched gills extending upward from the back, making them look as if they were carrying branches of trees on their shoulders. A rather unusual sight is a number of these slugs crawling upside down on the under surface of the water, supported by their ability to cling to the liquid's surface.

411

Attached to the rocks near the low tide level are the *molluscs.* These are the *chitons,* which differ from the snails in that they have a shell made of a series of transverse plates, usually eight in number, held together around the outside border by a layer of solid shell secreted by the mantle which lies beneath it. When pried

412

Looking like a walking bush, the *toad crab* carries his camouflage with him wherever he goes.

The spines of the *sea urchin* are often long and sharp. They should be carefully avoided by the seaside wader!

A *lobster* is bright red only after he has been boiled. In nature the colors are more subdued but very beautiful.

413

loose from the rock, the large flat foot can be seen. They feed on the algae growing on the rock surface and move slowly. Chitons are considered to be the most primitive of the molluscs.

A group of molluscs which occur abundantly along rocky shores is the *mussels,*representing bivalve molluscs, the ones with two shells. These shells are usually symmetrical. The young are free-swimming and have hook-like structures by which they attach themselves to the gills of fish, hitching a ride to their new home. When mature enough to settle down, they drop off and attach themselves to any permanent surface.

As soon as the shell begins to grow, they secrete from a gland on the under side a series of threads called "byssal threads". These are glued tightly to the base and as time goes on they secrete more until they are tightly bound to the surface and difficult to dislodge. Their feeding process is quite different from the method of the snails. Water is taken in through an opening in the shell and is passed through the body in such a way that it passes the mouth, where microscopic life is filtered out and taken into the stomach. Then it passes over the gills where oxygen is extracted, and the water is returned to the sea through another opening. Thus a constant current is kept running through the body to provide nourishment.

Mussels have a fantastic reproductive potential. If a piece of wood is put in the water it will be covered in a few weeks with hundreds of seed mussels per square foot. The competition is so great that only a few will be able to reach maturity, for there are any number of predators to destroy them. The chances of survival are so low that most animals have to produce large numbers of offspring in order to continue living at all.

The *starfish* are among the most interesting of all marine creatures. Their

The *pipefish* swims with the dorsal fin and stands upright in the water. When swimming this way in the *eelgrass,* he blends with the background and is almost impossible to see.

414

tube feet are arranged in rows down the center of each arm. As they project from the channel in which they rest, each foot extends until some solid surface is found and the sucker at the tip attaches to it and remains there until the foot is ready to be lifted to find a new purchase. Since a full grown starfish has several hundred of these tube feet, it is a wonder that they can be so well coordinated that the starfish can make steady progress in one direction. The tube feet at the end of the arms are longer than the others and apparently serve as feelers, since the starfish has very primitive eyes and can only distinguish between light and dark.

415

The tube feet are operated by a complex hydraulic system which begins at an opening on the upper side near the center, called the "madrepore". This seems to be a valve which controls the amount of water which enters into a ring canal just below. From this branch canals which extend to the end of each of the arms, or rays, and on either side of the canal are smaller tubes connecting with each of the tube feet. At the base of each foot is a small bulb, surrounded by a set of muscles. When these muscles squeeze the bulb, it forces the foot to expand and extend outward from the channel in which it rests

416

Spotted clown slugs are really snails which have lost their shells. They are small and often brightly colored.

Star coral lives as far north as Cape Cod. Unlike coral of tropical waters, it is not a reef builder.

and the sucker at the top can then be attached to any object with which it comes in contact. When the muscles relax, the tube can be unfastened and withdrawn to be replaced at another spot.

Starfish are carnivores, preying on molluscs and sometimes on barnacles. They feed by crawling up on top of a mussel or clam, spreading their arms on either side of the shell. Then by exerting a steady pull with the feet attached tightly to the shell, and aided by chemical secretions from the mouth opening underneath, they gradually pull the shell open. Then the stomach is protruded from inside the body and extended down into the clam, which is digested on the spot. They have remarkable powers of regeneration, and if one or two, or even as many as four, of the arms are broken or torn off, they produce new ones to replace them.

Protection from their enemies is provided by many small spines of calcareous material arranged along the back and at the margins of the rows of tube feet beneath. On the back these are surrounded by tiny pincers too small to be seen without a magnifying glass. These pincers are used to chop away any entangling seaweeds.

Starfish come in assorted sizes and with varying numbers of rays, although the most common number is five. The *red starfish* of the Pacific coast, a close relative of the small *blood starfish* found in the east, has small spines and a bright red or orange color. The larger species on eastern shores are the *Forbes starfish* and the *purple starfish.*

All of these belong to the *echinoderms,* which means "spiny-skinned." Another subdivision comprises the *brittle* or *serpent stars* whose rays are long and tenuous. They move with snaky motions of the arms and have no groove for tube feet beneath, but depend on the arms for locomotion. When tangled in the bases of kelp, or making their way in the crevices of a colony of sponges, it is almost impossible to dislodge them without breaking off one

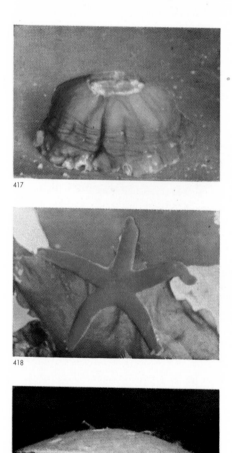

417

418

419

or two of the very brittle arms. The striking resemblance of the motion of the rays to that of a snake is responsible for one of the names of the group, and the ease with which they are broken for the other.

Another group in which spines are enlarged until the creature assumes an appearance much like that of a porcupine is the *sea urchins.* Projecting from the shell are the long protective spines which are articulated in a sort of joint at the base so that they can be moved. These strange, moving pin-cushions navigate about by using the combination of spines and tube feet.

The sea urchin feeds on vegetable matter or dead organic remains. The mouth has five hard, calcareous teeth used to scrape material off rocks on the bottom of the pools. They are

An *anemone* alarmed or touched, withdraws the tentacles and seals itself up except for a small hole at the top.

Most *starfish* are brightly colored and have five rays. If one is lost, a new one is regenerated to replace it.

Nature provided the *scallop* with jet propulsion. It can eject a stream of water and force itself rapidly along.

204

420

Wherever you may go along the seashore there are interesting habitats to study and explore. These students are examining a frond of seaweed for the many organisms that may be attached to it.

found along the North Atlantic coast, among the coral formations of the tropics and on the Pacific shore.

The *phylum crustacea* includes many animals which have in common the possession of jointed legs and a skeleton made of a tough, leathery material called *chitin,* often reinforced with some calcium in marine forms. They differ from the typical crustacean because of their sedentary existence attached to rocks or other substantial surfaces. Some project themselves farther into the water by means of a stalk, as do the *goose barnacles.*

A more typical example would be the *rock crab* found along the northern coast. Further south it is replaced by the blue crab, the important commercial crab of the east. The tidal zone is abundantly populated by the *green crab* crawling around under mats of seaweed. There are several species of commercial importance on the Pacific coast, too. The rock crab is rather oval in shape with the abdominal segments folded under the main part of the body in the shape of a *V.* The first pair of legs is much enlarged and armed with strong, heavy pincers. Even a small one can bite viciously, and once they get hold of some object, they cling with a bulldog grip that sometimes necessitates breaking the claw in order to pry it loose. If given an opportunity, crabs will usually make their escape, sidling off with a peculiar gait on the walking legs. They seem to prefer to walk sidewise, although they are capable of moving forward and backward and swim quite well.

The female crab carries the eggs for a period of time, attached to the underside of the abdomen which partially unfolds to make room for them. She carries several hundred eggs in this fashion. When the young larvae hatch, they drop off and become for a time members of the surface plankton animals in the sea. They are barely visible at first and go through a series

205

of complicated stages, after each of which they shed their shells and grow new ones. At the time of molting they are most vulnerable, since the shell is soft until the materials that compose it harden. This molting process continues in the adult stage, although the molts are less frequent then. Crabs in this condition are known as "soft-shelled crabs". When the young have reached a sufficient stage of advancement, they leave the plankton and settle down on the bottom.

Crustaceans are quite highly organized. They have well developed eyes which are on stalks so that they can be moved around for better vision. Around the mouth opening are a number of appendages similar in structure to the legs. These are used to handle the food which is first caught and broken up by the pincer claws and then passed into the smaller appendages which break it into pieces small enough to be taken into the stomach. The stomach has a series of toothlike structures on the inside which further grind up the food by their muscular action. They breathe by means of gills located in a chamber between the outside covering, or carapace, and the interior part of the body. Water is forced through this chamber in regular circulation and the feathery gills absorb oxygen from the water.

If you see a snail get up and quietly walk away, it will doubtless prove to be a snail shell inhabited by a *hermit crab*. Its body is long and the abdomen is coiled to fit the whorls of the snail shell, and soft, since its existence inside the shell demands a hard covering. At the tip of the abdomen is a small, hard structure used to hold the animal in the shell. The walking legs, claws, head, eyes and antennae all extend forward out of the shell. When a hermit crab grows too large for the shell he is in, he searches for another larger abandoned shell and moves into it. At the least sign of danger, he will withdraw the body into the shell while the opening is protected by the claws which are the last to be pulled in. As soon as the danger has passed, the head bobs up again and he is ready to pick up the shell.

A *hermit crab* takes shelter in a large snail shell, coiling its body inside with only the head and feet projecting.

A top-view of the "umbrella" of the *red jellyfish*. Underneath are long tentacles to capture food.

421

422

A sample of plankton from the water anywhere along the coast would contain great numbers of tiny crustaceans called *copepods*. Their numbers make them valuable as a key link in the long chain of food relationships of the sea, starting with the tiniest microscopic plants, called *diatoms*, and ranging to the largest

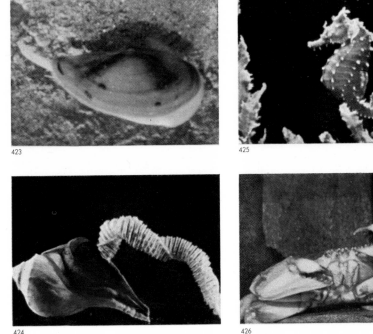

423

425

424

426

The *leaping clam* has a small siphon tube and a large, strong foot to pull himself rapidly through the soft mud.

A *conch snail* with a string of eggs. These peculiar chainlike egg masses can be often seen along the beach.

The unusual shape of the *sea horse* has made him one of the best known of marine animals in spite of his small size.

Many crabs are scavengers and will defend themselves vigorously, as this *rock crab* demonstrates.

fish and whales. They thrive in the cold waters of the North Atlantic and Pacific. Small enough to be barely seen, the commonest form, *calanus,* has a single eye, like Cyclops, in the center of the head and two long antennae which extend back beyond the end of the body.

The next important groups of crustaceans, in increasing order of size, are the *isopods* and *amphipods.* The former are *marine sowbugs,* flattened creatures with many legs, a little suggestive of a centipede in appearance though usually broader in relation to length. These crawl about over seaweed and are primarily scavengers of dead marine animals. One group of isopods has taken to the land, consisting of the *sowbugs* found under stones or rotting logs. Among the amphipods, the *scud* and the *beach fleas* are the most important. Though not very conspicuous, they occur all along the shore. The commoner types in tide pools are the scuds, which are usually under an inch long. In contrast to the isopods, they are narrow of body, compressed together on the sides. They may frequently be seen swimming on their sides across a tide pool with a rapid motion which might easily be confused with the appearance of a small fish.

The *lobster* is one of the most important crustaceans because of its value to man as a source of food. The largest of all the crustaceans, it attains a maximum size of over 30 inches and a weight of 36 pounds. Lobsters have

When the shell becomes too small for the *hermit crab,* he leaves and searches for a larger one to fit his new figure.

Beach fleas feed on rotting seaweed. These tiny creatures are found on sandy beaches, often annoying bathers.

a hard outer shell, called a carapace, which covers the head and thorax, while the abdomen is made up of several segments ending in a wide tail fin used for swimming. There are two large claws, one for holding food and the other with heavy, toothlike ridges used for cutting. These and the muscles which operate the abdomen form the greater part of the meat. Lobsters are scavengers naturally, feeding on all manner of dead life and sometimes capturing living food. Their breeding is similar to that of the crab, involving a period when the eggs are carried externally attached underneath the abdomen and a series of larval molts before the adult stage is reached.

Another interesting animal is the *sea cucumber.* Dark brown in color, the northern sea cucumber moves slowly across the bottom by means of several rows of tube feet. These and the five-parted design make it a relative of the starfish and the *sea urchin,* another *echinoderm.* The spines have been reduced to a series of calcereous plates imbedded in the skin and the body has become elongated and tubular. Around the mouth are several branching tentacles used to gather food. Powerful muscles cause the body to pulsate and take in water which is passed over the gills to supply necessary oxygen. Sometimes when the animal is captured, these muscles extrude much of the digestive tract which has somewhat the appearance of spaghetti. They have remarkable powers of regeneration.

Among the grotesque formations of coral, a host of animals and plants carry on their existence in a colorful pattern. The mere names—*brain, staghorn* and *organpipe*—give some indication of the pattern but no conception of the delicate colors they exhibit. Sponges, anemones, starfish and sea urchins vie with the bizarre shapes and patterns of tropical fish which glide among the protecting caverns of the coral itself.

Along the sandy shores and mud flats of the region south of Cape Cod to the coast of Florida the conditions of life are different from those of the rocky shores of the North Atlantic, the headlands of the Pacific coast or the coral reefs of the tropics. The beaches, the pounding surf and the shifting sands create a veritable desert as far as marine life is concerned. Only those few animals and plants which can gain a permanent foothold are able to survive these extreme conditions. Kick aside a mat of decaying seaweed and a swarm of beach fleas jump about in mad confusion. They are amphipod crustaceans, similar to the scud found skimming cross tide pools.

Except for the snails and hermit crabs, which are well armored, the animals which live here seek protection by burrowing down beneath the surface and extending their siphons, or tentacles, up to the water when the tide covers the land, drawing in their food and oxygen while they hide unobserved in the darkness underneath. There are two groups of animals which predominate in this type of habitat: the *bivalve molluscs* and the *worms.*

The bivalve molluscs are among the most important food resources of the shallow sea, including the *oyster, soft* and *hard-shelled clams,* and the *scallops,* as well as the mussels. The oyster varies from the usual pattern of these creatures in having no foot and the two valves of the shell unsymmetrical. It attaches to some solid object on the bottom and grows there, secreting a shell which is tightly affixed to it. Their breeding potential is fantastic; a single female may produce over 60 million eggs!

The clam burrows into the sand with the muscular foot and lies entirely buried except for the siphon tube which extends up to a small hole at the surface. Water is taken in through this tube and food and oxygen extracted from it as it passes through the body. Then it returns through a second tube, the excurrent siphon, to the outside. Living in the soft mud of the bottom is the *leaping clam* whose method of locomotion is quite unusual. The long foot is extended forward out of the shell and the tip is flared out like a fan. Then it is withdrawn, pulling the clam along with a leaping motion from which it derives its name. Similarly, the *razor clam,* so named from its resemblance to an old-fashioned straight razor, when placed on the sand, will use its foot to lift itself upright and then rapidly disappear under the surface.

At low tide the *kelp* and other *seaweeds* lie flat on the rocks. When the tide comes in, these seaweeds move about in the water, and many animals which seek shelter beneath them start to move around and look for food.

429

The bivalve which has learned to make use of jet propulsion for motive power is the scallop. It can swim rapidly through the water by opening and closing the two valves, forcing water out with a sudden snapping motion as the shell is closed, and thus propelling itself along over the bottom. Scallops have well developed eyes along the edge of the mantle, which look like tiny, steel-blue dots at the inner margin of the shell. The single strong adductor muscle is the only part of the scallop which is eaten.

In the same habitat, two other unusual creatures are found. One is the *sand dollar,* a relative of the sea urchin, the body flattened and the spines reduced to a very small size. They crawl slowly over the sand or mud, picking up bits of organic matter for food. The second is the *king,* or *horseshoe crab.* This unique creature, with his heavy covering of chitinous armor plate and long spiny tail, plows his way over the sand, digging up small crustaceans and worms. In structure, he seems to be part way between the crustaceans, because of the nature of the feet and claws, and the spiders, which he resembles in having platelike gill-books on the abdomen.

Many kinds of worms are found along the ocean, representing four different phyla or major groups. The most highly developed and varied in habits are the segmented worms, or *annelida,* of which the common *earthworm* is a well-known example. Sea worms occupy many habitats but are most abundant in sand and mud flats. In tide pools might be found the tiny *spiral tube worm,* which builds a limy case less than an eighth of an inch across, attached to seaweed, rocks or shells, and the *scale worm* with overlapping plates on his back. The *sand worm* is one of the most common of mud dwellers. It grows quite large, sometimes over a foot in length. Along the sides of the worm, projecting from each segment, are appendages called "parapodia", with fin-like structures used for swimming or burrowing. It also contains blood vessels, and through them is absorbed the necessary oxygen.

Interesting life may be found on and around wharves, jetties and pilings, especially at low tide. Seaweeds, hydroids and bryozoans abound, along with anemones, snails and sea slugs, and the marine equivalent of the termite known as the *shipworm* or *teredo.* Actually the shipworm is a species of clam which has learned how to use the front edge of the two shells to dig and burrow into wood.

Another animal often associated with this kind of habitat is a *tunicate.* These creatures, primitive relatives of the vertebrates, start out in life as if they were going to be quite well developed. But they later degenerate and secrete a heavy sheath or tunic about the body, attach themselves to a surface, and take in food through the openings or pores. Because of their habit of squirting water through these pores, they are known as *sea squirts.*

Coral reefs harbor bizarre species, one of them the *sea horse,* with its strange shape and prehensile tail. The males incubate the young. The eggs are attached to a pouch on the under side of the body and are carried there until they hatch.

The seaside is a vital storehouse, filled with a great number of useful products, and a place where the student of its life may find creatures of striking beauty and others whose habits and life histories are fascinating.

430

Falconers are accused of depleting the
population of *peregrine hawks.*

BIRDS OF PREY

Have you ever seen a *peregrine falcon* go into a "power dive" after a
starling . . . or watched a *marsh hawk* course over a meadow and suddenly pounce upon an unsuspecting *mouse?* Perhaps you have been privi-
leged to sight a *horned owl* gliding silently through a dark woodland in search
of an unwary *rabbit* . . . or you may have seen a *snowy owl* patrolling a beach,
its great yellow eyes agleam with hunger after a trip from the Arctic. Woe to
the *muskrat* it lights upon!

These are typical snapshots of birds of prey earning their living. What was
your feeling toward them while you read these brief descriptions of their
everyday habits? Did you think of them with distaste, as robbers, assassins,
murderers? Many people do.

Let us put some of our "good" and "bad" birds on trial.

211

431

Fewer than 1,000 pairs of *bald eagles* may be left in the U.S. They are often mistaken for a large hawk and shot.

To start, what is a bird of prey—or a predator, to use the scientist's term? Simply defined, the word means "a creature that lives by preying upon and devouring other animals".

Let's name a few. You say that's easy—a cruel hawk swooping upon and seizing a harmless *song sparrow* for its dinner! But what about the cruel *robin* that tugs a harmless *earthworm* out of the lawn to fill the yawning mouths of its nestlings? And if we must admit that the robin is a predatory bird, we must do the same for the *bluebird, mockingbird, Baltimore oriole* and many more of the "good" birds. They all live, wholly or partly, upon the bodies of the worms, grubs, insects and other animal life that they kill. By definition, many songbirds are predators—although we apply the term mostly to eagles, hawks, vultures, and owls.

Why do we label these particular groups of birds as gangs of criminals, and often destroy them as enemies? Isn't it because we delight in imposing our human moral standards upon wild life? It is wrong for a man to kill a man; therefore, we reason, it must be wrong for a bird to kill a bird.

212

We cannot expect song sparrows to match our human system—to breed insects systematically for their food! They must hunt, kill and eat their insect food where they can find it. If the natural enemies of song sparrows, such as *sharp-shinned hawks,* are reduced or eliminated, there may be too many sparrows competing for a limited food supply. This means that some of them will have to go. Nature's controls, other than predators, are starvation and disease. Doesn't this indicate that we should look with understanding eyes upon the woodland drama in which a sharp-shinned hawk captures a song sparrow in flight and snuffs out its life in an instant?

One of the leading conservation philosophers of our day, Dr. Irston Barnes, President of the Audubon Society of the District of Columbia, expresses his views on this subject of man's ethics and nature's laws in a most convincing way:

"In the world of nature," he says, "there are no good and bad birds. Each animal is chained by countless centuries of evolution to an instinctive pattern of behavior, the most basic of which pertains to the food it eats and the manner of its capture. Thus a hawk is powerless to alter its tastes or its manners. This dictate of nature assures that each form of life shall fulfill its destiny, that no chaos of individual choices shall destroy nature's balance of resources, and that no essential job shall be left undone. The very fact that a form of life exists is clear testimony to its rightness; each form has its essential role in a healthy wildlife community."

432

A hawk soars over his farmyard and the man with the hoe rushes for his trusty shooting-iron. . . . A hunter roaming the October woods flushes a horned owl that has been dozing in a tree. He shoots it and congratulates himself upon having dispatched a "fierce and vicious" killer that he fancies is directly competing with him for grouse and other game. By what logic it is "vicious" for a horned owl to kill a rabbit, but an act of rugged sportsmanship when the deed is done by a man? A rancher surveying his grazing lands from a plane

Because they do such good sanitation work, *African vultures* are never molested and have become quite tame.

Man-made nesting boxes, if large enough, are quite acceptable to the handsome *kestrel hawk.*

433

213

434

435

Goshawks come to the States at 9 to 11 year intervals when prey is scarce on their northern breeding grounds.

These young *horned owls* are fed everything from rodents and insects to snakes and even skunks!

spots a *golden eagle* wheeling gracefully, his gaze intent upon a ground squirrel that would make a succulent meal. The rancher recalls lurid tales of eagle depredations upon livestock, so he shoulders his gun and draws a bead; the great golden bird plummets earthward. The man in the plane did not thrill to the magnificent powers of flight of the eagle, far more wondrous than those of his mechanical bird. Obviously he would not agree with naturalist Olaus Murie that a dead eagle is both an economic and a spiritual loss.

Then there are the "bird lovers" who put out feeding stations and proceed cheerfully to commit mayhem on all the "bad" birds that are attracted. They apparently feel the Creator slipped up a bit when He gave us starlings, jays, hawks, owls, vultures and other predators.

Hawks and owls have never had an easy life. Both groups have been persecuted widely, hawks more so than owls. Hawks are day-flying birds, and most of the owls are nocturnal, so man is less aware of their activities.

Game farms produce abnormal concentrations of birds in open pens completely lacking in escape cover such as briar patches and shrubbery. This situation allows even the slowest of hawks to dine on birds that are usually too swift for them to capture in a natural environment. Many a gamekeeper makes his generalizations about predation from the highly artificial situation he creates on his game farm.

In recent times game managers discovered that the key to wildlife abundance is food and cover. They found that under normal conditions predators exert a negligible influence in determining the abundance of game. They pointed out that in some instances predators actually aid the game by helping to control the populations of rodents which sometimes prey upon the eggs and young of game birds. They stated, too, that predators are responsible for developing alertness and speed in game species, characteristics that make them of interest to sportsmen.

Sportsmen's organizations which not long ago found it impossible to say

214

anything good about the birds of prey are now speaking up in their defense and urging their members not to kill them indiscriminately. Ducks Unlimited has gone to the expense of publishing a bulletin on hawks. It concludes with this statement: "Unless any of them (hawks) are doing harm to you, let them go their way in peace. They have their place in nature and have their appeal to all those who appreciate beauty and adaptation to their mode of life. Do not allow your sympathies for their prey to turn your heart and hand against them. There is more in this Predator-Prey relationship than meets the eye. Dame Nature fitted them for their role and she is a wise old Dame and knows what she is doing. Don't forget that you, Mr. Man, are the greatest predator of them all, and a wanton destroyer if ever there was one."

Until we invent some sort of atomic blast that will eliminate rodents but not men, we will need the predators to help keep the rodents in check. One pair of meadow mice could be responsible for one million relatives within a year's time if their fecundity was not disturbed. Nature has wisely provided controls for the mouse population. Not only the birds of prey, but a wide variety of mammals, eat mice as staple food.

A surprising amount of predation on game birds and songbirds, as well as other creatures, is upon what biologists call "surplus populations"—in other words, individuals that cannot be supported by the environment and which in most instances would perish whether eaten by the flesh-eaters or not. The web of life in the out-of-doors is such a complicated one that the natural forces of nature rather than mathematics must be relied upon.

436

Because public sentiment usually lags considerably behind scientific research, it is not surprising that legal protection for the birds of prey has been slow in coming. Hawks, owls, eagles and vultures were omitted when most birds were extended protection by the Migratory Bird Treaty between Great Britain and the United States in 1918 and also in the Convention with Mexico in 1936. However, all but eight states

Shrikes usually live in open country where they raise four to six young.

A *shrike* eats insects mostly, but will sometimes impale mice and small birds for a future snack.

437

215

438

The *California condor* is a living link with the Ice Age. Only 60 still fight against extinction. Any intruder within a half-mile will alert this bird.

have laws which protect at least some of the hawks, owls and eagles. Most states exempt the *accipters* or so-called "bird hawks" from protection. This has resulted in very little attempt at enforcing the laws because, generally speaking, the only persons who can distinguish between the protected and unprotected hawks are those who would not shoot them anyway.

Recognition of the weaknesses of present legislation has resulted in the development of considerable sentiment for protection of all hawks and owls. So far only two states and one province have taken this bold step—Connecticut, Michigan, and Alberta—but others are pondering it. A clause in such legislation, permitting the taking of protected birds by the farmer on his own property when such birds are in the act of doing actual damage, protects the land-owner who may suffer from the depredations of those few individual hawks that develop a taste for poultry.

It is generally recognized that a high percentage of North American hawks from widely scattered areas are funneled into fairly narrow flight lanes during migrations. Thus, wholesale slaughter of hawks at vantage points along their flyways, due to absence of protecting laws in adjourning states, can

439

This *red-tailed hawk* is a masterly glider. Soaring
for hours over farming country, he makes an easy
target for farmers and sportsmen.

nullify much of the protection these birds receive on their breeding grounds.

Some conservationists are advocating that all hawks be protected during
migrations (September 1 to November 30 and March 1 to April 30) by an
Act of Congress. This would be comparable to the federal statute which
protects the *bald eagle* at all times. Except during migrations, hawks would
continue to be under the jurisdiction of state laws.

Discovery of a hawk slaughtering ground on a lookout in the Kittatinny
Mountains of Pennsylvania led to the establishment in 1934 of the Hawk
Mountain Sanctuary near Allentown where once shooters killed and maimed
hundreds of hawks and eagles every week-end during migration.

Other famous hawk-watching locations are Cape May in New Jersey, and
Duluth, Minnesota, where great numbers of hawks swing down the north
shore of Lake Superior and come right over the city.

There can be no doubt that the tide is turning in favor of the birds of
prey. Bishop Robert W. Hatch of Connecticut, who admits that he once
classified all hawks as "big chicken hawks" or "little chicken hawks" has
written this eloquent expression of his "conversion":

440

441

442

"To me the hawk is the supreme expression of the amazing orchestra of nature, from which no note can be subtracted without serious consequence to man himself. Hawks are an integral part of that orchestra, as well as an expression of its vast score of checks and balances. They are important to us. When we destroy them, through ignorance or sentimentality, we release an army of other creatures, like rodents and insects, which was never meant to be released. It would be crass, however, to think of them only in terms of economics. Far more significant are their beauty, their expression of wildness in an age which has lost touch with the God-created things of this earth."

Vultures are big black birds, which characteristically soar in wide circles in the sky. Their naked heads are small for the size of the bird, as contrasted with the much larger heads of hawks and eagles. Also in this family are the *turkey vulture, black vulture,* and *California condor.*

The black vulture is largely confined to the South, but the turkey vulture may be found in the northern states and even into Canada, though it is nowhere common in the north.

These huge birds soar for hours at

No wonder *barn owls* are called "monkey-faced"! The grown male will bring rats to the female incubating her eggs.

Young *saw-whet owls* can be picked off their branch! They will keep their brown plumage all summer long.

The *saw-whet* is only eight inches long, but as fearless as he is small. He is named for his strange cry.

218

These nearly adult *barn owls* are aptly termed "living mouse traps". They have a huge appetite for rodents.

The *osprey* is an aerial fisherman who provides better sport for the angler by eating stunted fish.

Is a *Cooper's hawk* "bad" because he kills to live? Individuals may prey on poultry—but many do not.

443

a time, utilizing thermals that make it possible for them to glide without seeming to move a feather. They have a 6-foot wing-spread. When flying, the outer wing feathers are separated like the fingers of a hand.

The turkey vulture's plumage is rusty black, its head and neck being bare. The exposed skin is red. Vultures have weak bills and feet, hence usually are incapable of killing live animals. Virtually all of their food is carrion—dead livestock or wildlife.

The turkey vulture breeds from the Gulf of Mexico north to western Connecticut, western New York, and northern Minnesota. It winters from southern New Jersey and the Ohio valley southward.

African vultures soaring overhead are often the first indication to a traveler in Africa that a native village is at hand. These small vultures are tame because they are never molested in view of their sanitation work.

One of the most fascinating of African birds is the *secretary bird*. It stands about three feet tall and has a wing span of seven feet. Stalking through the bush, the secretary bird captures *snakes, scorpions, lizards*

444

445

219

Audubon's caracara is depicted on the Mexican flag and may be seen in Florida and Texas with its black crest.

The hooting of the *horned owl* is often a hair-raising sound and a threat to many wild creatures.

and *rats,* which it kills by stamping on them.

The *giant California condor* is a link with the Ice Age. It has existed through eons of time down to the present. Unfortunately there are only about 60 survivors of this fascinating species and they are located in the mountains of Southern California. The last stronghold of the birds is in the Los Padres National Forest where a sanctuary was established for them in 1947 by the U.S. Forest Service.

Condors nest in niches in rugged rock cliffs and do not breed until they are four or five years old. Normally they do not nest more often than every other year, probably because a young condor must be fed and cared for by its parents until it is more than one year old. Only about five young condors have been raised to flying maturity annually in recent years. This has just about compensated for the death of adult condors, so the population has not varied materially.

The condor has a greater wingspread—8½ feet to 10½ feet—than any other North American bird.

Kites resemble *falcons,* except that the wide wings of the *Everglade kite* are more like those of a *buteo.* Generally they have long, narrow wings and airy, graceful flight. The kite family consist of the *white-tailed kite, swallow-tailed kite, Mississippi kite,* and *Everglade kite.*

Florida's Everglade kite is the third rarest bird in America, ranking behind the *whooping crane* and California condor. There may be fewer than 100 Everglade kites in Florida, the only state where they occur.

The Everglade kite probably has more specialized feeding habits than any other North American bird. It eats only fresh-water snails of the genus *ampullaria.* To search out these snails the kite flies low over its marsh habitat. Most if not all of the remaining Everglade kites in Florida live in the Lake Okeechobee marshes. In the fall they make easy targets for those duck hunters who find the going a bit dull and have little hesitation about exercising their marksmanship on any hawk-like bird that comes over.

Illegal shooting alone is not responsible for the Everglade kites' decline, however. Once fairly common in Florida, much of its habitat has been ruined by extensive drainage. When the snails are destroyed by drying up of their marsh homes, the kites must move elsewhere. Often there has been nowhere to go and they have perished. Fluctuation in the water level of Lake Okeechobee may yet exterminate the snails and the kites as well.

Accipiters are swift-flying hawks with short, rounded wings and long tails. They are usually found in woodlands and do not often soar. Accipiters are sometimes called "blue darters" because of their astonishingly rapid flight.

The *goshawk,* largest of the accipiters, is bold and defiant. It migrates southward into the States in numbers at 9 to 11 year intervals. These "invasions" apparently coincide with a shortage of prey on its northern breeding grounds.

The goshawk breeds mainly in Canada from Newfoundland and Alaska southward to the northern United States.

The *sharp-shin* is a remarkable bird. It feeds mostly on small birds, often sparrows or warblers. It also captures small mammals on occasion.

Usually it nests in an evergreen and is quite common in the extensive wild woodlands of eastern Canada. Birds from this area are seen in considerable numbers as they migrate southward along the hawk flyways.

Bird watchers sometimes have trouble separating the sharp-shin from the *Cooper's hawk.* The latter, however, is considerably larger and has a rounded tail in contrast to the square tail of the sharp-shin.

The sharp-shinned hawk breeds throughout all temperate and subarctic North America; it winters, after migration, from British Columbia, Iowa, and the Great Lakes, southward to Panama.

The Cooper's hawk is an enlarged edition of the sharp-shin. As with all accipiters, its typical flight is four or five flaps and a glide. The Cooper's hawk perches out of sight in a tree and waits for a bird or small mammal to come along. Because of its secretive habits, even bird watchers do not often see it.

Cooper's Hawks often are responsible for losses of chickens for which the more conspicuous soaring hawks are blamed. However, individuals of almost any of the larger hawks may develop poultry-taking habits. Therefore, it stands to reason that *individual* hawks should be controlled where necessary to protect poultry, but that hawks should never be killed just because they belong to a certain species.

The Cooper's hawk breeds from southern Canada south to Florida, the Gulf Coast, and northern part of Mexico.

The most conspicuous hawks are the *buteos.* They are good-sized, with

Adult *condors* care for their young for over a year. They cannot breed until they are five or six years old!

448

221

449

450

Rabbits and other small animals are brought to the *golden eagle's* eyrie to feed their ravenous youngsters.

The *white gyrfalcon* is a powerful flyer who will sortie into our northern states from its Arctic home during winter.

broad wings and fan-like tails. They frequent the open countryside where they usually may be seen soaring overhead.

The buteos are *red-tailed, Harlan's hawk, red-shouldered hawk, broad-winged hawk, Swainson's hawk, short-tailed hawk, rough-legged hawk, ferruginous rough-legged hawk,* and *Knider's hawk.*

When one sees a large, broad-winged hawk with a fan-like tail soaring slowly in the sky, the chances are good that it may be a red-tail. There is no distinct banding on the under side of the tail, and when the hawk banks so that the sun reflects the brilliant rusty red of its tail, we are then certain of our identification.

The reason this bird is called a "hen hawk" is that it frequently is seen in farming country, but the description is inaccurate because the red-tail seldom takes poultry.

The red-tail's beauty and its mastery of the air should be enough to win it friends. Anyone who has watched it spiral from one column of air to another cannot help but sense its grace and color.

Some red-tailed hawks are very dark, such as the *Harlan's hawk,* which is virtually black. Others are extremely pale, like the *Krider's hawk,* which is nearly white. Even in the various races of the red-tailed hawk there are individuals that have erratic coloration.

Crows often harass the red-tails, but they keep just out of reach of the hawks' long claws, for they seem to realize that they might suffer if the hawks became overly annoyed by their attentions.

Red-shouldered hawks will live in built-up areas if they are not persecuted. They particularly like wet woodlands and river bottoms and are often found in farming country.

The three eggs take nearly a month to hatch. The hawks may often be seen perched on the lower branches of trees near water areas. From these vantage points they make quick forays for mice, shrews, crayfish and frogs. The red-shoulder is very fond of insects; in fact, they make up a major part of its diet.

Those capable mimics, the *blue jays,* can imitate the red-shoulder's call to perfection. Until you get on to this ruse you may think that red-shouldered hawks have suddenly become very numerous.

The red-shouldered hawk breeds from Nova Scotia, southern Quebec, and Ontario south to Florida and the Gulf of Mexico and west to the Great Plains.

Eagles resemble the buteos or "buzzard hawks" but they are much larger and have longer wings. The *bald eagle,* our national emblem, and the *golden eagle* are the two widely-distributed eagles of North America.

451

Golden eagles may be seen occasionally in the east but they are typically birds of the west. Except at close range it is not possible to see the golden head feathers which give this eagle its name. It appears to be dark all over except for some white at the base of the tail.

Golden eagles are widely distributed over about half the globe. They prefer rugged, mountainous country with open stretches for hunting. They take a variety of prey—ground squirrels, rabbits, woodchucks and other small mammals. They will take larger mammals on occasion, including skunks and raccoons, as well as birds. Some golden eagles develop the habit of eating young lambs or pigs, but according to careful studies of their food habits, this is rare and is no excuse for persecuting all of them. They also eat a good deal of carrion. Many observers, seeing an eagle feasting on a deer or a lamb, will assume that the bird killed it, whereas it likely was dead when

452

Often dubbed "chicken hawk", the *red-tail* dines chiefly on small rodents found on its long hunting flights.

These small *screech owls* come in two colors: rufous brown or a gray. They once were considered as ill omens.

Though mainly southerners, you see *turkey vultures* up north, identified by the upward arc of the wings.

453

223

454

Looking like white ghosts, *snowy owls* come southward in search of food. Their lovely plumage makes them highly prized.

the eagle arrived. The same thing is true of a great many other birds and mammals that eat carrion on occasion. Because pheasant feathers are found around a fox den does not necessarily mean that the fox killed the pheasant. He may have found the corpse waiting for him on a highway.

Golden eagles usually nest on cliff ledges or in tall trees. Most species of birds defend what is known as a breeding territory. They drive off other birds of their own kind. Doubtless this is nature's way of preventing depletion of food supply. The golden eagles defend a much larger territory than most birds, the average being about 36 square miles. They will fight off any other golden eagles that are found in "their" territory and may even harry hawks and owls on occasion.

There has been a good deal of publicity about the shooting of golden eagles from airplanes in Texas and certain other western states. One airplane hunter boasts that he has downed 512 of these great birds. Ranchers pay for the time of the airplane hunters and there is every indication that the depredations of the eagles have been greatly exaggerated, perhaps deliberately by those who wish to collect the bounty for shooting them.

It is estimated that the present population of our national emblem, the bald eagle, in the United States is less than 1,000 pairs. Many eagles can be seen on coins and seals, but unfortunately the living bird is now rare. Its major stronghold in the United States is in Florida, but even there, extensive development has eliminated many favorite eagle haunts.

It takes about four years for a young bald eagle to develop its distinctive white head and tail. Until that time it is often mistaken for a large hawk or perhaps a golden eagle. With millions of gunners afield who know little about bird identification, it is perhaps surprising that any eagles survive rather than that a number are killed each year. The sad fact is that only a few pairs of eagles now remain in areas where once they were fairly common. It is to be hoped that we will never have to follow the example of Finland which erected a monument on the site where the last *Finnish sea eagle* nested.

Bald eagles are believed to mate for life, though if one dies another mate is usually found. Normally the same nest is used year after year, new material being added each season. A huge nest in Ohio measured 12 feet in depth and 8½ feet across the top. When it finally collapsed of its own weight, two tons of debris were deposited on the ground.

Fish is the bald eagle's favorite food. One of the dramatic sights of the out-of-doors is to watch an eagle pursue an osprey with a fish and force the smaller bird to drop its prey. The eagle then plunges earthward and often captures the fish before it hits the water. Eagles occasionally eat ducks that are wounded or victims of lead poisoning.

455

Only representative of the *harriers* in North America is the *marsh hawk*. It breeds in meadows and marshes from the Gulf of St. Lawrence to the Gulf of Mexico. The marsh hawk's long, pointed wings, long tail, white rump patch, and its habit of skimming low over farmland and marsh make it easy to identify.

Ospreys are highly specialized fish-eating hawks. There is only one species, which includes five subspecies but they are all very widely distrib-

Proof that *snowy owls* are good scavengers and should be protected are these rat bone piles around their nests.

The *African secretary bird's* long, delicate looking legs belie their real function—that of killing its prey.

456

457

458

It's fun to turn detective and find out what *owls* eat—these clean, odorless pellets solve the mystery.

The "singing" *red-shouldered hawk* is a sure harbinger of spring. A highpitched call earned his nickname.

uted throughout both hemispheres.

The osprey is always associated with water, though is not fussy whether it be seacoast, lake, or stream. When it sights a fish, an osprey plunges into the water, sometimes almost disappearing from sight to capture its prey. There are a few records of ospreys having sunk their talons into fish that were too large for them. The birds were pulled under and drowned.

Casual bird watchers often confuse the osprey with the bald eagle. There should be no mistaking the two species, however, since the osprey's whole breast is white, whereas the white on the eagle is limited to its head and tail.

Perhaps because of their regal bearing and their resemblance to eagles, ospreys are usually protected by state law and public sentiment, whereas other hawks and fish-eating birds often find that persecution is their lot. The osprey feeds mainly on fish that are not desired for commercial or sport purposes, as is true of most fish-eating birds.

The range of the osprey is almost world-wide. In the western hemisphere it breeds from Newfoundland and northwestern Alaska south to the Bahamas and to western Mexico. It breeds in most of Europe, Asia, Australia, and northern Africa.

Anatomically the *caracaras* are closely related to the true falcons but otherwise they are more like the vultures. They are long-legged and sluggish in their movements.

The caracara's domain is the prairie. It prefers open country where palms or yuccas are available for nest sites. It is a more attractive bird than the black or turkey vultures. It is easy to identify with its conspicuous white patches on the neck and breast and its contrasting black cap. It usually flies near to the ground, but sometimes soars in characteristic vulture fashion. If no carrion is available, the caracara will readily eat snakes, lizards, frogs, etc.

Audubon's caracara is the national emblem of Mexico. It graces the country's official seal. The bird is depicted with a rattlesnake in its mouth.

The *falcons* are speedy and handsome. They have long tails and long, pointed wings. Their wing-strokes are rapid and they seldom soar. Falcons include the *gyrfalcon, prairie falcon, peregrine falcon, merlin,* and *kestrel.*

The peregrine is one of the fastest flyers in the bird world. It has been clocked at 175 miles an hour in a dive. It is truly master of the air and apparently is able to capture any prey that it fancies. Usually the victim is taken in the air. Sometimes, especially with larger birds, the prey is hit with the peregrine's strong feet and knocked to the ground where it is captured.

Birds are the peregrine's usual diet, but the species vary from jays and meadowlarks to plovers and small mammals, depending upon area.

In the wild, peregrine falcons are partial to cliff ledges as nesting sites; hence they are usually found in rugged terrain, often along sea-coasts, though river gorges and other locations are not uncommon. Their distribution throughout the world seems erratic and unplanned.

Although peregrines usually are associated with wild areas, they have no hesitancy about nesting on skyscrapers in the hearts of great cities where they pursue pigeons and starlings down man-made canyons.

Although falconers will train other hawks, their favorite is the peregrine. Falconry has often been described as the "sport of kings" and was practiced in medieval times. An elaborate ritual surrounds the sport and the falcons are hooded during training.

In the United States falconry is a controversial pastime. Some bird protectionists accuse the falconers of being responsible for the decline of the peregrine population, asserting that aeries are consistently robbed and that adult birds are live-trapped to supply the demand of falconry practitioners. The falconers usually admit that some of their followers are over-zealous and indiscreet but they deny most of the charges, saying that they are among the staunchest supporters that the hawks have and that their birds either escape or are released after a year or two.

The gyrfalcon is a rare visitor to the United States. It occurs in black, gray, and white color phases. It is larger than the peregrine but very similar to it in appearance.

Grasshopper hawk would be a more appropriate name for the *sparrow hawk.* The American settlers named it after the sparrow hawk of Europe with which it has less in common than with the *kestrel* of Europe. *American kestrel* is a good name. Kestrels may often be observed as they perch on utility wires from which they dart to capture their small prey. The kestrel is just a little larger than a robin and many casual observers fail to realize that it is a hawk. It is often found in built-up areas.

Kestrels may often be observed hovering like a helicopter over their hunting grounds, watching intently

The *sharp-shinned hawk* feeds mostly on small animals, sparrows and warblers.

459

460

Much persecuted, the *golden eagle* deserves a better break. Hunters often kill off breeding stock.

for insects and mice which are captured in their curved claws. The pointed wings and long tail identify this species as a falcon. The red color of the tail and its small size distinguish it from the other falcons.

The sparrow hawk breeds in tree cavities and nest boxes from Florida and the Gulf of Mexico north to Newfoundland, southern Quebec, and Saskatchewan.

Let's turn now to the owl. Owls are characterized by large heads and eyes, facial discs, chunky bodies, and upright perching position. Most of them are night-hunters and their flight is noiseless because the soft edges of the wing feathers muffle the sound of the wingbeats. An owl's eyes are fixed in their sockets, but its neck is very flexible, allowing it to about-face quickly. The iris can be quickly expanded, permitting it to utilize every bit of light in the night woods. This iris contracts in the daytime, but an owl can see perfectly well by day.

Anyone can find out what owls eat by examining the pellets that they regurgitate or spit up. These neat little bundles contain the indigestible portions of the creatures they consume—bones and feathers tightly packed in an outer layer of fur.

There are 18 species of owls in North America. They vary from the *elf owl* of the southwest, about the size of an *English sparrow,* to the *great gray owl* of Canada, measuring 27 inches long.

Barn owls are often called *monkey-faced owls* and anyone who has seen one will agree that the nickname is appropriate. These long-legged birds appear almost white in flight. They like open country and eat whatever rodents are most common, whether they be ground squirrels, mice, rats, or others. They sometimes take over church belfries or nest in barns, tree cavities, abandoned buildings, or caves.

Young barn owls are covered with white down and have a ludicrous appearance. When they are 50 to 60 days old they leave the nest for the first time. The parents, however, continue to feed them for more than a month. Barn owls eat thousands of rodents and only a few small birds.

Because most owls are creatures of the night, many superstitions about them have developed. Most of these have their origins in early times. Fortunately for the *screech owl,* it is better regarded today. It is the best known of all our North American owls and is the only small owl that has ear tufts.

The screech owl comes in two colors: a rufous brown, and gray. These are color phases and have no relation to the age or sex of the bird. An individual does not change its color.

Screech owls occur in open woodlands, orchards and towns. They usually nest in tree cavities, but will accept bird houses if they are large enough and if sawdust is placed on the floor.

The tremulous, screeching whistle of the screech owl is distinctive and is quite different from the calls of other owls.

Screech owls are not fussy about their diet and will eat everything from moths and frogs to birds and bats. They are very bold in defending their nests and have been known to knock off the hats of passers-by.

"Tiger of the air" and "Bubo, the executioner" are two of the colorful titles that have been applied to the *horned owl.* This is one of the most magnificent of all wild birds.

From 18 to 25 inches in length, this is the largest of our "tufted" owls. Like most predators, it takes whatever food is most abundant and easily available. Usually this means rodents, with a variation of insects, snakes, wild birds and poultry. Now and then it will capture domestic cats, skunks, and even *barred owls.*

Horned owls do not build their own nests but take over the abandoned nests of other birds such as red-tailed hawks and herons.

About every four winters bird watchers in the United States and

The fluctuation of one lake level might exterminate the *Everglade kites* in the U.S. by destroying its food—snails.

461

462

Owls, contrary to popular belief, aren't blind by day but they usually hunt at night when their eyesight is superb.

Canada are treated to a *snowy owl* invasion. Snowy owls are large white birds that are abroad during the daytime and therefore are very conspicuous. They are most often seen along seacoasts and lake shores. Because they are big and spectacular and make handsome trophies, many of them are shot each winter when they migrate south in numbers.

The *saw-whet owl* is the most diminutive of all northern owls, being only eight inches long. A beautiful little bird, it is seldom seen even in areas where it is fairly common because it is so completely nocturnal. It gets its name from its call, which sounds like the filing of a saw.

A NOTE ON NATURE
COLOR PHOTOGRAPHY

Sᴵɴᴄᴇ ɴᴀᴛᴜʀᴇ is the whole wide universe in which we live, a nature photograph can, conceivably, be of almost anything—a star galaxy, a magnification of a virus taken through the electron microscope—or a pansy in your own back yard. Thus, of necessity, this discussion is limited to the type of nature photographs found in this volume.

It is, of course, also influenced by the character of the author's experience both as an editor and as a photographer. I have spent nearly twenty-five years in the graphic arts business in positions that necessitated the purchasing and judging of photography, both black-and-white and color. As an editor I have been one of the guiding hands in the Audubon Nature Program since its inception and most of the color photographs in this volume have passed under my scrutiny before being purchased. Our objective in the Audubon Nature Program has been to buy color nature photographs, taken from life, that would reproduce well when printed in sizes not larger than 4 by 5 inches which is the largest size we could conveniently use. My photographic experience has been intensive during the last three years but has been admittedly confined to color photography with small size cameras. Thus I have been concerned largely with photography intended for photo-mechanical reproduction, which of course rules out photographs taken primarily for projection or salon prints.

This brings me to the first point I wish to make. The effectiveness of a color photograph cannot be judged entirely by its reproduction. Obviously, if you shoot the Grand Canyon on 35 mm. film, the only way you'll ever see it again in anywhere near the same scale is to project the film on as large a screen as possible. When a vast scene of this sweep is reproduced in small size its meaning and impact are practically lost.

This is a lesson we learned early in the program and for this reason the majority of the pictures chosen have been close-ups. A single camellia (356) filling a negative does more to reveal the character as well as the color of the flower than a wide angle shot of a whole field of flowers (190) which ends up on a printing plate as so many dots of color.

This is also the reason why we have shown so many small objects larger than they exist in life. Few people have ever stopped to study and admire the unusual design of a single caraway seed (45)—yet you'll see one here magnified nearly ten times. A similar close-up of the teeth on the edge of a blade of sawgrass (265) taken with a 35 mm. lens on a Leica with the bellows at full extension (exposure factor nearly 45x) is an instance of extreme close-up photography without the use of a microscope.

There are many other good close-ups in this volume that emphasize the second point I would like to make which is also one of the guiding principles governing the selection of pictures for the Audubon Nature Program. Confined as we were to the book page and a small format, we deliberately sought the interesting detail pictures that people rarely saw, or overlooked because they required close observation and even magnification to reveal their character and beauty. In this connection we have tried to reproduce subjects that are not to be found in the usual nature guide, so that this volume and the program as a whole would gain in value by the wealth of original material reproduced in color for the first time.

This demand on our part for close-ups of living subjects (there are not more than half a dozen museum shots in the book) has forced our contributing photographers to use the latest advanced photographic techniques to give us pictures with the qualities of significant color, good detail in both shadow and highlight, adequate depth of field and fully stopped action, to say nothing of interesting composition and color variety in group selections.

Because so many devotees of nature are also camera enthusiasts, and because we have often been asked how to take the type of color photograph that is used in the Audubon Nature Program, I would like to list the qualities, as we see them, that are needed for a good nature color shot—a shot taken for reproduction—and give a brief outline of the equipment and techniques generally used.

First, it might be well to explain to the technically minded that the color plates made for the Audubon Nature Program were, in the first few months, 120-line screen letter-press (example—Camouflage in Nature). Later, we went to a 133-line screen (Favorite Wildflowers). Then we tried 133-line offset (Life in the Everglades) and finally settled on 150-line offset (Seeds and Seed Pods), which is now our standard method of reproduction. This book is printed by offset lithography, but the earlier coarse screens have not been remade. Where subjects from these earlier plates have been included, we have photographed the dots from the black-and-white reproduction proofs, and thereby converted the letter-press plates to offset. This word of explanation is simply to explain the subtle variations of printing quality to be discerned on close examination. A study of these variations with a screen finder, in relation to the subject matter photographed, will prove a valuable lesson to those dealing in the graphic arts and interested in reproducing transparencies having a wealth of fine small details. The search for a perfect solution to this problem is never ending, and the day may yet come when we'll be able to do long-run mass printing, without a screen, and with the colors in perfect register—which is what you have when you look through a good clear color transparency.

Now, as to the qualities needed in a good color shot, would it be laboring the obvious to say that color is of first importance? I would go so far as to say *significant* color. Everything has color to some extent, but significant color

232

implies that the color in the picture has meaning. There are many photographs taken to reveal design, structure and function that can better be taken in black and white, and even still better revealed by a line drawing. The color camera is not the last word, nor is it an all-seeing eye. It is often extremely limited, particularly in stopping action or getting pictures under adverse light conditions. All of which is to say that unless color is beautiful, or significant, or an aid to identification and the understanding of function or adaptability to environment, it is often meaningless and confusing. Color may be drab and lacking in beauty, but may nevertheless be important to the naturalist, even though uninteresting to the popular reader. We have deliberately included a number of drab, monochromatic pictures in this book, usually to show nature's art of protective coloration (290, 295, 325).

Color must be representative of what the photographer saw when he took the picture. Notice that I do not insist on fully accurate color. I am convinced that accuracy in color is impossible. A photographer has no way of reproducing exactly the original conditions and lighting that existed when he took his nature shot, and thus he cannot compare the three-layer dye image on his film with the multi-hued scene that he photographed. And when his transparency is still further removed from the original by breaking it up into dots and printing it on paper in four inks, to be viewed by reflected rather than transmitted light, it is a wonder that there is any similarity whatsoever left. As a matter of experience, however, there is a remarkable retention of values through this complicated process of photo-mechanical reproduction. The extraordinary popularity and realism of color photography revealed through the printed page is convincing evidence to this fact.

This willingness to accept representative color in place of accurate color does not excuse bad exposures. Most nature photography is done with 35 mm. cameras at less than thirteen cents an exposure. There is little excuse for the serious 35 mm. worker not to bracket his exposures. By "bracket" I mean take a meter reading, then take one shot on the reading, another a half stop over, and another a half stop under. Workers with 4 by 5 cameras, using Ektachrome, may find bracketing too expensive and may be better off taking two shots, one on each side of the plate holder, at exactly the same exposure and then developing and drying one film before doing the same to the second. With Ektachrome, a variation of about two minutes in the first developer will compensate for about a half stop over or under exposure.

Over-exposed transparencies appear thin and washed out. Under-exposed shots appear dense in all colors. A picture with uneven exposure, or rather with an unevenly illuminated subject, taken without sufficient light in the shadows, can usually be spotted by the character of the green leaves if any are present. These under-exposed greens take on a dark, turquoise blue cast that is quite unnatural. You often find these unnatural greens in pictures that are otherwise excellent, simply because there was insufficient light in the background areas.

And what about backgrounds?

A second quality needed in a good nature shot is sharpness of detail in the subject focused upon—but does the background need to be sharp? or true in color? or even real? As far as this editor is concerned, I look upon it entirely as a matter of expediency. I would rather produce colorful, sharp, useful and salable pictures, even though the backgrounds are out of focus, or even use an old piece of linoleum for color contrast, than take an impossible purist's position and decry all such devices as "nature faking". As a matter of fact, there are literally hundreds of pictures that cannot be taken unless they are *arranged* and *designed.* And if the nature photographer is to abrogate all creative innovation and become merely a mechanical shutter-tripper—well— he may derive great lonely satisfaction from his reportorial photography, but he is not doing justice to his subject or his pocketbook.

I am sure that both scientists and the public want to see in pictures the subjects named in the captions. If you shoot a small yellow bug against a mass of yellow petals (280), you may present an interesting picture in protective coloration, or a puzzle picture—where's the bug?—but you have probably made it impossible to see what the bug is like. Even though you don't set up a feeding station against a green, blue or brown background, you should try to photograph each subject against some contrasting background or complementary background that will make it stand out—if only to get it into a position where you can throw the background out of focus. Backgrounds, therefore, can be in or out of focus depending upon whether or not they are important. But in either event there is no excuse for the main subject not being sharp.

The examination of a great many bird and insect nature photographs reveals a fairly common weakness; when the subject focused upon fails to fill the negative then a lot of extraneous matter is taken in. It is true that the Kodachrome and Ektachrome emulsions are relatively grainless and that both will stand a considerable degree of enlargement, but there is a limit as to how far a small image can be blown up without loss of definition and detail. Any editor would much prefer to receive a larger negative than a small one, and a well filled negative than one where the subject of interest occupies a corner of it. Pictures of this character are probably due to a weakness in the photographer's pocketbook rather than in his intentions, because in order to fill a negative properly you need a wide assortment of lenses and a camera that will enable you to switch from one to the other at a moment's notice. This is not the cheapest type of equipment to own and operate, but it is almost essential for most types of nature work.

In line with filling the negative with the subject of interest comes an equally important point of the pose, or composition, or angle of view from which the picture is taken. The use of the word "pose" is liable to misinterpretation. Most nature shots are as unposed as you can want, but the bird or animal or insect or flower that is the subject of the picture assumes a position, or rather the photographer assumes a position in relation to it. That position may or may not reveal the full characteristics of the subject. A dead-on, low angle, full-faced view of a centipede may present a startling picture, but will fail utterly to reveal the length of the animal and the number of legs. Similarly, a large number of birds, animals and insects cannot be adequately revealed from any one angle, but to be completely understood must be taken from a number of angles, and these sequential pictures are combined in the reader's mind's-eye to build up the full proportions and structure of the subject.

This brings me to the last of these qualities needed in a good nature color photograph, which is that the nature photographer should certainly be willing to take a sequence of shots where necessary. It doesn't really make much sense to try to indicate the metamorphosis of a monarch butterfly by only showing one stage of it. You will find six stages in this book (230, 231, 232, 233, 234, 235), but there is an equal number of others that could have been included. Similarly, in any process of hatching, molting, metamorphosis or growth, the nature photographer will find a wealth of sequence shots that will be as fascinating to take as they will be to exhibit.

Obviously, all this requires an immense amount of patience, to say nothing of an immense amount of study. And when study and patience are added to all of the foregoing qualities there is a good likelihood that the photographer, whether he be amateur or professional, will turn out top grade work; provided, of course, that he has the equipment and the technical knowledge with which to use it.

As for equipment, the bewildering array of photographic equipment offered at any large camera store and advertised in the various photographic magazines is enough to confuse all but the most determined camera fan. I have spent a number of years working my way up through the simpler types of cameras to those of more complex design, and reaching that point at which you can read all the photographic magazines and not want to buy a new piece of equipment, because you now understand what most of the gadgets will do and what their limitations are.

A lot of the confusion and complexity in the business seems to me to be unnecessary. There is very little standardization in the industry. Among exposure meters, for example, there are two scales and, if you include European meters, five different scales of measurement. While a number of cameras have interchangeable lenses, hardly any one make will accept the lenses of another. This makes it difficult to acquire a truly versatile battery of equipment except at considerable cost.

All of this is by way of warning to any amateur who is thinking of embarking on a career of serious nature photography. My heart-felt suggestion would be that he spend the first few months reading the magazines and studying the field and the equipment to be used, and then borrow or rent a camera, if not two or three different kinds of cameras, before he settles on any one design. There is no camera that will do everything. They all have advantages and disadvantages, and if you are going to take up photography with any seriousness you might as well master the subject at the start and assume full control over the problems involved.

I do not wish to imply by the foregoing that some good nature shots cannot be obtained with simple cameras or even with a Brownie. Obviously, if the light is good and the subject focused upon is fairly large and between six and ten feet from the camera, there is a good chance that you may come off with an acceptable picture; but if the subject is small and you have to bring the camera up within a foot or even six inches of the bird or insect, or if it is a flying squirrel in a tree or a bird of paradise at the top of a rain-forest or an Egret wading in a marsh across the opposite side of a stream, you are going to have extreme difficulty getting either type of picture without either close-up devices on the one hand or a long distance telephoto lens on the other.

In using either close-up devices or long lenses, the advantage of a reflex camera or reflex housing, which will enable you to look through the lens and see exactly what you are getting and whether you are sharp or not, is of the utmost importance. Most range finder cameras operate within a fairly narrow limit. The range finder on a Leica, for instance, will operate with a 35 mm., 50 mm., 85 mm., 90 mm. and 135 mm. lens, but when you start using the Leica for close-up or telephoto work, you either have to add fixed-focus close-up devices to it, and disregard the range finder, or screw the camera on the back of a reflex housing with bellows or telephoto lens, which turns it into a reflex camera. Once converted with a reflex housing it is an excellent instrument for nature work.

The single lens reflex camera of the type of the Exakta or Rectaflex or Hasselblad is equally good for nature work because it enables you to see exactly what part of your negative is being covered, whether your background is sharp, too sharp or not sharp enough, and whether your depth of field is adequate to keep the subject sharp both front and back. All of these factors have to be imagined when shooting with a rangefinder camera, because you are never looking through the lens itself, and you do not see in your viewfinder the effect that you get by changing the aperture.

I would venture to suggest that probably the most useful lens in nature work whether with an Exakta, Rectaflex, or a Leica reflex housing with bellows, is the 135 mm. lens. Most popular hand-held 35 mm. cameras, even the more expensive varieties, come equipped with 50 mm. lenses, but the 135 mm. lens has the advantage that with various extensions, either with bellows or focusing mounts, it can be used to focus on infinity or to focus on objects down to actual size (1 to 1). This wide variation in focusing power is of tremendous value in close-up work where there is a need to fill the negative with the subject in view. This accomplishment is also the property of a remarkable new Makro-kilar lens which is built on the zoom principle in a deep set helical focusing mount that enables you, with a twist of your wrist, to focus from 1 to 1 to infinity. A lens of this character can only be used with a reflex camera.

Lest you visualize most nature photographers running around and shooting from the hip, let me assure you that most of them use a tripod, and a firm one, on every occasion possible, and only resort to hand held shots when the photograph is not obtainable by any other method. Color film being so slow, it is rarely possible to expose it at speeds greater than 1/50 of a second, although the new, fast Ektachrome and Anscochrome can be shot at 1/100 of a second and even faster in good light. A tripod is good insurance that the resulting picture will be sharp and not blurred by camera motion.

Finally, good quality color can hardly be taken with any degree of predictability without minute attention to lighting. The light may come from the sun, it may come from flash bulbs or electronic speed-lights, but whatever the source, it has to be adequate for the picture you are taking. As most people who shoot color know, a hazy, overcast day with a lot of moisture in the air and hence a lot of light bouncing around results in better color photography than a day of sharp, contrasting bright sunlight. Whenever you have to shoot in sharp sunlight, it is almost essential that you fill in the shadows by some means, either by throwing light into the shadows with a reflector, or using a flash, or changing your position so that the sun is more directly behind you and you are not faced with hard, sharp outlines of shadow and highlight due to the acute angle of the sun coming from the side.

All this attention to balancing the light on a color subject is due to the fact that the color response of Kodachrome, Anscochrome and Ektachrome is much narrower than the color response of the human eye. The human eye has an automatic iris which opens in the dark and closes in the sunlight, and does so with no attention on your part whatsoever. The iris on a camera, however, not only has to be opened and closed by hand, but the opening itself bears a fixed relation to the speed of the shutter. Your eye has no shutter. Therefore, at any given fixed opening and speed, there is a measured amount of light reaching the film, and that amount of light will produce shadows of a certain density and highlights of a certain degree of lightness according to the lighting conditions present.

The ability of a film to respond to varying quantities of light at the same time and produce an acceptable image is called its latitude. The latitude of most color films can be said to be in the range of about 2½ stops, which simply means this: if you have measured your exposure correctly with a meter and you miscalculate, you can be in error about one stop over or one stop under and still get a usable image, although the color in either case may be degraded by your miscalculation. The latitude of black and white film is much broader than that of color film, which accounts for the fact that almost anyone can take a Brownie camera and point it and click the shutter and get a picture. Unless the photographer is independently wealthy and is willing to waste numerous exposures in trial and error, it is essential that the elements of good exposure should be mastered and a light meter correctly used whenever exposing color film. Obviously, care has to be taken to balance the ratio of highlight and shadow with fill-in lights into the shadows when the contrast range is too great, and allowances made for dark and light subjects, side-lighting, and other conditions.

With a moderately expensive camera, an assortment of lenses, a light meter and adequate lighting or reflecting equipment, it also seems strange to me that so many well equipped nature photographers should still pursue what I would call a helter-skelter shooting schedule. In other words, they take their camera and equipment and go out into the field or the marsh or the boat or the forest, and with their eyes alight with anticipation they shoot whatever comes to hand. I do not doubt that this is fun, and from a recreational point of view I think it is all to be admired, but I believe that the project method, the deliberately planned shooting schedule, is even more rewarding and more satisfying if it is pursued.

Under the project method, the nature photographer determines beforehand what he is going to shoot and what kind of pictures he is going to take and then lays his plans accordingly. This may necessitate reading up for a week on how a beaver builds his dam or raccoons wash their food or how termites build protective tunnels from the ground to the wood timbers of a house, or how paper wasps masticate wood pulp and turn it into paper in building their complicated, multi-celled nests. The photographer on any one of these assignments would take advantage of the research that has already been done in the field to determine in advance what are the significant things to be seen in studying any of these creatures, what are their characteristic modes of behavior, what changes they go through in the course of their life cycles, how they eat, reproduce, rear and train their young, what structural changes they themselves go through physically in the course of their life, what is unique and interesting about them that would be worth photographing. Once these salient points have been determined, then it becomes a most challenging assignment to try to capture these episodes in color on film. It is one thing to pluck a big, fat, green tomato worm off a plant or take its picture on the green leaf, but it takes no end of patience, time, careful lighting and probably a sleepless night or two to photograph each significant stage as that worm goes through all the subtle changes that turn it into a moth.

Nowhere near enough has been written about how the very capable nature photographers that are working for Walt Disney achieve their remarkable sequences of film shown in BEAVER VALLEY, THE VANISHING PRAIRIE and THE LIVING DESERT. I do know enough about them to report that most of them have worked hard and long developing devices, lights, blinds, tunnels and all the other contraptions needed to photograph nature's creatures without being seen or suspected. Oftentimes when a photographer develops a piece of equipment he would prefer to use it to take pictures, rather than advertise it. The very obvious thing about good nature photography is that it is usually preceded by a great deal of study and the photographer has himself to become a naturalist before he can resume the roll of a photographer.

Most of the work of photographing animals in their native habitat is done from blinds or with long lenses. These two devices are used frequently in the photography of birds although one quite famous bird photographer, Eliot Porter, has publicly described his technique of lowering a bird's nest, slowly, with young in it in successive stages until he can get it near enough to the ground to focus his lights and camera. (Land Birds of America, McGraw-Hill, 1953.) This, of course, necessitates cutting off the limb and rigging up ropes that will suspend the limb in approximately the same position as it was in originally. He has found that if the fledglings are at least two or three days old there is an irresistible urge on the part of the parents to keep them well fed and warm even though the nest is dropped ten or twenty feet, all of which has enabled Mr. Porter to gather some very remarkable nest site photographs. Other nature photographers, notably the president of the DuPont Company, have concentrated on the characteristics of flight, and by the use of very high speed electronic flash units and electronic shutter trippers have succeeded in stopping birds in mid-air to show characteristics of wing beat and the formation of feathers as they brake the air for a landing.

The photography of each living thing presents an individual problem. Taking pictures of fish, for example, is most exacting. There is a great deal of it being done today with under-water cameras in air tight housings and men diving under the water with aqualungs. This is a fascinating but a dangerous sport, and hardly a pastime for the amateur. The problems of good color photography under water are many. In the first place water itself gives everything a bluish tinge, and the deeper you go the less light you have. In using a reflex camera under water, you have to contend with the turbulence and the refraction of the water between your eye and the ground glass, so that a range finder type of camera is probably more effective. You can see a split image come together, whereas under water it is difficult to tell whether a ground glass image is sharp or not. Even the taking of little fish in tanks presents problems because of their rapid movements and the necessity to restrict those movements and bring them close to the front edge of the tank where they will be in focus. Men who have worked with tropical fish have usually placed a special glass in the tank to move the specimen forward to the desired position, or they have suspended a small photographic tank inside the larger tank and confined the fish in that small space so that it cannot move out of focus. Here again speed-lights are necessary in order to stop movement.

The insect world, too, presents a fascinating array of photographic subjects, and fortunately a great many insects can be captured and kept alive in bottles or cages or even in a well screened room—carefully separated from the rest of your house—so that it is possible to watch and photograph moths, butterflies, and praying mantises while they go through all their fascinating changes and stages of life. But to catch insects on the wing and photograph them in flight takes a reflex camera and a man who can think as an insect does and move almost as quickly. Roman Vishniac is one of the few individuals who has pursued this fascinating hobby, and he has succeeded in stopping a dragon fly in mid-air, and caught a large number of other insects in flight.

Flowers are practically the easiest of all nature subjects to photograph, but don't let their ease and accessibility fool you. A riot of color does not necessarily make a good photograph; it is one thing to focus your camera on a blazing azalea bush, and it is quite another to show the structure of one single flower and the details of its tiny stamens. Few photographers have taken the time to photograph sequentially the growth of a plant or the development of a flower from its early budding through its full bloom and to the formation of its seed head and the resulting seeds.

Fortunately a great many good flower shots are possible with relatively simple cameras—that is, any focusing camera that can be equipped with a close-up lens and a focusing frame. A focusing frame is simply an arrangement of wire or wood extending out from the camera the exact distance to which the close-up lens is focused, and shaped in such a way that it exactly describes the field of view. Such a device is relatively easy to operate; you just poke it at the flower in question, and when the flower is in the exact center of the frame you press your shutter release. Devices of this kind do not, of course, permit you to study the depth of field or the sharpness or fuzziness of the background, and much better flower pictures can be taken with a single lens reflex camera or reflex housing.

The best flower pictures are probably taken with a view camera and three speed-lights. I know one very capable photographer, a Mr. Charles Johnson, who is a partner of Scott-d'Arazien, one of the country's largest firms of industrial photographers. Charlie spends his spring and fall weekends touring the New England countryside with a station-wagon loaded with photographic equipment. From the size of his tripod, the size of his 4 x 4 view camera, and the number of lenses that he usually carries with him, along with a "Rube Goldberg" of a speed-light, you would think he was out to shoot a steel mill, but he is in search of simple wild flowers. He uses the three lights to stop action and fill in the background when photographing a rare sprig of trillium deep in the forest where the light is insufficient for normal color exposure and where the breeze is too brisk to permit a long time exposure. He always uses a tripod and usually takes from half an hour to an hour to make any one picture. He rarely, if ever, disturbs the specimen he is shooting but will frequently compose the background around it so as to make it more attractive and natural than it was when he found it. He has even been known to spray a flower and its leaves gently with a fine mist from a perfume atomizer to give it that fresh blush of dew that you often find on foliage in the early morning.

There is an amazing wealth of life and color even in plants that do not flower—in mosses, lichen, leaves and barks. William Amos once did a fascinating series of pictures for the Nature Program all of which were taken on a forest floor in an area probably not more than 100 feet square.

And after you have exhausted the animals and birds and insects and fish and flowers and plants of this world there is still the whole field of inanimate nature to photograph—sunrises, sunsets, stars, weather changes, significant cloud formations, the fascinating world of minerals, and the equally fascinating world of astronomy. The big thing to remember is that a professional nature photographer in shooting any of these subjects does so with a purpose in mind, with a story to tell, with a truth to be revealed.

Lastly, there is one natural creature that has been photographed to death and only infrequently been photographed with intelligence and insight, and that is man himself. Both men and women have been photographed as clothes-horses, as eaters and drinkers of food and wine, as workers of machines, as drivers of cars, but only rarely are men, women and children photographed for themselves alone as human beings, as part of nature, in an effort to reveal their adaptabilities to their environment, the development of their skills, and the expression of their aspirations and achievements. Edward Steichen came very close to showing how this should be done with his memorable collection of photographs from all over the world, recently exhibited at the Museum of Modern Art under the title of The Family of

Man, and subsequently published in book form. A closer and more revealing record of man's activities can be found, however, in some of the records brought back by anthropologists who have lived alone with isolated tribes or small communities of people and have reached such a degree of intimacy that they have been allowed to snap pictures of the daily lives of the people around them in such a way that their full character and behavior comes through. Unfortunately, few of these pictures are easily available for public inspection, but the very idea of trying to reveal the nature of man to man himself by unobtrusive candid photography is a challenge that should fascinate the possessor of any good miniature camera.

The camera is more than a mechanical instrument. It is held by two hands, it is focused by a seeing eye, which in turn is controlled by a knowing, discerning brain. What the brain sees, how it sees it, and the instant it tells the hand to click the shutter constitute an interpretation of nature that is far more than just a photograph. If focused on the world around you, animate, inanimate or human, with both interest and intelligence, a camera can lead to knowledge and insight that are of value both to the photographer himself and to those who view his work. That work, incidentally, is of value quite apart from the prices such pictures bring or the frequency with which they are exhibited or sold. To get good pictures, a photographer first has to study, observe closely, develop patience, and acquire the technical skill of a craftsman. All of this can be most satisfying to himself alone, even though his work is never used professionally.

CONTRIBUTING PHOTOGRAPHERS

and the Plate Numbers of Their Pictures

Allen, Arthur A., 446

American Museum of Natural History, 6, 32, 164

Beatty, Dorothy, 339, 363

Bleitz, Don, 438, 448

Broun, Maurice, 439

Cadbury, B. Bartram, 401, 405, 407, 408, 409, 410, 411, 413, 414, 417, 422, 423, 426, 427, 429

Cadbury, J. M., 444

Calkins, John, 347

Chace, Lynwood, 158, 160, 169, 323, 330, 334, 390

Collins, Steven, 142, 152, 314, 325, 337, 368, 374, 386, 397

Colvin, Lily, 178, 191

Conklin, D. R., 31

Crich, W. V., 29

Crockett, Harry L. and Ruth, 173

Cruickshank, Allan D., 115, 119, 121, 124, 129, 140, 150, 272, 274, 298, 299, 303, 304, 306, 315, 326, 371, 372, 382, 436, 437, 454

Cruickshank, Helen, 141, 155, 159, 195, 255, 266

Davidson, W. T., 166, 180, 369, 381

Drahos, Nick, 348

Gottscho-Schleisner, 359, 391

Grierson, Stan, 167

Grimes, Samuel, 453, 461

Gurien, Jay, 33, 34, 35, 36, 37, 38, 39, 40, 41, 42, 43, 44, 45, 46, 47, 48, 49, 50, 51, 52, 53, 54, 55, 56, 57, 58, 59, 60, 62, 63, 64, 65, 66, 67, 68, 69, 70, 71, 72, 73, 74, 349, 351, 356, 358, 367

Haist, G. M., 181

Harlow, William, 335, 340, 355, 362, 376

Harrison, Hal H., 11, 13, 22, 109, 112, 117, 123, 125, 126, 127, 128, 131, 134, 137, 139, 179, 201, 204, 211, 286, 316, 317, 318, 329, 393, 430, 435, 452

Hermes, Robert, 16, 143, 144, 145, 146, 147, 149, 151, 153, 156, 161, 162, 163, 165, 168, 170, 171, 378

Hess, Lilo, 213, 214, 240, 275, 276, 277, 278, 279, 280, 281, 283, 284, 285, 287, 288, 289, 290, 291, 293, 294, 295, 296, 297, 300, 301, 302, 303

Hike, E. J., 193, 212

Hill, Edward A., 324, 328

Hollister, J. M., 309

Hood, A. W., 15, 18

Hood, Mary V., 8, 12, 431

Howard, Edwin J., 282

Hunn, Max, 23

Jackson, Torrey, 433, 440, 442, 443

Jahoda, Wm. J., 61, 135, 370, 375

Johnson, Charles, 25, 175, 187, 188, 192, 194, 196, 200, 202, 205

Johnson, G. Blake, 75, 76, 77, 78, 79, 80, 81, 82, 83, 84, 85, 86, 87, 88, 89, 90, 91, 92, 93, 94, 95, 96, 97, 98, 99, 100, 101, 102, 103, 104, 105, 106, 107, 108, 462

Jones, Billy, 357, 363

Kaston, B. J., 198, 343, 365

Knight Photos, Don, 190, 199, 206, 210, 352

Lower, George, 399, 404, 406, 416, 419, 421, 424, 425

Mallett, Sabra, 110, 118, 130, 132

Matteson, Clifford, 203

Maurice, Scally, 176, 185

Meng, Heinz, 434, 445, 451, 459

Miller, Paul, 182, 209

Miller, Wilford, 292

Mohr, Charles E., 148, 154, 157, 305, 307, 308, 312, 313, 320, 321, 322, 327, 331, 332, 373, 377, 379, 383, 385, 387, 389, 394, 402, 420, 447, 450, 455, 457, 458

Mohr, J. L., 428

Mooney, Mark, 388, 395

Morgenson, D. C., 360, 366

Morrow, R. W., 172, 184

Palmer, Eric, 460, 449

Passmore, Lee, 310

Pluemer, W. A., 319, 380, 384, 392

Porter, Eliot, 111, 113, 114, 116, 120, 122, 133, 136, 138, 243, 244, 245, 246, 248, 249, 250, 256, 258, 259, 260, 262, 263, 264, 267, 268, 269, 270, 271

Quitt, Louis, 215, 217, 218, 219, 220, 221, 222, 228, 229, 230, 231, 232, 233, 234, 235, 236, 237

Rapho-Guillumette Photos, 1, 3, 4, 5, 14, 17, 24, 336, 344, 345

Renfro, Alfred, 396, 398

Robinson, Dorothy T., 311

Rue III, Leonard Lee, 10

Sage, Ruth, 177, 183, 342, 361

Sanborn, A., 441

Scott, A. H., 216, 223, 224, 225, 226, 227, 238, 239, 241, 242

Sherman, Charles, 247, 251, 252, 253, 254, 257, 261, 265

Shostal Press, 2, 7, 9, 19, 30

Simon, J. R., 21, 197

Simpkins, John, 354

Smiley, L. T., 174, 207, 208

Steinmetz, J. J., 26

Van Wormer, Joe, 20, 28

Walcott, Charles E., 333

Walgreen, Myrtle R., 346, 353

Warrick, E., 186, 189

Williams, Woody, 400, 403, 412, 415, 418

INDEX
TO ILLUSTRATIONS

THE FIRST REFERENCE after each entry, in **boldface type,** is the illustration number; the second number is the page on which the illustrations appear. Wherever important or significant, the scientific classification name is given in *italics*.

A

acacia, *Acacia,* **336,** 164

African cheetah, *Acinonyx jubatus,* **106,** 49

African lion, *Panthera leo,* **86,** 41

African secretary-bird, *Sagittarius serpentarius,* **456,** 225

African vulture, **432,** 213

agrias butterfly, *Agrias sp.,* **240,** 112

agriope, silver, **256,** 121

alligator, *Alligator mississippiensis,* **250,** 119

alligator, **89,** 42; **92,** 43; **101,** 47

American bittersweet, *Celastrus, scandens,* **33,** 19

American cranberry bush, *Viburnum trilobum,* **353,** 170

American egret, *Casmerodias albus egretta,* **243,** 115

American flying squirrel, *Glaucomys,* **96,** 45

anemone, sea, **400,** 196; **405,** 199; **417,** 204

anemone, wood, **201,** 93

anhinga, *Anhinga leucogasta,* **251,** 119

anolis lizard, **285,** 137

ant, (galleries) **307,** 149; (hill) **305,** 148

apple, *Malus pumila,* **68,** 31

apple, *Malus sylvestris,* **354,** 171

apple, love, **55,** 26

arbutus, trailing-, **187,** 88

armadillo, nine banded, **388,** 189

avocado, *Persea americana,* **37,** 21

azalea, *Rhododendron* sp., **344,** 167

B

baboon, **31,** 16

backswimmer, *Notonecta, undulata,* **163,** 76

badger, *Taxidea taxus,* **8,** 5

bagworm case, **332,** 160

bald eagle, *Haliaeetus leucocephalus,* **431,** 212

Baltimore checker spot butterfly, *Euphydryas, phaeton drury,* **224,** 104

Baltimore oriole, *Icterus galbula,* **317,** 152

bank swallow (nests), *Riparia riparia riparia,* **328,** 158

barberry, Japanese, **36,** 20

barn owl, *Tyto alba,* (adult) **443,** 219; (young) **440,** 218

barn swallow, *Hirundo erythrogaster,* **304,** 147

barnacle, goose, **406,** 199

barnacle, rock, **401,** 197

bat, red, **379,** 185

beach flea, *Orchestia* sp., **428,** 208

beaded rockweed, *Ascophyllum nodosum,* **407,** 199

beans, black, **46,** 24

bear cubs, *Ursus americanus,* **28,** 15

bear, koala, **1,** 1

beaver dam, **372,** 181

beaver lodge, **311,** 150

bee, carpenter-, **319,** 154

bee, honey, **105,** 48

beetle, diving, **147,** 70

berries, juniper, **368,** 177

bird, African secretary-, **456,** 225

bison calves, *Bison bison,* **21,** 12

bittern, least, **274,** 132

bitter-root, *Lewisia rediviva,* **197,** 92

bittersweet, American, **33,** 19

black beans, *Vigna* sp., **46,** 24

black pilot snake, *Elaphe obsoleta obsoleta,* **13,** 9

black walnut, *Juglans nigra,* **50,** 25

blackbird, red-winged, (female) **116,** 55; (male) **110,** 52 blackbird, yellow-headed, **141,** 68

black-eyed peas, *Vigna* sp., **46,** 24

black-eyed susan, *Rudbeckia hirta,* **208,** 95

blood root, *Sanguinaria canadensis,* **203,** 94

blue flag iris, *Iris versicolor,* **202,** 93

blue heron, great, **150,** 72

blue jay, *Cyanocitta cristata,* **318,** 153

blueberry, lowbush, **337,** 165

bluebird, eastern, **109,** 51

blue-headed vireo, *Vireo solitarius,* **382,** 186

bobcat, *Lynx rufus,* **12,** 8

bougainvillea, *Buginvillaea* sp., **357,** 172

box turtle, *Cistudo bauri,* **248,** 118

box-elder, eastern, **383,** 187

brown pelican, *Pelecanus occidentalis carolinensis,* **272,** 129

brown thrasher, *Taxostoma rufum,* **115,** 54

buckeye, flame, **338,** 165

bug, electric light, **165,** 78

bug, water, **171,** 81

bullfrog, *Rana catesbeiana,* **166,** 79

bumblebee, *Bombus pennsylvanicus,* **276,** 133

bumblebee moth, *Hemaris thysbe,* **276,** 133

burdock, lesser, **387,** 189

bush-tit, *Psaltriparus minimus,* **306,** 148

butterfly, agrias, **240,** 112

butterfly "antennae," **396,** 193

butterfly, Baltimore checker spot, **224,** 104

butterfly, caligo, **273,** 131

butterfly, callithea, **213,** 99

butterfly, Compton tortoiseshell, **241,** 112

butterfly, dead leaf, **296,** 141

butterfly, dog face, **242,** 113

butterfly "drinking straw," **398,** 193

butterfly, European cabbage, **238,** 111

butterfly, monarch, **229,** 108; **230,** 108; **231,** 109; **232,** 109; **233,** 110; **234,** 110; **235,** 110

butterfly, mourning cloak, **239,** 111

butterfly, orange sulphur, **216,** 101

butterfly, painted lady or cosmopolite, **225,** 105

butterfly, viceroy, **236,** 111; **237,** 111

butterfly-weed, *Asclepias tuberosa,* **189,** 89

C

cabbage butterfly, European, **238,** 111

cactus, hedgehog, **173,** 83

cactus, mound, **178,** 84

caddis flies, *Phryganea interrupta,* **293,** 140

calf, **30,** 16

California condor, *Gymnogyps californianus,* **438,** 216

California poppy, *Eschscholtzia californica,* **190,** 89

caligo butterfly, **273,** 131

callithea butterfly, *Callithea* sp., **213,** 99

camellia, *Camellia japonica,* **356,** 172

Canada thistle, *Cirsium arvense,* **52,** 26

caracara, *Caracara cheriway,* **446,** 220

caraway, *Carum carvi,* **45,** 23

cardinal, *Richmondena cardinalis,* (female) **136,** 64; (male) **129,** 61

cardinal flower, *Lobelia cardinalis,* **385,** 188

carpenter-bee, **319,** 154

cat, **87,** 42

catalpa, *Catalpa* sp., **339,** 165

catbird, *Dumetella carolinensis,* **134,** 63

caterpillar, saddleback, **397,** 193

caterpillar, slug, **300,** 143

caterpillar, spicebush, **93,** 44

caterpillar, stick, **290,** 140

caterpillar, tomato sphinx, **294,** 141

catkins, willow, **343,** 166

cecropia moth, *Platysamia cecropia linnaeus,* **217,** 102; **218,** 102; **219,** 102; **220,** 102, **221,** 103; **222,** 103; **297,** 142

chameleon, *Anolis carolinensis,* **247,** 118

checker spot butterfly, Baltimore, **224,** 104

cheetah, African, **106,** 49

cherry, *Prunus cerasus,* **367,** 177

chicks, **14,** 9

chimpanzee, *Pan,* **94,** 44

Chinese hibiscus, *Hibiscus rosa-sinensis,* **349,** 169

Chinese lantern plant, *Physalis alkekengi,* **51,** 25

chipping sparrow, *Spizella passerina,* **117,** 56

cicada-killer, *Sphecius* sp., **395,** 192

clam, leaping, **423,** 207

clam, soft-shelled, **410,** 200

clown slug, *Triopha carpenteri,* **415,** 203

cocker spaniel, **108,** 50

cocoon, **333,** 161

collie pups, **5,** 3

columbine, white Rocky Mountain, **182,** 86

Compton tortoiseshell butterfly, *Nymphalis j-album,* **241,** 112

conch snail, **424,** 207

condor (young), *Gymnogyps californianus,* **448,** 221

condor, California, **438,** 216

Cooper's hawk, *Accipiter cooperi,* **445,** 219

copperhead snake, *Agkistrodon mokasen,* **283,** 136; **375,** 182

coral, northern star, **416,** 203

coral reefs, **399,** 195

corn, *Zea mays,* **34,** 20

cosmopolite or painted lady butterfly, **225,** 105

cotton, *Gossypium* sp., **62,** 29

cottontail rabbit, *Sylvilagus*, **78**, 36
cottontail rabbit, *Sylvilagus floridanus*, **275**, 132
cottonwood, *Populus deltoides*, **340**, 166
coyote, *Canis latrans*, **20**, 12
crab apple, *Malus* sp., **363**, 175
crab, hermit, **421**, 206; **427**, 208
crab, horseshoe, **402**, 197; **404**, 198
crab, rock, **426**, 207
crab spider, yellow, **103**, 48
crab, toad, **411**, 201
currant, Indian, **57**, 27
cynthia moth, **286**, 138
cypress, pond, **270**, 128
cranberry bush, American, **353**, 170
crayfish, *Cambarus*, **77**, 36

D

dandelion, *Taraxacum officinale*, **61**, 29
dead leaf butterfly, **296**, 141
deer mouse, **331**, 160
diamondback rattlesnake, *Crotalus adamanteus*, **271**, 129
diving beetle, *Dysticus fasciventris*, **147**, 70
dock, *Rumex crispus*, **49**, 25
dogbane, *Apocynum cannabinum*, **60**, 29
dog face butterfly, *Colias (Zerene) cesonia stoll*, **242**, 113
dogwood, eastern flowering, **393**, 191
downy woodpecker, *Dendrocopus pubescens*, **371**, 180
dragonfly, *Anax junius*, **144**, 68; **145**, 69; **146**, 69
dragonfly, *Anisoptera*, **107**, 50
duck, wood, **159**, 75
duck hawk, *Falco peregrinus anatum*, **312**, 150
Dutchman's breeches, *Dicentra cucullaria*, **174**, 83

E

eagle, bald, **431**, 212
eagle, golden, (adult) **460**, 228; (young) **449**, 222
eastern bluebird, *Sialia sialis*, **109**, 51
eastern box turtle, *Terrapene carolina*, **370**, 180
eastern box-elder, *Acer negundo*, **383**, 187
eastern flowering dogwood, *Cornus florida*, **393**, 191
eastern skunk, *Mephitis mephitis*, **374**, 182
eggs of the pond snail, **156**, 74
egret, American, **243**, 115

electric light bug, *Lethocerus americanus*, **165**, 78
elephant, *Elephas maximus*, **81**, 38
eucalyptus, *Eucalyptus* sp., **39**, 21
European cabbage butterfly, *Pieris rapae linnaeus*, **238**, 111
everglade kite, *Rostrhamus sociabilis*, **461**, 229
eye of toad, **80**, 37; **85**, 40

F

fawn, Virginia white-tail, *Odocoileus virginianus*, **22**, 13
fern, giant holly, **70**, 32
ferret, *Mustela nigripes*, **98**, 46
field sparrow, *Spizella pusilla*, **111**, 52; (nest) **130**, 62
finch, purple, **99**, 46; **135**, 64
firethorn, *Pyracantha coccinea*, **42**, 22
fish, leaf, **291**, 140
fish, weed, **295**, 141
flame buckeye, *Aesculus splendens*, **338**, 165
flamingo, *Phoenicopterus ruber*, **257**, 122
flea, beach, **428**, 208
flicker, northern, **315**, 151
flies, caddis, **293**, 140
flower cardinal, **385**, 188
fly, house, **381**, 185
fly, May, **151**, 72
flying squirrel, American, **96**, 45
flying squirrel, northern, **16**, 10
foal, **9**, 6
foam-flower, *Tiarella cordifolia*, **204**, 94
forsythia, *Forsythia* sp., **341**, 166
fox cubs, red, **11**, 7
fox squirrel, *Sciurus niger*, **244**, 116
foxtail grass, *Setaria* sp., **72**, 33
fringed gentian, *Gentiana crinita*, **198**, 92
frog, tree, **90**, 43; **259**, 123; **378**, 184

G

gallinule, purple, **269**, 127; **303**, 145
galls, insect, 321, 155
gay-wings, *Plygala paucifolia*, **205**, 94
gentian, fringed, **198**, 92
giant holly fern, *Polystichum munitum*, **70**, 32
giant scallop, *Pecten magellanicus*, **419**, 204
giant swallowtail, *Papilio cresphontes cramer* **227**, 106
gibbon, **4**, 3
giraffe, **7**, 5
goat, mountain, **292**, 140

golden eagle, *Aquila chrysaëtos*, (adult) **460**, 228; (young) **449**, 222

goldfinch, *Spinus tritis*, (male) **127**, 60; (young) **124**, 59

goldstar-grass, *Hypoxis hirsuta*, **200**, 93

goose barnacle, *Lepas anatifera*, **406**, 199

goshawk, *Accipiter gentilis*, **434**, 214

grape, *Vitis* sp., **40**, 21

grapefruit, *Citrus paradisi*, **58**, 28

grass, foxtail, **72**, 33

grass, goldstar-, **200**, 93

grass, poverty, **47**, 24

grasshopper, **377**, 184

grass-pink orchid, *Calopogon pulchellus*, **186**, 88

gray squirrel's nest, **327**, 158

great blue heron, *Ardea herodias*, **150**, 72

green iguana, *Iguana iguana*, **95**, 45

green sea urchin, *Strongylocentrotus droehbachiensis*, **412**, 201

grey squirrel, *Sciurus carolinensis*, **83**, 39

grosbeak, rose-breasted, **132**, 63

gum, sweet, **67**, 31

gyrfalcon, white, **450**, 222

H

Hall's honeysuckle, *Lonicera japonica halliana*, **65**, 30

hawk, Cooper's, **445**, 219

hawk, duck, **312**, 150

hawk, red-shouldered, **458**, 226

hawk, sharp-shinned, **459**, 227

hedgehog cactus, *Echinocereus engelmanni*, **173**, 83

hermit crab, *Pagurus bernhardus*, **421**, 206; **427**, 208

hermit thrush, *Hylocichla guttata*, **138**, 65

heron, great blue, **150**, 72

hibiscus, Chinese, **349**, 169

hobblebush, *Viburnum alnifolium*, **348**, 169

hog-nose snake, *Heterodon simus*, **301**, 144; **302**, 144

holly fern, giant, **70**, 32

honesty, *Lunaria annua*, **63**, 30

honey bee, *Apis mellifera*, **105**, 48

honeysuckle, *Lonicera* sp., **350**, 169

honeysuckle, Hall's, **65**, 30

hooded skunk, *Mephitis macroura*, **32**, 17

horned lark, *Otocoris alpestris*, **299**, 143

horned owl, *Bubo virginianus*, (adult) **447**, 220; (young) **435**, 214

horned toad, *Phrynosoma*, **100**, 47

horseshoe crab, *Limulus polyphemus*, **402**, 197; **404**, 198

house fly, *Musca domestica*, **381**, 185

house wren, *Troglodytes aedon*, **128**, 61

hummingbird, ruby-throated, **298**, 143

hyacinth, water, **154**, 73; **261**, 124; **266**, 126

I

ibis, wood, **264**, 125

iguana, green, **95**, 45

Indian currant, *Symphoricarpos orbiculatus*, **57**, 27

Indian pipe, *Monotropa uniflora*, **211**, 96

indigo snake, *Spilotes corais couperi*, **255**, 120

insect galls, **321**, 155

Io moth, *Automeris io fabricius*, **223**, 104

iris, blue flag, **202**, 93

J

jack pine, *Pinus banksiana*, **361**, 174

jack-in-the-pulpit, *Arisaema triphyllum*, **207**, 95

Japanese barberry, *Berberis thunbergi*, **36**, 20

jay, blue, **318**, 153

jellyfish, red, **422**, 206

junco, slate-colored, **118**, 56

juniper berries, *Juniperus virginiana*, **368**, 177

K

kangaroo, **17**, 11

kelp, **429**, 209

kestrel, *Falco sparverius*, **433**, 213

kite, Everglade, **461**, 229

koala bear, **1**, 1

L

ladyslipper, queen, **185**, 87

ladyslipper, yellow, **179**, 85

lambs, **2**, 2

lark, horned, **299**, 143

leaf fish, *Monocirrhus polyacanthus*, **291**, 140

leaping clam, *Yoldia limatula*, **423**, 207

least bittern, *Ixobrychus exilis exilis*, **274**, 132

leech, *Placobella parasitica*, **143**, 68

lesser burdock, *Arctium minus*, **387**, 189

lilac, *Syringa* sp., **358**, 172

lilac, mountain, **366**, 176

lily, spider, **253**, 120

lily, swamp, **268**, 126

lily, tiger, **180**, 85

lily, water, **155**, 73

lily pad, **157**, 74

lion, African, **86,** 41
lion cubs, **21,** 12
lizard, anolis, **285,** 137
lobster, *Homarus americanus,* **413,** 201
locust, *Cicada* sp., **267,** 126
loggerhead shrike, *Lanius ludovicianus,* (adult) **437,** 215; (young) **436,** 215
long-billed marsh wren, *Telmatodytes palustris,* **326,** 157
lotus, *Nelumbium nelumbo,* **64,** 30
love apple, *Solanum integrifolia,* **55,** 26
lowbush blueberry, *Vaccinium angustifolium laevifolium,* **337,** 165
luna moth, *Actias luna,* **297,** 142
luna moth, *Actias luna Linnaeus,* **215,** 100
lupines, *Lupinus* sp., **193,** 91

M

magnolia, saucer, **359,** 173
manatee, *Trichechus manatus,* **246,** 117
mandrill, *Mandrillus sphinx,* **82,** 39
mangrove, red, **260,** 123
maple, red, **355,** 172
maple seeds, *Acer* sp., **365,** 176
marigold, marsh-, **194,** 91
marsh wren, long-billed, **326,** 157
marsh-marigóld, *Caltha palustris,* **194,** 91
May fly, **151,** 72
meadowlark, western, **114,** 54
measuring-worm, *Synchlora aerata,* **280,** 135; **287,** 138; **288,** 139; **289,** 139
melaleuca, *Melaleuca* sp., **48,** 24
milk snake, *Lampropeltis doliata,* **91,** 43
milkweed, *Asclepias* sp., **177,** 84
milkweed, *Asclepias syriaca,* **369,** 179
millet, *Panicum miliaceum,* **59,** 28
mockingbird, *Minus polyglottos,* **139,** 66
mole, *Scalopus aquaticus,* **389,** 190
mole tunnels, **320,** 154
monarch butterfly, *Danaus plexippus Linnaeus,* **229,** 108; **230,** 108; **231,** 109; **232,** 109; **233,** 110; **234,** 110, **235,** 110
moss-pink, *Phlox subulata,* **196,** 92
moth, bumblebee, **276,** 133
moth, cecropia, **217,** 102; **218,** 102; **219,** 102; **220,** 102; **221,** 103; **222,** 103; **297,** 142
moth, Cynthia, **286,** 138
moth, Io, **223,** 104
moth, luna, **215,** 100; **297,** 142
moth, old wife, **282,** 136
moth, urania, **214,** 100
mound cactus, *Echinocereus mojavensis,* **178,** 84
mountain-ash, *Sorbus aucuparia,* **347,** 168

mountain goats, **292,** 140
mountain-laurel, *Kalmia latifolia,* **391,** 190
mountain lilac, *Ceanothus integerrimus,* **366,** 176
mourning cloak butterfly, *Nymphalis antiopa Linnaeus,* **239,** 111
mouse, deer, **331,** 160
mouse opossum, *Marmosa,* **84,** 40
mud-dauber wasp (nest), **329,** 159
muskrat, *Ondatra zibethica,* **152,** 73

N

nine banded armadillo, *Dasypus novemcinctus,* **388,** 189
northern flicker, *Calaptes auratus,* **315,** 151
northern flying squirrel, *Glaucomys sabriuus,* **16,** 10
northern sea cucumber, *Cucumaria frondosa,* **409,** 200
northern star coral, *Astrangia danae,* **416,** 203
nutmeg, *Myristica fragrans,* **71,** 33

O

oak, white, **73,** 33
ocotillo, *Fouquieria splendens,* **360,** 174
okra, *Hibiscus esculentus,* **35,** 20
old wife moth, **282,** 136
opossum, *Didelphis virginiana,* **10,** 6; **258,** 122
opossum, mouse, **84,** 40
orange sulphur butterfly, *Colias eurytheme boisduval,* **216,** 101
orchid, grass-pink, **186,** 88
Oregon sunshine, *Eriophyllum lanatum,* **212,** 97
oriole, Baltimore, **317,** 152
osprey, *Pandion haliaetus,* **444,** 219
ostrich, *Struthio camellus,* **79,** 37
otter, *Lutra canadensis,* **254,** 120
owl, **97,** 45; **273,** 131
owl, barn, (adult) **443,** 219; (young) **440,** 218
owl, horned, (adult) **447,** 220; (young) **435,** 214
owl, saw-whet, (adult) **442,** 218; (young) **441,** 218
owl, screech, **452,** 223
owl, snowy, **454,** 224
owl, snowy, (meal) **455,** 225
owl's eyes, **462,** 230
owl's pellet, **457,** 226

P

paint-brush flower, *Castilleja* sp., **209,** 96

painted bunting, *Passerina ciris*, **245**, 117

painted lady or cosmopolite butterfly, *Vanessa cardui Linnaeus*, **225**, 105

painted turtle, *Chrysemys picta*, **167**, 79

paper wasp, *Polistes annularis*, **392**, 190

paper wasp's nest, **334**, 161

partridge-berry, *Mitchella repens*, **192**, 90

peanut, *Arachiz hypogaea*, **69**, 32

pear, *Pyrus* sp., **352**, 170

peas, black-eyed, **46**, 24

pelican, brown, **272**, 129

penguin, **6**, 4

peregrine, *Falco peregrinus*, **430**, 211

persimmon, *Diospyros virginiana*, **345**, 168

phoebe bird, *Sayornis phoebe*, **316**, 152

piddock, wood, **309**, 149

piglets, **26**, 14

pilot snake, black, **13**, 9

pine, Jack, **361**, 174

pine cone willow gall, **308**, 149

pineapples, wild, **249**, 118

pink, moss-, **196**, 92

pipefish, *Syngnathus fuscus*, **414**, 202

pitcher-plant, *Sarracenia purpurea*, **384**, 187

poinciana, royal, **54**, 26

pomegranate, *Punica granatum*, **74**, 33

pond cypress, *Taxodium ascendens*, **270**, 128

pond snail, *Physa gyrina*, **153**, 73

poppy, California, **190**, 89

porcupine, *Erethizon* sp., **15**, 10

potter wasp, *Eumenes fraternus*, **390**, 190

poverty grass, *Andropogon scoparius*, **47**, 24

prairie dog, **325**, 156

purple finch, *Carpodacus purpureus*, **99**, 46; **135**, 64

purple gallinule, *Ionornis martinica*, **303**, 145; **269**, 127

Q

queen ladyslipper, *Cypripedium reginae*, **185**, 87

R

rabbit, cottontail, **78**, 36; **275**, 132

rabbit, snowshoe, **277**, 134; **278**, 134; **279**, 135

raccoon, *Procyon lotor*, **29**, 16

rail, Virginia, **140**, 67

raisin, *Vitis*, **40**, 21

rattlesnake, *Crotalus horridus*, **104**, 48

rattlesnake, diamondback, **271**, 129

red bat, *Lasiurus borealis*, **379**, 185

red fox cubs, *Vulpes fulva*, **11**, 7

red jellyfish, *Cyanea capillata*, **422**, 206

red mangrove, *Rhizophora mangle*, **260**, 123

red maple, *Acer rubrum*, **355**, 172

red starfish, *Henricia* sp., **418**, 204

red-eyed vireo, *Vireo olivaceus*, **133**, 63

red-shouldered hawk, *Buteo lineatus*, **458**, 226

red-tail, *Buteo jamaicensis*, **439**, 217; **451**, 223

redwing blackbird, *Agelaius phoeniceus*, (female) **116**, 55; (male) **110**, 52

rice, wild, **38**, 21

robin, *Turdus migratorius*, (female) **123**, 59; (young) **121**, 57

robin's nest, **125**, 60

rock barnacle, *Balanus balanoides*, **401**, 197

rock crab, *Cancer irroratus*, **426**, 207

rock weed, beaded, **407**, 199

Rocky Mountain columbine, white, **182**, 86

root, bitter-, **197**, 92

rose, wood, **44**, 23

roseate spoonbill, *Ajaia ajaia*, **252**, 120

rosebay, *Rhododendron maximum*, **351**, 169

rose-breasted grosbeak, *Pheucticus ludovicianus*, **132**, 63

rose-mallow, *Hibiscus moscheutos*, **206**, 94

round-leaf sundew flower, *Drosera rotundifolia*, **172**, 83

royal poinciana, *Delonix regia*, **54**, 26

ruby-throated hummingbird, *Archilochus colubris*, **298**, 143

S

saddleback caterpillar, *Sabine stimulea*, **397**, 193

saguaro, *Cereus giganteus*, **210**, 96

salamander, **313**, 150

salamander, spotted, **142**, 68

sandworm, *Nereis virens*, **408**, 200

saucer magnolia, *Magnolia soulangeana*, **359**, 173

sawgrass, *Cladium effusum*, **265**, 125

saw-whet owl, *Aegolius acadica*, (adult) **442**, 218; (young) **441**, 218

scallop, giant, **419**, 204

scarlet tanager, *Piranga olivacea*, **126**, 60

scorpion, water-, **162**, 76

screech owl, *Otus asio*, **452**, 223

sea anemone, *Metridium dianthus*, **400**, 196; **405**, 199; **417**, 204

sea cucumber, northern, **409**, 200

sea horse, *Hippocampus hudsonius*, **425**, 207

sea urchin, green, **412**, 201

seal pup, **18**, 11

secretary-bird, African, **456**, 225

sedge, *Carex*, **53**, 26

sharp-shinned hawk, *Accipiter striatus*, **459**, 227

shrike, loggerhead, (adult) **437**, 215; (young) **436**, 215

shrimp, *Mysis relicta*, **168**, 79

silver agriope, *Agriope argentata*, **256**, 121

silverbell, *Halesia monticola*, **364**, 175

skunk, eastern, **374**, 182

skunk, hooded, **32**, 17

slate-colored junco, *Junco hyemalis*, **118**, 56

slug, clown, **415**, 203

slug caterpillar, **300**, 143

snail, **314**, 151

snail, conch, **424**, 207

snail, pond, **153**, 73

snail, tree, **262**, 124

snail, yellow, **403**, 198

snail eggs, pond, **156**, 74

snake, black pilot, **13**, 9

snake, copperhead, **283**, 136; **375**, 182

snake, hog-nose, **301**, 144; **302**, 144

snake, indigo, **255**, 120

snake, milk, **91**, 43

snapping turtle, *Chelydra serpentina*, **170**, 80; (hatching) **169**, 79

snowshoe rabbit, *Lepus americanus*, **277**, 134; **278**, 134; **279**, 135

snowy owl, *Nyctea nyctea*, **454**, 224; (meal) **455**, 225

soft-shelled clam, *Mya arenaria*, **410**, 200

song sparrow, *Melospiza melodia*, **119**, 56

spade-foot toad, *Scaphiophus holbrookii*, **386**, 188

spaniel, cocker, **108**, 50

spanish-needles, *Bidens bipinnata*, **394**, 192

sparrow, chipping, **117**, 56

sparrow, field, **111**, 52; (nest) **130**, 62

sparrow, song, **119**, 56

spatulate-leaved sundew, *Drosera intermedia*, **380**, 185

spicebush caterpillar, *Papilio troilus*, **93**, 44

spider, yellow crab, **103**, 48

spider's nest, **310**, 150

spider's web, **323**, 155

spider lily, *Hymenocallis palmeri*, **253**, 120

spiderwort, *Tradescantia virginiana*, **184**, 87

spittlebug, **324**, 156

spoonbill, roseate, **252**, 120

spotted salamander, *Ambystoma maculatum*, **142**, 68

squirrel, American flying, **96**, 45

squirrel, fox, **244**, 116

squirrel, grey, **83**, 39

squirrel's nest, grey, **327**, 158

squirrel, northern flying, **16**, 10

star coral, northern, **416**, 203

starfish, red, **418**, 204

stick, caterpillar, *Lycia cognataria*, **290**, 140

sumac, *Rhus* sp., **66**, 30

sundew, round-leaf, **172**, 83

sundew, spatulate-leaved, **380**, 185

sunfish, *Centrarchidae*, **102**, 48

sunfish, *Lepomis gibbosus*, **160**, 76

sunflower, *Helianthus annuus*, **59**, 28

swallow, bank, (nests) **328**, 158

swallow, barn, **304**, 147

swallowtail, giant, **227**, 106

swallowtail, tiger, **228**, 107

swallowtail, (larvae) **281**, 136

swamp lily, *Crinum americanum*, **268**, 126

sweet gum, *Liquidambar styracifolia*, **67**, 31

sycamore, *Platanus occidentalis*, **43**, 22

T

tadpole, **158**, 75

tanager, scarlet, **126**, 60

tanager, western, **120**, 57

tapir, **23**, 13

thistle, Canada, **52**, 26

thrasher, brown, **115**, 54

thrush, hermit, **138**, 65

thrush, wood, (adult) **113**, 54; (young) **112**, 53

tiger, *Panthera tigris*, **75**, 35

tiger lily, *Lilium tigrinum*, **180**, 85

tiger swallowtail, *Papilio glaucus Linnaeus*, **228**, 107

toad, *Bufo americanus*, **148**, 70

toad, eye of, *Bufo*, **80**, 37; **85**, 40

toad, horned, **100**, 47

toad, spade-foot, **386**, 188

toad crab, *Hyas coarctatus*, **411**, 201

tomato sphinx caterpillar, **294**, 141

trailing-arbutus, *Epigaea repens*, **187**, 88

tree, tulip, **362**, 175

tree frog, *Hyla*, **90**, 43; **259**, 123; **378**, 184

tree of heaven, *Ailanthus altissima*, **56**, 27

tree snails, *Liguus* sp., **262**, 124

treehopper, *Thelia bimaculata*, **284**, 136

trillium, white, **195**, 91

tulip tree, *Liriodendron tulipifera*, **362**, 175

turkey-beard, *Xerophyllum asphodeloides*, **181**, 85

turkey vulture, *Cathartes aura*, **453**, 223

turtle, **25**, 14

turtle, *Chrysemys picta*, **88**, 42

turtle, box, **248**, 118

turtle, eastern box, **370**, 180

turtle, painted, **167**, 79

turtle, snapping, **170**, 80; (hatching) **169**, 79

turtle, wood, **76**, 36

U

urania moth, *Urania*, **214**, 100

V

veeries, *Hylocichla fuscescens*, **137**, 65
venus fly-trap, *Dionaea muscipula*, **176**, 84; **373**, 182
viceroy butterfly, *Limenitis archippus Cramer*, **236**, 111; **237**, 111
violet, white, **188**, 88
vireo, blue-headed, **382**, 186
vireo, red-eyed, **133**, 63
Virginia rail, *Rallis limicola*, **140**, 67
Virginia white-tail fawn, **22**, 13
virgins-bower, *Clematis virginiana*, **183**, 86
vulture, African, **432**, 213
vulture, turkey, **453**, 223

W

walnut, black, **50**, 25
walrus, *Odobenus rosmarus*, **3**, 2
wasp, paper, **392**, 190
wasp, potter, **390**, 190
wasp nest, mud-dauber, **329**, 159
wasp nest, paper, **334**, 161
water bug, *Belostoma flumineum*, **171**, 81
water hyacinth, *Eichornea crassipes*, **154**, 73; **261**, 124; **266**, 126
water lily, *Nymphaea odorata*, **155**, 73
water lily, white, **175**, 84
water-scorpion, *Ranatra fusca*, **162**, 76
water tiger, *Dysticus larvae*, **161**, 76
water through microscope, **164**, 77
web, spider, **323**, 155
weed, butterfly-, **189**, 89
weed fish, **295**, 141
weigela, *Weigela* sp., **346**, 168
western meadowlark, *Sturnella neglecta*, **114**, 54
western tanager, *Piranga ludoviciana*, **120**, 57
white gyrfalcon, *Falco rusticolus*, **450**, 222
white oak, *Quercus nigra*, **73**, 33

white Rocky Mountain columbine, *Aquilegia caerulea alba*, **182**, 86
white trillium, *Trillium grandiflorum*, **195**, 91
white violet, *Viola primulifolia*, **188**, 88
white water lily, *Nymphaea odorata*, **175**, 84
wild pineapples, *Tillandsia* sp., **249**, 118
wild rice, *Zizania palustris*, **38**, 21
willow catkins, *Salix* sp., **343**, 166
willow gall, pine cone, **308**, 149
winter wren, *Troglodytes troglodytes*, **122**, 58
witch-hazel, *Hamamelis virginiana*, **342**, 166; **376**, 183
wood anemone, *Anemone quinquefolia*, **201**, 93
wood duck, *Aix sponsa*, (male) **159**, 75
wood ibis, *Mycteria americana*, **264**, 125
wood piddock, **309**, 149
wood rose, *Ipomoea tuberosa*, **44**, 23
wood thrush, *Hylocichla mustelina*, (adult) **113**, 54; (young) **112**, 53
wood turtle, *Clemmys inscupta*, **76**, 36
woodchuck, *Marmota monax*, **19**, 12
woodpecker, downy, **371**, 180
wren, house, **128**, 61
wren, long-billed marsh, **326**, 157
wren, winter, **122**, 58

Y

yellow crab spider, *Misumena*, **103**, 48
yellow ladyslipper, *Cypripedium pubescens*, **179**, 85
yellow snail, *Tylodina fungina*, **403**, 198
yellow-headed blackbird, *Xanthocephalus xanthocephal*, (male) **141**, 68
yellowjackets, **322**, 155; **330**, 159
yellowthroat, *Geothlypis trichas*, **131**, 62
yew, *Taxus* sp., **335**, 163
yucca, *Yucca* sp., **41**, 22

Z

zebra, **24**, 13
zebra butterfly, *Heliconius charitonius Linnaeus*, **226**, 105